Sudd

Having his Baby

...and a lot can happen in nine months!

Acclaim for Charlotte Lamb, Lynne Graham and Emma Goldrick

About BODY AND SOUL

"Charlotte Lamb's innovative mind brings readers yet another challenge to enjoy."
—*Romantic Times*

"Lynne Graham's strong-willed, hard-loving characters are the sensual stuff dreams are made of."
—*Romantic Times*

"Emma Goldrick's light humorous touch combines with delectable characters giving readers a wonderful lasting impression."
—*Romantic Times*

Having his Baby

Charlotte Lamb
Lynne Graham
Emma Goldrick

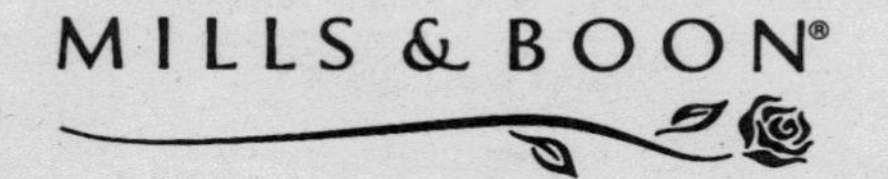

All the characters in this book have no existence outside the imagination of the author, and have no relation whatsoever to anyone bearing the same name or names. They are not even distantly inspired by any individual known or unknown to the author, and all the incidents are pure invention.

Harlequin Mills & Boon Limited,
Eton House, 18-24 Paradise Road, Richmond, Surrey, TW9 1SR

HAVING HIS BABY

Body and Soul, Angel of Darkness and *Baby Makes Three* were first published in separate, single volumes by Mills & Boon Limited.
Body and Soul in 1994, *Angel of Darkness* in 1994
and *Baby Makes Three* in 1993.

ISBN 0 263 80878 5

05-9803

Printed and bound in Great Britain
by Caledonian Book Manufacturing Ltd, Glasgow

Charlotte Lamb was born in London in time for World War II, and spent most of the war moving from relative to relative to escape bombing. Educated at a convent, she married a journalist, and now has five children. The family lives in the Isle of Man. Charlotte Lamb has been writing for Mills & Boon® since 1973 and has written over a hundred books. She has sold more than 45 million copies, which have been published around the world.

BODY AND SOUL

by

CHARLOTTE LAMB

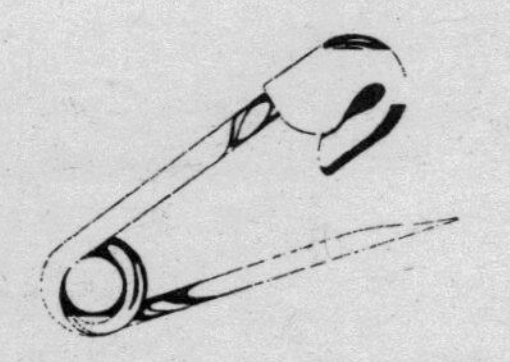

CHAPTER ONE

MARTINE was late, and in a hurry, so she leapt out of her taxi and ran across the pavement towards the Mayfair restaurant, too intent to notice the man in evening dress who got out of a parked car on the other side of the road and headed in the same direction.

There was a moment when either of them could have held back, but, although they glanced briefly at each other, neither of them stopped. Martine thought she was nearer and would get there first; but he moved faster.

They collided in the revolving door. Which promptly jammed—with them crushed together inside one section. Martine looked up, her eyes as stormily green as northern seas. The eyes that met hers were black, cold, irritated.

'If you back out, that will free the door!' said a deep, dark voice with a faint foreign accent which she couldn't identify.

'If you had had the manners to let me go first this wouldn't have happened! *You* step back!' she snapped.

It was all his fault, and Martine didn't like his peremptory tone, or the fact that she had been forced so close to him. You couldn't have got a sheet of paper between them, in fact—which meant that his body actually touched hers, making her very aware of his powerful build. He might be wearing civilised evening dress but underneath it was a distinctly primitive body: six feet of muscle and bone and smooth, tanned skin, a face that could have been carved out of granite.

'There's no point in arguing about whose fault it is!' he bit out. 'Just wriggle backwards.'

'Any wriggling can be done by you,' Martine informed him.

Just because she was almost a foot shorter than him, fine-boned and slender, he needn't imagine that she was a helpless female and a pushover. She wasn't backing down, even if it meant they stayed jammed in this door all night.

He stared down into her angry green eyes, and she bristled like a cat faced with danger, the hair standing up on the back of her neck.

Something about the arrogant tilt of his head, the sleek black hair, the cool eyes, reminded her of a man she had once loved, but who had walked out on her to marry a girl with rich parents. Three years had gone by since then, and Martine had dated other men, but never fallen in love like that again, and never meant to. She had been badly hurt once. She didn't intend to repeat the experience.

'Look, even an idiot should see that the easiest way of freeing the door would be for you to back out,' he coldly pointed out.

'Oh, very well,' Martine said, shifting sideways to get into a better position for wriggling out. His foot was in the way. Her elegant little black shoes had thin, high heels, like stilettos. She felt one of them sink into the top of his polished shoe.

He started violently, took a sharp breath, and said something under that breath which she couldn't quite hear but which sounded suspiciously like swearing.

'Sorry,' she said, and met glittering black eyes.

'You did that deliberately!' he accused.

'Don't be ridiculous! I was simply trying to get out. How was I to know you would put your foot in the way?'

He eyed her with dislike. His nostrils flared, a white line of rage around his mouth.

'I suppose I'll have to get us out of here or we'll be here all night,' he muttered. 'Just stand still, will you?'

Turning sideways, he began to slide past her, his body pressing against hers in the process, his long thigh pushing past, his arm brushing her breast. Despite herself she felt a sharp needle of sexual awareness stab through her and tensed in shock.

'Hey! Watch it!' she hissed, guessing that he was inflicting his intimacy on her deliberately in male revenge because she hadn't been the one to back out.

It was a mistake to say anything. It made him stop, dead, looking down at her with those dark, narrowed eyes barely inches above her own, their bodies still touching. 'Don't flatter yourself,' he said through his teeth. 'This isn't giving me any thrill at all, I assure you.'

Martine reddened crossly. 'Oh, just get a move on, will you?' she muttered. 'We're attracting a crowd!'

There were people on the inside of the restaurant, trying to get out, and another couple on the pavement, trying to get in, all watching them and grinning. They were providing live entertainment and Martine felt very silly and very angry. She hid it, giving their audience helpless smiles and shrugs.

Her reluctant companion finally squeezed out backwards, and Martine immediately pushed the revolving door to emerge in the restaurant, murmured an apology to the people waiting, slid out of her silk evening jacket and handed it to a hovering waiter.

'Is Mr Redmond here, yet?'

'If he is, he'll be in the bar, miss.'

Behind her she heard the revolving door turning and was aware of a looming presence emerging.

She ignored him.

As she walked into the circular, discreetly lit bar, she saw a faint reflection swimming in the black glass lining the wall behind the bar counter. First herself, slender, in black georgette, her face thrown into odd prominence, a pale, shimmering oval, her neck long and slim, a white magnolia pinned just above her breasts, at the edge of her deep neckline, her dark auburn hair coiled low on her nape; and, walking behind her, a head taller than her, the black-haired foreigner in his stiff white shirt front and black jacket.

She had to admit they made an interesting composition in black and white; the only colour visible was the dark flame of her red hair.

She halted to look around the room. There were a few people in the bar, but there was no sign of Charles, which didn't surprise her. He was often unpunctual, but then he had so much on his mind. Since the death of his wife he had buried himself in work; sometimes he didn't seem quite sure which day of the week it was! She only hoped he would remember that he had asked her to have dinner here tonight.

He had just flown back from New York that morning and hadn't been in to the office since landing; had stayed at home, resting after the trip.

He had made their date for tonight from New York. No doubt he wanted to talk to her out of the office; there was always too much going on there for any possibility of a private conversation, and since much of the information he needed to give her was very confidential they chose their meeting-places carefully.

She sat down at one of the empty tables. Immediately a waiter came over. 'What will you have to drink, madam?'

'Oh...just a glass of sparkling mineral water, please,' she said, crossed one slender, shapely leg over the other, her fine, filmy skirt riding up a little so that she had to stroke it down over her knee. Casually glancing around the bar, she found herself looking into black eyes on the other side of the room, eyes that had been watching her smoothing down her skirt, had coldly assessed her legs, risen to give the same unimpressed speculation to her figure and face.

Martine gave him a glacial stare back. She never liked getting looks like that—as if she were an object, not a human being. Some men used it as a silent insult. She had the feeling this one did, especially remembering the way he had spoken to her while they were jammed in the revolving door.

He calmly detached his gaze, looked down, shot his cuff back to allow a glimpse of his gold wristwatch and frowned, then got to his feet. Martine stiffened, thinking for a few seconds that he was coming over here to her table.

Instead he walked out of the bar without giving her another look. Several women in the room watched him avidly.

OK, he had his points, especially when you saw him in a good light, thought Martine. She liked tall men, especially when they moved like that. The tan was striking, too. He probably stripped well; his body had interesting proportions: broad shoulders, slim hips, long, long legs.

Catching herself up, she grimaced. What was she thinking about? Men like him were nothing but a disaster. She hadn't had a man in her life for almost a year, that was the trouble, and however hard she worked, however many hours she put into her job, she still felt pretty blue at times. Frustration and loneliness must be having a dire effect on her brains for her to look twice at that guy, though!

She crossly took a couple of salted almonds from the bowl in the middle of the table and popped them into her mouth while she, too, consulted her watch.

Where was Charles?

She had no sooner thought the question than she saw him hurrying towards her, a thin, slight, fair man in a well-cut dark suit.

'Sorry,' he apologised, sliding into the seat next to her. 'Am I late, or were you early?'

'I've only been here a moment,' she lied, smiling at him, her eyes faintly anxious as she absorbed the air of weariness he habitually wore. She hadn't seen him for a week and was struck by the way he was ageing. He was only forty-five, but he looked older; there were lines around his mouth and eyes, his skin had a grey tinge.

The waiter brought her drink, looked at Charles expectantly.

'My usual, Jimmy,' Charles told him with a smile.

'Yes, Mr Redmond,' said the waiter, beaming, pleased because Charles had remembered his name.

Charles ate here frequently. He lived in a luxurious penthouse flat a short walk away; this was his nearest local restaurant and he liked the place. He had a married couple who ran his home. Mr Wright was his chauffeur and handyman, and looked after his clothes; Mrs Wright cleaned and cooked in the flat. But Charles let them have three evenings a week free, and came here to eat.

The waiter walked away and Charles turned back to smile at Martine.

'That's my favourite dress, you always look lovely in it,' he said, and a faint flush crept into her face. She had put on the black georgette because whenever she wore it Charles told her how much he liked it.

Working for him meant a constant succession of important social gatherings for which she required a large and very expensive wardrobe, so she had plenty of clothes to choose from. She got a special allowance for clothes and Charles encouraged her to buy from good designers because as his personal assistant she was always representing the bank and Charles felt she should look expensive and elegant at all times. It was the image he wished the bank to convey: moneyed, sophisticated, cool.

'Thank you, Charles, you look very elegant yourself tonight,' she murmured, and he gave her a rueful little quirk of the mouth.

'Why, thank you.' He didn't sound convinced. No doubt he knew his suit no longer fitted perfectly, revealed how thin he was getting, emphasised the fact that he had lost even more weight since she last saw him.

Charles had never been heavily built, but after his wife's death two years ago he had lost weight as if his flesh was melting away. That hadn't been the only change in him. His hair had been a lovely pale gold; the shock of Elizabeth's death had left him with a sprinkling of silver hairs and a haunted look in his blue eyes.

He had been driving and had emerged unscathed himself with a few minor bruises and cuts and a slight head injury. Elizabeth had been killed instantly; Charles had never quite got over it. He blamed himself and was guilty because he had not died too. If they had had children it might have been easier for him to recover from the shock, but he and Elizabeth hadn't yet got around to a family.

'Thanks, Jimmy,' he told the waiter as the man appeared with a double whisky and soda on a silver tray. 'I'm expecting another guest to join us—would you keep an eye open for him? His name's Falcucci, Bruno Falcucci.'

'An Italian gentleman, would he be, sir? There's a gentleman making a telephone call in the foyer who's talking in Italian. I'll check if it's Mr Falcucci, shall I?'

'Thanks, Jimmy,' Charles said, smiling at him again.

Ice clinked in the glass as Charles took a swallow of whisky.

'Who's joining us?' Martine asked, faintly disappointed because she had been looking forward to dinner alone with him, but not taken entirely by surprise because Charles often used social occasions to smooth a business deal, and she was frequently included in the party, whether it was lunch or dinner or a cocktail party.

'A cousin of mine,' Charles said with a glint of mischief in his blue eyes.

As startled as he had obviously expected her to be, Martine said, 'You've never mentioned having any close relatives.'

Charles had, from time to time, told her something about himself and his background, and other members of staff at the bank had dropped the odd crumb of gossip. She had gained the impression that Charles had no near family, and very few close friends. He had always been so wrapped up in his work, even while his wife was alive, and since her death he had cut his social life almost to nil.

His friends were largely colleagues or business acquaintances, most of them married, with family commitments, making Charles an odd man out on most social occasions. That was why he had fallen into the habit lately of taking Martine along with him to any private gathering to which he was invited.

They weren't romantically involved, simply very good friends as well as close colleagues; it suited them both to have an escort for an evening now and then, and they were both deeply involved in their work.

Charles had told her that he had been an afterthought by his parents, both of whom, apparently, had been in their late forties when he was born, their first and only child, a much loved and indulged one. Perhaps having old parents had made him so serious, so tied to duty and work?

They had died long ago, when he was a young man, leaving Charles an enormous fortune and the major interest in the family merchant bank. Charles had once said that he had begun to work as soon as he left university, and hadn't noticed much about the world outside banking until he was nearly forty himself. That year he had been in Paris at an international conference and met a beautiful French model half his age, Elizabeth, raven-haired, tiny, exquisite. Charles fell like a ton of bricks, married her just weeks later, only to lose her again within two years, a tragedy which made him, for Martine, a deeply romantic, star-crossed figure.

She felt highly protective towards Charles, as well as liking him.

'Bruno is the only close relative I have,' Charles said now, giving her a smiling, rueful shrug. 'And I've only met him a couple of times; he lives in Switzerland.'

'Switzerland? And he's in banking, of course,' she said with a wry expression.

Charles looked amused suddenly. 'You think that follows naturally? Well, you're right, he is in banking, I suppose it was in his genes. Or perhaps his mother talked him into joining a bank? Anyway, he works for the Swiss Bank Corporation at the moment, but tonight I intend to ask him to join us.'

Martine's green eyes widened. 'Oh, I see.' Now what did that mean? she wondered, startled.

Charles went on quietly, 'I don't want anyone else to know this, Martine; I'm telling you because I trust you completely. I want you to know, I've just made a new will, leaving my shares in the bank to him. There's nobody else for me to leave them to.'

Martine felt cold suddenly. 'You're talking as if... good heavens, you're only forty-odd. You'll marry again, Charles. Oh, I know you still miss Elizabeth, and it isn't easy to get over things like that, but you sound as if you've given up on life, and you mustn't! There's plenty of time to think about making wills!'

Charles gave a faint, wry smile. 'After working in banking for years, Martine, I'd have thought you knew better than that! It is never wise to put off making a will.'

Frowning, she shrugged. 'In principle, no, but...'

'In practice, too. You should make one yourself. One never knows what's around the next corner.' His blue eyes had that haunted look again; he was thinking about Elizabeth and that crash.

Martine put a hand on his arm, comforting silently, and he gave her a quick, crooked smile, coming back to the present moment.

'Anyway, I've made my will. Actually, Bruno should have had shares in the bank long ago; his mother was my father's only sister! But my grandfather refused to leave anything at all to his daughter, Una, because she married against his will—a Swiss doctor she met on a holiday at Lake Como. Her parents disapproved violently. First, Frederick was a foreigner, and secondly he was not in banking. Worst of all, he had very little money, but he was apparently a delightful man, a good man and a good doctor. Una was very happy with him, but her father never forgave her for marrying him, so he left all his money to my father.'

'That does seem unfair,' Martine agreed. 'It must have made your aunt very unhappy.'

'I'm sure it did.'

'And it led to a family feud!' Martine murmured, and Charles laughed.

'You have a disconcerting streak of romanticism!'

She blushed. She always tried to hide it; it didn't go down well in banking circles, for one thing, and, for another, it had led her into a painful love-affair and left her with a broken heart and bitter disillusion.

'I suppose it was something along those lines, though,' Charles shrugged. 'My parents exchanged

Christmas cards with Aunt Una but they never visited Switzerland, and Aunt Una never came back to England. This big gulf opened up between them.'

'How sad!' It seemed pretty childish to Martine, but the things people did to each other often were, she thought.

Charles sighed. 'It is really, isn't it? Sad and very stupid. When my parents died I lost contact with Aunt Una altogether, but she died a few years ago, and Bruno wrote to tell me. I happened to be going to Switzerland on that banking commission tour so I looked him up while I was there, and I liked him.'

'Does he know you've made him your main beneficiary?' Martine shrewdly asked.

Charles gave her an amused look. 'Not yet.'

Martine's eyes narrowed speculatively. This Bruno Falcucci might not know yet that Charles had left the Redmond share of the bank to him, but he would know that Charles was unmarried and had no other heir, and, if he was shrewd, as he probably was if he was a senior bank executive, he would probably have worked out that he had a chance of persuading Charles to leave him some money.

'Did you invite him to come to London, or is he here off his own bat?'

'He rang me last week to say he had to come to London on business,' Charles informed her, still looking amused. 'What a suspicious little mind you've got!'

'I didn't say a word!'

'You don't need to! I can read your thoughts—after all, I know you very well, Martine.' He looked down into her green eyes and they exchanged an intimate, laughing look.

At that instant somebody strolled up to the table and Charles glanced round, exclaimed, stood up, holding out his hand, his drawn and tired face lighting up.

'Ah, there you are, Bruno! I was beginning to think you had forgotten all about tonight!'

'I've been looking forward to the evening all week,' a deep, cool voice drawled.

Martine sat there transfixed, her mouth open and her nerves in shreds. It would be him, wouldn't it?

Of all the men in the world, she had had to pick on Bruno Falcucci to take an instant dislike to! It hadn't occurred to her for an instant that the man she had got stuck in the revolving door with might be the man she and Charles were waiting for.

Charles was smiling, gesturing to include her in the circle. 'Bruno, I want you to meet my right hand—Martine Archer, my personal assistant for the last four years.'

Martine numbly held out her hand.

Bruno Falcucci took it, his powerful tanned fingers swallowing up her small, pale ones.

She risked a glance upwards. His black eyes coldly mocked her. He said something polite and distant. She answered with equal remoteness. He released her hand.

'Sit down, have a drink; their whisky is very good,' Charles told him.

'I don't drink spirits.' He looked at Martine's glass. 'Is that mineral water? I'll have the same, thank you.'

'I'd forgotten you don't drink,' Charles said, made a face.

'Like your assistant here, I like to keep a cool head,' Bruno Falcucci drawled, and Martine gave him a flicking glance. Oh, very funny! she thought.

Charles ordered the drink, adding, 'And bring the menus, Jimmy, will you? Now, Bruno, what sort of business brings you to London?'

'Banking,' the answer smoothly came.

Charles laughed. 'Of course. Is it confidential? Shall we change the subject?'

'I can't talk in detail about it, I'm afraid. You may read about it in the financial Press some time, but not yet.'

'Well, how long do you plan to stay? Can you tell us that?'

'A week, maybe two. Then I might take a holiday—fly on to Greece, perhaps, or even as far as the Caribbean. I want to relax for a while, unwind, get some sun before I go back to work.'

'You have an amazing tan already!' said Charles. 'Don't you think so, Martine?'

She gave another brief glance in Bruno Falcucci's direction; let her lids droop indifferently over her eyes again. 'Amazing,' she said offhandedly.

She felt Bruno looking at her closely, considering her rich auburn hair, the fine-boned face with the warm, curved mouth and fierce green eyes, before running his gaze down over her body in arrogant appraisal.

Her flush deepened and she felt the back of her neck prickle.

'Where do you go for a holiday?' he asked her.

She shrugged, reluctant to answer.

'Oh, Martine doesn't like hot countries,' Charles answered for her. 'Like most redheads, her wonderful skin doesn't like too much sun. But we had a terrific time in Sweden last summer, didn't we, Martine? And Switzerland was fun a couple of years ago.'

'Especially the *après-ski*, no doubt,' Bruno drawled.

He was making no attempt to hide what he was thinking, his gaze flicking from her to Charles and back again, glinting with cynicism.

He suspected her of having an affair with Charles, she realised. He couldn't be serious! Charles was almost old enough to be her father!

Oh, he was still very good-looking in a weary way, but he had no energy, his hair was thinning and turning silver, his elegant, fine-cut features had a distinct look of strain. She was deeply fond of Charles, she felt sorry for him; but that was all. She resented Bruno Falcucci's speculative stare, the cool cynicism in his eyes.

The head waiter arrived. 'Have you chosen yet, sir?' he asked Charles, who looked at the others.

'I'm ready to order—how about you two?'

Martine nodded. So did Bruno.

She chose melon and sole with a salad; Bruno chose melon, too, with prosciutto, followed by a steak, also with a salad; and Charles ordered melon followed by an omelette with a salad. He ate almost nothing these days. He would probably just pick at his food.

While they waited to be told their table was ready Charles and Bruno talked about the international banking situation. Martine listened intently, absorbing with a faint dismay the fact of Bruno Falcucci's swift, hard intelligence. Charles knew what he was talking about, but he was like a machine running on half-power lately—he kept fading, losing interest, missing vital points. She began to suspect that Bruno could run rings around him.

There was no doubt about it. The man was potentially lethal. And she had a sinking feeling that Charles wouldn't listen if she tried to warn him, would just laugh at her.

The head waiter came back, smiling. 'Whenever you're ready, Mr Redmond . . .'

'Shall we go in?' suggested Charles, rising. Martine got to her feet. He put a hand under her arm in a gallant gesture, to which she submitted, smiling at him, her eyes affectionate. He was always chivalrous, an old-fashioned man in many ways; she liked that.

Out of the corner of her eye, she caught sight of Bruno Falcucci's face: jet eyes watching her with sardonic amusement, mouth wry. Martine's smile stiffened into anger. It was going to be an ordeal to sit through a meal with that man across the table. She wished she couldn't read his mind so clearly, but it was as if his thoughts leapt across the table to her—or maybe he was actually allowing her, or willing her, to pick up what he was thinking!

Yet why should he? She frowned, letting Charles steer her into the dining-room. Her imagination was really working overtime, surely? She was building Bruno Falcucci up into some sort of bogeyman!

She was seated between the two men at the table, but from then on she turned all her attention, and her body, towards Charles, practically ignoring the other man except when she had no option.

Bruno Falcucci leaned back in his chair, a brooding presence, watching her out of narrowed eyes, physically dominating the circle they made: herself, Charles and him, around this table, with his wide black-clad shoulders, his deep chest and hard face.

Charles dominated the talking, though, and was too absorbed in his favourite subject, international finance, to be aware of the silent duel going on across the white-damask-covered table with its spray of dark red roses in the centre. The dining-room was shadowy, and a softly shaded lamp gave them exactly enough light in which the table glittered with crystal glass, silver cutlery and fine bone china and their faces glowed, now in shadow, now in light, like shifting masks.

It was towards the end of the meal that Charles finally asked Bruno Falcucci the question Martine knew he had been planning to put to him.

'How would you feel about leaving your present job, Bruno, and coming to work for us in a rather more senior position?'

If Bruno was surprised he didn't show it. There was a beat of time when he just sat there, as if absorbing the possibilities, then he calmly said, 'That's a very flattering offer, Charles. I would need to know precisely what you had in mind, of course, and I'd need time to think it over, but in principle I'm certainly interested.'

Charles beamed. 'I hoped you would be. You wouldn't regret the decision if you accepted, Bruno, I promise you that. You could have a splendid future with us, far more exciting than anything you have in prospect at the moment. Ours is a family bank and you are my only male relative.'

He shouldn't be stating the situation quite so frankly. He was betraying the weakness of his position, Martine thought, watching Bruno Falcucci closely, her green eyes sharp and hostile.

He was watching Charles, and his face was a polite mask. Martine would have given a good deal to know what he was thinking, whether he was excited, triumphant, elated. He gave no clues.

'I'll get Martine to put together a proposition for you, setting out all the terms,' Charles promised as he called for the bill. 'And after you've had time to digest the contents, we can talk it over. I'm going to be frank with you—I think your mother should have been provided for in her father's will; she should have had shares in the bank.'

Bruno nodded. 'She should.'

There was a ruthless set to his jaw, the spark of anger in his black eyes. If Charles thought Bruno did not resent the way his mother had been treated, he was clearly wrong. Bruno resented it bitterly. Martine shivered. She hoped Charles hadn't made a fatal mistake. Yet what threat could Bruno present to him? Charles owned a majority of the shares in the bank; Bruno couldn't hurt him.

Charles smiled at him, apparently blithely unaware of the dark feeling in the younger man. 'I want to make up for the past, Bruno. I want you in the family business, where you belong.'

Martine shifted restlessly, frowning. Haven't you got eyes? she wanted to ask Charles. Can't you see what he's like under the good looks and the formal good manners?

Bruno flicked one of those brief, cold glances her way. Charles might not be picking up her agitation, but Bruno Falcucci was, and her dismay didn't bother him. He looked into her eyes, then away, one black brow curling sardonically.

A hard spot of red burnt in her cheeks. She knew what that lifted eyebrow had said. She might oppose him but she wouldn't be a problem, he could deal with her.

Well, that was what he thought! They would see about that.

Charles signed the bill, folded some notes into the leather wallet in which the bill had arrived, and stood up, yawning, looking suddenly drained and white.

'I'm sorry, Martine,' he said in a wearily apologetic voice. 'I'd planned to drive you home myself, but I'm barely able to stay on my feet—will you be very cross if I just put you into a taxi back to Chelsea?'

'Don't worry about it,' she began, but Bruno interrupted.

'I have my car parked outside; I'll drop her off.'

'I thought you said you were staying at the Savoy? There's no need to drive out to Chelsea, I can easily get a taxi.' Martine certainly didn't want him driving her home. The very idea of being alone with the man even for five minutes sent shivers down her spine.

'It's still early. I would enjoy a drive along the river,' he shrugged.

Charles beamed. 'And you can get to know each other! That's a wonderful idea, I should have thought of it myself. Martine is indispensable to me, Bruno. She can tell you all you need to know about the way the bank runs.'

His car was parked across the street. As he began to walk towards it Martine caught Bruno Falcucci's secret smile, and tensed. If she hadn't known how it would upset Charles she would have slapped his face.

Turning away, she walked with Charles to his car, watching him with concern.

'You look quite ill, Charles. You've been working too hard for far too long. I think you need a long holiday. Why don't you take a few days off work and get away?'

'I will, soon,' he said quietly, bent and kissed her cheek. 'You're my guardian angel—don't think I'm not aware of it. Now, be nice to Bruno. I want him to join us, Martine, sell the bank to him. I've done some quiet research on him and he has quite a record, he's pulled off some brilliant deals. Even if he wasn't family, I'd want him, but as he is a Redmond, even though his name is different, I'm determined to get him by hook or by crook.'

'Well, in that case I'll do what I can,' she promised as Charles got behind the wheel of his silver Rolls. She meant what she said, despite her private reservations about the man. She would certainly sell the bank to Bruno Falcucci, but she doubted if it would be necessary. She had the feeling no persuasion would be required to get him to join them. He had always planned to do so.

Charles smiled at her through the window as he started the softly purring engine.

'I know I can always trust you. Goodnight, Martine, see you tomorrow.'

He drove off and she turned to find Bruno Falcucci right behind her, lounging against a long, sleek, vintage black Rolls-Bentley. It was one of the loveliest cars she had ever seen; her mouth watered at the sight of it. She loved old cars.

He opened the passenger door, his body graceful as he held the door for her. 'Where am I to take you?'

'Do you know Chelsea?' she curtly asked, having already discovered that he had been to London a number of times.

He nodded. 'Vaguely. I make for Parliament Square and head off along the Embankment, right?'

She nodded. 'I live a stone's throw from the Tate Gallery, I'll guide you after we get to Millbank.'

She slid into the Bentley's interior, instinctively stroking the soft, pale cream leather seats, giving the dashboard an appreciative inspection.

'Is this yours, or have you borrowed or hired it?' she asked as Bruno got in beside her.

His tanned hands lightly holding the wheel he turned his black head and gave her a long, cool look.

'It's mine. I just bought it.'

It must have cost a fortune; she wondered how much he earned a year to be able to afford a toy like this. Well, she would find out soon, when he and Charles began negotiations.

'You aren't married, Mr Falcucci?'

He shook his head, that sardonic smile in evidence again.

'Have you ever been?' she asked.

'No, have you?'

'No,' she said tersely.

'You're a devoted secretary, though,' he drawled. 'Lucky Charles.'

He turned his head again, deliberately, to meet her stare and Martine let all her dislike and distrust of him show in her face.

'If you hurt Charles in any way I'll kill you!' she told him.

His brows shot up and he gave her that cool, sardonic smile, then took her breath away by what he said next.

'If he was going to marry you, he'd have done so long ago, you know. You're wasting your time waiting for him; which seems a pity, looking the way you do.' His dark eyes flicked down over her body and a wave of heat flowed through her. Softly he added, 'I'm sure a lot of men would be only too happy to help you forget Charles. I might even volunteer myself!'

Martine went dark red, her hands clenching, her teeth together, but she refused to play his game by answering or defending herself, explaining that he was wrong. Information was power, Charles had taught her long ago. Never give it away, use it for your own purposes and do so sparingly. So she let Bruno Falcucci imagine that he had hit on the truth, just gave him one icy glance, then said in a tight, brusque voice, 'Take the next turn on the right, would you?'

The Bentley spun round the corner and began moving along the wide street of rather stately Victorian houses.

'No comment, then?' Bruno Falcucci asked her, watching her out of the corner of his eyes.

'Stop here, please,' was all Martine said.

He braked and turned towards her but she was already getting out of the car. She slammed the door then bent towards the window and he leaned over to wind it down to hear what she said.

Martine looked into his gleaming, dark eyes. 'Remember, if you hurt Charles, I'll make sure you pay for it,' she said, then turned on her heel and walked away.

CHAPTER TWO

'YOU have to admit,' said Annie, one of the share analysts, some months later, 'he's an asset to the bank!'

'Oh, please, no puns this early in the morning!' winced Martine.

'You've got no sense of humour where he's concerned, that's the trouble,' complained Annie, who was a year younger, and very pretty: small, fair, bubbly, and very popular with the men. 'And you've dodged my question! He's the hottest thing we've acquired in years. Look at that Ambleham-Tring merger—I hear we've picked up a lot more business from that, and his client list has doubled since he arrived.'

'Haven't you got any work to do?' Martine was staring at her VDU, frowning over the string of figures coming up. 'Because if you haven't, I have. With Charles ringing in to say he's working at home today, and our trip to Rome starting tomorrow, I've got so much to do I'll be working until very late tonight, so get off my desk and go away, Annie!'

'In a minute,' Annie said, wriggling like a child on the edge of the desk, her small feet swinging back and forth. 'I wanted to ask you something . . .'

'Well, what?' Martine irritably asked, wondering how Annie could be so thick-skinned. What did you have to do to get rid of her?

'Has he got a woman tucked away somewhere? I mean, he hasn't dated anyone since he joined us, he says he isn't married, and I can't believe he's gay, so is there someone in the background?'

'I don't know, I don't care, and will you please shut up about Bruno Falcucci, get off my desk and let me get on with my work?' Martine frequently wished she had never heard the man's name, let alone met him. He had been here nearly four months and she sometimes felt as if the whole place revolved around him. It certainly did as far as the female staff were concerned. They couldn't stop talking about him; half of them were in love with him and the others were simply fascinated.

Except Martine, of course. If anything, she disliked him more now than she had the first day she'd met him.

She had watched grimly while he became a director and immediately began to dominate board meetings, making himself the centre of power on the board, a voice to be reckoned with, pushing Charles further and further out of the picture.

It was what she had feared from the beginning, but Charles would not listen even now. He had smiled gently when she pointed out that Bruno had taken over some of his own clients, some of the most lucrative, at that.

'At my suggestion, my dear girl!' he had insisted. 'I'm trying to shed some of my workload. You told me I was working too hard, remember!'

'I didn't tell you to hand some of your best clients over to Bruno Falcucci! And you never told me that was what you were planning!'

He had given her a wry, apologetic look. 'I knew you'd get agitated and lecture me on your favourite subject!'

Eyes startled, she'd asked, 'What do you mean?'

'Bruno,' Charles had said, laughing softly as she flushed dark red. 'Now, don't deny it—you're paranoid where he's concerned. You think he has horns and a forked tail!'

'Yes,' she had said then, soberly. 'I don't trust him, and I only hope you aren't making a serious mistake, letting him get into such a position of power at the bank.'

Her uneasiness had not lifted a few weeks after this discussion with Charles, on the cool autumn morning when Annie sat on her desk and would not stop talking about Bruno Falcucci.

'Shoo,' she told Annie, pushing her off her desk, and Annie turned a laughing face to her.

'Oh, come on, I bet you're secretly crazy about Bruno too—you just won't admit it!'

'I'd rather date Dracula!' Martine snapped just as her office door opened.

She and Annie both looked round, both froze in confusion. Bruno stood in the doorway, his dark eyes hooded and unreadable, his powerful body briefly at rest, which she already knew was rare for him since he was perpetually in motion, a man with burning energy always racing against the clock, or himself, or the world, she wasn't sure which.

'What's Dracula got that I haven't?' he drawled, and Annie began to giggle, half in relief because he didn't seem angry, half with embarrassment because she didn't know how much of the earlier conversation he had overheard.

'Don't tempt me,' Martine said, and Bruno looked into her eyes, his mouth twisting.

'Could I?'

Annie's eyes grew enormous, fascinated. She looked from one to the other and waited to hear more.

'No,' Martine said through her teeth.

Bruno held the door open. 'Weren't you just going, Annie?' he asked in a bland voice. She hesitated, wanting to stay and eavesdrop, but Bruno's eyes were hypnotic. Reluctantly she swayed her way across the room towards him. Martine watched Bruno watch Annie. There was a distinct gleam in the dark eyes. Annie was a pocket-sized blonde Venus—high breasts, tiny waist, rounded hips—and she knew how to move to make men stare. Bruno was staring now.

Annie paused to smile up at him; Martine couldn't see her face but she saw the way Bruno smiled down at her.

'Dracula hasn't got anything you haven't got,' Annie said, and giggled.

'Then why aren't you scared?' Bruno asked and bent towards her, lip curling to show his teeth, pretending to be about to sink his fangs into her throat.

Annie shrieked in delight and fled.

Bruno straightened and looked across the room. Martine coldly met his laughing gaze and the laughter stopped; his face tightened and turned cold. He walked towards her, letting the door slam behind him.

Her nerve-ends quivered in alarm at something in his stare. He stopped beside her desk, and for an instant of panic she was afraid he was going to touch her, kiss her.

She went crimson, then white, shrinking back from him.

He watched her inexorably.

'One of these days I'm going to tell you why you can't stand the sight of me,' he said softly. 'And then you'll really hate me.'

'I already do!'

It came out before she could stop it, and she bit her lip in shock. She hadn't meant to be so up-front about her real feelings; she was horrified that she should have lost control like that. In her work she often came up against men she loathed and despised, but she knew better than to let her view of them show!

'I'm sorry,' she said edgily, not quite meeting his gaze. 'I lost my temper, please forget I said that.'

If he told Charles she knew the reaction she would get. Charles would be appalled. He was aware she didn't trust his cousin but he expected her to have a little self-control and to keep her private opinions to herself. And, in fact, so did she. She was angry with herself for losing her cool.

'I never forget anything,' Bruno murmured, and she believed him. She had already discovered what a fantastic memory he had; he seemed to know everything about every public company and many in private hands. The tiniest detail was retained in his mind and could be conjured up out of nowhere when he needed it. They used state-of-the-art computers to do work Bruno could do in his head and seemed to find child's play.

'That's up to you,' she said, trying to hide her faint dismay. No doubt one day she would pay for having lost her temper. She suspected him to be a man who took his revenge for past wounds. That was why it worried her that Charles seemed to trust him so implicitly. She was afraid that one day Bruno Falcucci would make Charles pay for the way the Redmond family had treated Bruno's mother.

She swallowed, looked at the screen in front of her and changed the subject. 'Have you seen the latest Japanese figures?'

'More or less as I predicted,' he shrugged.

'Yes, right again, as usual!' Martine said with saccharine sweetness.

He laughed. She couldn't even make him angry. It was infuriating. She wished he would go away, he was ruining her morning.

'I am rather busy,' she told him coldly. 'So unless you wanted to tell me something important...?'

'Charles just rang me from his home,' he said. 'About the Rome conference...'

'Yes?' She was flying to Rome with Charles the following day for an international banking conference, and was rather looking forward to the trip. It was ages since she had been anywhere interesting, and it would mean getting away from the office and Bruno Falcucci for a little while.

'His doctor has advised him to stay in bed for a week, so he won't be able to go,' Bruno coolly said.

'What's wrong? Is he ill?' Martine anxiously asked but Bruno shook his head.

'Just tired, I gather. A touch of flu, too, maybe. Nothing serious, but his doctor thinks he needs complete rest. He asked me to explain to you, and say how sorry he is to miss the Rome trip.'

'Of course; I understand, though,' Martine said, deeply disappointed, her face falling. 'I can't say I'm surprised, he has looked quite exhausted the last few days. He really needs a long holiday, but a week in bed would be a good start. Well, I'd better cancel everything, but I don't think we'll be able to reclaim the price of the air tickets. The hotel can be cancelled without a problem, of course.'

She put out a hand to the phone but Bruno caught hold of her wrist, his fingers cool and light, yet making her aware of their potential strength.

'No, don't cancel anything. The trip is still on, it's just that I'll be taking Charles's place.'

Martine stiffened. 'You?'

His mouth curled. 'Sorry, I know I'm no substitute for Charles in your eyes, but you'll have to put up with my company for a few days, I'm afraid. Charles wants the bank represented. He was making a speech on the pros and cons of monetarist policy and he wants me to read it to the conference.'

Martine knew all about that speech; Charles had discussed it with her at great length. She could have delivered that speech for him, if he'd asked her, but Charles hadn't even considered that, she realised, her mouth taut.

Bruno considered her expression, his brows crooked. 'Charles has a rather old-fashioned view of women's place in banking, doesn't he?'

'Which you share?' she bitterly suggested.

'You do enjoy thinking the worst of me, don't you? No, as it happens, I don't, but Charles was obviously ill and I couldn't very well argue with him. Have you got all his documentation, by the way? Tickets, etcetera?'

She nodded and began to get up. Bruno moved back just enough to let her pass; she picked up the scent of his aftershave and decided she didn't like it.

She found the folder containing all the travel documents for Charles, and handed it to Bruno.

'The name on the tickets will have to be changed. I'll do that.'

'Don't worry, my secretary will deal with it,' he said, turning to walk out. 'See you tomorrow, on the plane.'

She glared after him, half inclined not to turn up. Only her loyalty to Charles made her decide to go. Someone had to keep an eye on Bruno Falcucci.

They met at Heathrow, in fact, in a chaotic, overcrowded terminal building. All planes were delayed by fog in the London area. Bruno and Martine bought piles of newspapers and magazines, drank lots of bitter black coffee, tried to ignore screaming babies, restless children, the whine of the Tannoy, the discomfort of the seats they sat on.

At last the fog lifted and planes began to take off. They were two hours late in leaving for Rome, in the end.

The chauffeur-driven car they had ordered was not waiting to meet them when they arrived. They had to take a taxi, there were long queues and a black, relentless rain was falling. Rome sulked under sagging clouds and grey skies. Looking up, Martine felt very depressed.

By the time they got to their hotel, which sat near the top of the Spanish Steps, she was barely able to stand, and very fed up. She collected her key and went straight to her room, which turned out to be charming: beautifully furnished and with a magnificent view over the huddled roofs, towers and cupolas of the city.

The rain was still teeming down, lashing along streets, trickling down windows, spilling from the gargoyles on churches, splashing in gutters, forming rivers down the Spanish Steps.

Martine leaned on the window for a while, gazing out. There was a magnificent desolation about the scene spread out below her, and her eyes wandered from building to building, absorbing the atmosphere. Even in the rain Rome was noisy, bustling, over-full of people and vehicles. She heard the blare of horns, police whistles, people shouting to each other, people quarrelling loudly, the clatter of feet on old pavements.

Sitting there with the window open made her shiver after a while. She stood up, closed the window and went into her modern bathroom to take a long, warm, fragrant bath, pouring deliciously scented bath oils into the water before she climbed gratefully into it.

Bruno had suggested that they meet for dinner at eight o'clock in the bar. The first gathering of the conference was at nine o'clock the following day, and was scheduled to take place at another hotel, the Excelsior, which was a popular conference centre with efficient modern facilities, next door to the United States embassy and close to the via Veneto. Most of the delegates were also staying at the Excelsior, but Charles had wanted to have a peaceful bolthole to make for when conference politics grew too hectic. It often helped to be able to escape for a while. The lobbying began at breakfast and went on until well into the night, and if you could get away you had a better chance of preserving your sanity, Charles said.

After her bath, Martine went to sleep on her bed, wrapped in her thick white bathrobe, a quilt over her. Her dreams were as chaotic as the traffic in the Rome streets; she twisted and sighed in her sleep, her body restless, overheated.

She woke up with a start when someone knocked sharply on the door. For a second she was totally disorientated. While she had slept, night had fallen; the room was dark, only the flash of a neon light somewhere nearby in the city to show her the furniture, the high oblong of the window.

She lay on the bed, staring blankly; then somebody knocked on the door again, louder, peremptorily.

Stumbling off the bed, she went to the door and opened it on the chain, blinking in the light from the corridor.

It was Bruno, in evening dress, looking the way he had the night she first saw him—ultra-civilised, menacingly primitive. It was a very disturbing mix, added to which, just the sight of his smooth-skinned, closely shaven face and sleek black hair, his gleaming jet eyes, his powerful body, sent a strange quiver of weakness through her. Ever since she had met him she had been both alarmed by and hostile to him, working on instincts buried inside her, too deep for her to be quite sure what it was about the man that set all her alarm bells jangling.

'Aren't you dressed yet? We said eight o'clock,' Bruno reminded her, his gleaming eyes roaming slowly over her dishevelled, damp coils of auburn hair, her flushed face, the short white robe which left her long legs bare and revealed the deep cleft between her breasts.

She instinctively put up a hand to pull her robe lapels together to hide her breasts, and saw Bruno's mouth twist in wry comprehension.

'I must have fallen asleep,' she stammered. 'Why don't you get yourself a drink in the bar, and I'll only be ten minutes, I promise!'

She shut the door quickly, afraid he would notice she was trembling. Switching on the light, she leaned on the elaborately carved oak bed for a moment, to steady her nerves. What on earth was wrong with her? Maybe she had picked up some bug? The same one Charles had got? She wouldn't be surprised. That was how she felt—ill, feverish, weak-legged, shivery.

She didn't want to get dressed, do her hair, have dinner alone with Bruno Falcucci; she didn't feel strong enough.

But how could she get out of it? They were here representing the bank, standing in for Charles; she couldn't simply duck out of her responsibilities, she would be letting Charles down. She must pull herself together.

Her hands cold and shaking, she began to get ready. She had picked out her dress before she had her bath: a dark green velvet, figure-hugging, with a deep scoop neckline along which ran a Greek key pattern in gold thread, a tight waist and very short skirt which left her long legs bare. It was formal and elegant, but once she had put it on Martine had second thoughts.

She stared at herself in the mirror, biting her lip. She had forgotten just how tight the dress was, and how short the skirt! It made her feel half-naked. Charles had always liked the dress, that was why she had packed it, but wearing it for Charles was one thing—wearing it when she was going to spend an evening alone with Bruno Falcucci was something else. The very thought of it made her hair stand up on the back of her neck.

She looked at her watch, and groaned. There was no time to change, either. If only she hadn't fallen asleep on the bed! She still had to do her hair and her face. She picked up her brush and began to work hurriedly.

When she walked into the hotel bar she saw Bruno watching her from a table on the other side of the room and an atavistic shudder ran through her.

Déjà vu, she told herself hurriedly. That was what it was, *déjà vu*, because this was almost a re-run of the night they'd met—and she remembered with another shudder the way their reflections had shimmered in the dark glass behind the bar. It had seemed significant then; more so now.

He's dangerous to me, she thought. Dangerous to Charles. To the bank.

Yet there was something darker involved, something she had never quite faced.

She did so now. I'm afraid of him, she admitted, ice trickling down her spine. He terrifies me.

She thought of Charles's pale face and tired eyes, the sadness in his heart, and she hated Bruno Falcucci. Charles was helpless against him; he didn't have the drive or the desire to fight back if he was attacked, but Bruno wasn't going to destroy Charles if she could stop him, so she pushed her fear away and began to walk towards him through the crowded bar.

Her auburn hair glowed like dark flame in the light of chandeliers, her oval face a classical cameo, green-shadowed eyes, elegant nose, wide, full, generous red mouth. Her slender, rounded figure swayed under the tight dark green velvet, the low neckline drawing eyes to her high, white breasts, her pale legs moving gracefully, the skirt constantly sliding up to give glimpses of her slim thighs.

The lively hum of voices, the clink of glasses, the laughter, died away and people's heads turned to watch her, although Martine herself was completely unaware of her effect on the others in the bar because she was too absorbed in staying cool, getting herself under control.

The only watching eyes of which she was aware were Bruno's; she didn't meet them but she felt them fixed on her, black, brilliant, intent, and the way they watched her made a pulse beat hard in her throat.

He stood up to greet her, she slid into the deep-upholstered seat beside him, and the noise in the bar broke out again.

'That was quite an entrance!' Bruno drily said. 'What will you have to drink?'

She looked at his glass and wasn't surprised to see that it was mineral water with a twist of lime in it. 'The same as you, thanks.'

He ordered the drink and handed her a menu. 'I've already decided what I want, but take your time to choose. The food is terrific here, and as it is a special occasion I thought we might try a glass or two of an excellent Italian wine they have on their list. You do drink wine, don't you?'

'Sometimes, not often,' she agreed, looking at the menu and realising suddenly that she was hungry. She hadn't eaten on the plane because she hated unreal food, and with surprise it dawned on her that her last meal had been breakfast at the airport. 'What a huge menu! I don't know what half these dishes are!' Remembering suddenly that he was a Swiss of Italian extraction, she asked him, 'Can you recommend something?'

He shifted along the seat and leaned over her shoulder. She felt his thigh touching hers, his arm against her, smelt his cologne.

'This is probably good at this time of year,' he suggested, pointing. 'Autumn is the best time for wild mushrooms, and I love them served with seafood.'

Martine read the name of the dish falteringly: *funghi e frutti di mare*.

'Mushrooms and seafood?' she asked.

'Exactly.' Bruno's deep voice had a husky tone, she felt his warm breathing on her bare shoulder.

'OK, I'll have that,' she hurriedly said, nervously aware of his body somehow even closer. 'And I suppose I'll just have pasta for the main course.' She would have moved away then but Bruno shook his head, pointing to the menu again.

'Don't be so predictable!' he softly said, very close to her ear. 'Try the *saltimbocco* . . .'

'What's that?'

'It means...hmm..."jump in the mouth"...it's veal escalope, rolled in ham, flavoured with sage, fried and then simmered in Marsala wine. Very rich, but it's a Roman speciality, you must try it once, at least. While you're in Italy, and especially in Rome, you must be more adventurous, take a few risks for once in your life!'

She tensed, picking up the undertone, the hidden meaning, and hedged instinctively. 'Risks and banking don't go together!'

'Oh, but they do,' he drawled. 'Lending money is always a risk, but if you don't gamble you don't accumulate, as you know very well. You've been working for Charles for too long. Charles has the excuse of being middle-aged, but you're not.'

'Charles isn't middle-aged!' she threw back, flushed and angry now. 'He's only in his forties.'

Bruno laughed coldly. 'That *is* middle-aged!'

'Yes, well, Charles is still very...' She broke off the sentence, not sure how she had been meaning to finish it, and Bruno finished it for her in a hard, sardonic voice.

'Attractive? Was that what you were going to say? I know you worship the ground he walks on, and I'd be curious to know why you're so fixated on a man who was at university before you were even born! Does he remind you of your father? Or didn't you have a father? If I had a crude mind, I'd suspect it might be Charles's money you were really interested in, and that thought did occur to me before I got to know you, but I've realised you aren't that materialistic. No, it's Charles himself, isn't it?' His dark eyes watched her tense profile closely. 'You have a real problem, Martine. The gap's too wide. You'd regret it bitterly sooner or later if Charles was crazy enough to take what you're dying to give him.'

Her face was burning and a choking rage filled her throat. She turned on him furiously, her green eyes stormy with resentment.

'How dare you...?' She stopped as the waiter approached. Quivering, dark red, Martine had to swallow the words boiling to get out.

Bruno was as cool as the ice-cubes in their drinks. He smiled blandly at the waiter. 'Ah, ready to take our order? Right.' He ordered for them both, without consulting Martine again, which at any other time would have infuriated her, but which she accepted without comment then because she knew she couldn't have said a word without her voice shaking.

By the time the waiter had gone Martine had had time to work out what she really wanted to say to Bruno, but, before she could start, someone else came up to their table.

Before she actually spoke, Martine picked up the heady, musky fragrance of her perfume. It enveloped them like a cloud.

'Bruno, *caro*!' a warm voice said, and Bruno got up, smiling. Martine watched coldly as he was engulfed in what looked like a very passionate embrace. The woman was in her thirties, her black hair wreathed at the back of her head in coils and pinned there with a huge black lace bow, her skin olive, but glowing with a golden tan she had not got in Italy at that time of year. She had a figure like a fairground switchback, curving in and out exaggeratedly: full, warm breasts, a tightly belted waist, with rounded hips giving a curved line to the black satin evening suit she wore. It glittered with diamanté on the neck and cuffs and hem. Diamonds shone in her ears, at her throat, at her wrists; her hands sparkled with rings, too.

She was certainly not a wallpaper person, thought Martine drily. In fact, she obviously dressed to be noticed, in every sense of the word.

The way she was kissing Bruno, they must surely have been lovers at one time. Good friends didn't kiss on the mouth like that. So, that was the sort of woman he liked?

Martine's green eyes chilled. Every little detail about him was important, told her new facts about him, might help her defeat whatever he had planned against Charles. But she wouldn't have expected him to like a woman who looked like that.

A second later, Bruno turned her way to introduce her. 'Angelina, this is a colleague from London, Martine Archer. Martine, this is the wife of an old friend of mine, Angelina Fabri.'

Martine smiled politely and coldly, offered her hand. The other woman took it, her own smile equally cool, studying her with shrewd, sophisticated eyes.

'You are in banking?' She spoke English with a strong Italian accent, her phrasing slightly off most of the time. 'Yes, I can tell you are. A career woman, obviously. And if it gives you all you need, why not? For some women it is the answer; we don't need to get married these days, after all!'

Martine kept her face cool, her teeth together, but she knew she had just been patronised and insulted.

Bruno smoothly intervened, openly amused by the instant hostility between the two women.

'I think your friends are about to leave, Angelina.'

She turned to look across the room at a group near the door, and waved, nodding.

'Yes, I must go, *caro*! Will we see you while you're here? Now, promise we will!'

'I'll do my best. Give Carlo my best wishes, tell him I'll ring, as soon as I can. Unfortunately, I have too many engagements during the conference, but my last day here is free, maybe we could meet then?'

'You must come to dinner, *caro*. Arrange it with Carlo. *Ciao*!' Angelina gave him another hug, nodded dismissively to Martine, and walked away.

Bruno sat down again, gave Martine an amused glance. 'Well, you and Angelina didn't hit it off, did you? A pity, she's a warm-hearted woman...'

'So I noticed,' Martine said.

'Miaow!' he murmured, laughing silently. 'Well, that's Angelina; it doesn't mean anything, she's always very over the top whatever she does.'

'Does her husband know she's so...fond...of you?'

The icy sting in her voice didn't bother him; his eyes had a mocking gleam in them.

'Carlo? He adores her just the way she is... they have a very happy marriage. She's a wonderful mother, they have four boys and two girls, she runs their home to perfection—Carlo's a very lucky guy and he knows it.'

Martine stared at him, uncertain now about his relationship with the Italian woman, wishing she knew the truth about that, about every other aspect of his life. What sort of man was Bruno Falcucci?

They went into dinner a few minutes later. The meal was superb; the wine matched it. Martine only intended to drink one glass, but without noticing it drank far more because the waiter kept refilling her glass.

They talked about the conference over the table at first, then as the evening wore on Martine talked less and less. She was feeling light-headed, dreamy, a heat and excitement running through her veins. Across the table Bruno watched her with those hypnotic eyes while they drank their coffee.

'Liqueur?' he suggested as the wine waiter arrived with his rattling trolley of bottles.

She hastily shook her head. 'I've already drunk too much wine. I don't want a headache in the morning.' She looked at her watch. 'In fact, I think I should be on my way to bed now; we have to get up very early, and there's a very crowded day ahead of us.'

On their way to the lift she paused to look out through the main doors at the Rome night.

'It's stopped raining. What I wanted to do this afternoon was take a walk around the city, but I couldn't go out in all that rain.'

'Why not take a short stroll now?' suggested Bruno.

'It's much too late, and I haven't got my coat with me,' she said, but she was drawn towards the door, tempted in spite of common sense.

'We needn't walk far, just look down the Spanish Steps,' Bruno said, putting an arm around her, pushing the door open.

While she was still thinking about it she found herself outside the hotel, in the warm autumn night. The torrential rain had washed the sky and the city clean; the air was soft and still, stars shone over the Roman rooftops and a crescent moon sailed above them.

'It's magical,' she breathed, staring around her. With the rain over, everyone had come out to enjoy the city. The night was full of people, walking, talking, the lights of cafés and bars, the sound of guitars, of someone singing Italian with a throb in his throat.

'You don't want to catch a chill. Put my jacket round your shoulders,' Bruno said, and she looked round in surprise as she dropped his evening jacket around her.

'What about you?' she asked. He looked like a toreador in his black trousers and waistcoat; he had that atmosphere of arrogance, high courage, disdain. 'Aren't you cold just in your shirt-sleeves and that thin waistcoat?'

He shook his head. 'Don't worry about me, I'm tough. Do you want to window-shop? If we go down the steps we'll be in the via Condotti and you can pick from Gucci, Bulgari and a lot of other designer-label places.'

'Going down the steps would be fine,' she said wryly. 'It's coming up again in this dress that could be a problem. The skirt's so tight.'

Bruno's dark eyes wandered slowly over her, lingered on her long, smooth legs. 'That dress is dynamite,' he murmured, and her colour deepened.

She turned away hurriedly and began to wander along the road. She didn't know quite how it had happened but in her dreamy mood her hostility had got lost somewhere, Charles pushed to the back of her mind. She was too wrapped up in the romance of the Rome night.

Passing a dark shop doorway, she heard a movement, a sound; there was a couple standing in the shadows, a skinny boy in jeans and a young girl in a brief tight skirt and red sweater. They were passionately kissing, bodies pressed so fiercely against each other that it was hard to say where one began and the other ended. As Martine paused to stare, the boy's hand began to slide up inside the girl's tiny skirt and the girl gave a little moan.

Martine spun to walk away and cannoned into Bruno.

He had seen the young couple too. He looked down at Martine, who was breathing raggedly, shivering as if she was cold.

'I...we...we'd better go back inside,' she stammered, her face darkly flushed.

Bruno followed her as she headed back towards the hotel, but as they passed another shop he suddenly grabbed her and pulled her into the doorway.

She gave a cry of protest, looking up angrily, and then his mouth was on her own, hard, hot, compelling. It was as if he had lit a forgotten fuse inside her; she began to shake, a flame leaping through her veins, her whole body going up in fire, an explosion that left her helpless.

Her lips parted moistly under the invasion of his tongue; she felt her legs give under her, and put her arms around his neck and clung to him, shuddering in a reaction she couldn't stop or understand.

It was a long time since anyone had made love to her. She had buried desires, needs, hungers that she refused to feel. They had betrayed her once; she wouldn't give them another chance.

Tonight though, the wine must have loosened her inhibitions, allowed her hidden emotions to escape. Deep inside her she felt the beat of an erotic drum. Her fingers clenched in his hair, closed on the firm nape of his neck, moved down his back, passionately aware of the male strength of the warm body under the evening shirt, aching to touch him more intimately, unconsciously moving invitingly against him, her hips pressing closer.

Bruno gave a thick groan, his leg sliding between her thighs, his hand under the jacket still hanging from her shoulders. She felt him unzip the velvet dress; it parted; Bruno's hand slid inside and caressed her bare back, followed the curve of her spine downwards to her buttocks, his fingers inserting themselves into the top of her tiny silk briefs.

The dark, breathing absorption they shared was suddenly broken by the sound of running feet, screams, shouting.

They spun apart, very flushed, out of breath. A teenage boy ran past the shop doorway. They saw a woman's handbag clutched in his hand. Before Bruno and Martine could move a whole string of people ran past after the boy, screaming angrily in Italian. A police whistle sounded near by; the boy dived down the Spanish Steps. The crowd followed him.

The sound of the pursuit died away into the city. Martine shakily did up her zip without looking at Bruno, her head averted. All the excited heat had evaporated, and she was suddenly very cold.

'Come to my room, Martine,' Bruno said with an urgency that made her stiffen.

She turned on him, her face white now. 'I feel sick, do you know that?' she broke out. 'You got me drunk, you knew I wasn't used to drinking, and you kept pouring wine into me, right the way through dinner. You had this in mind all the time, didn't you? You set me up, and it nearly worked. I almost fell for the oldest trick in the book.'

There was a silence you could have cut with a knife. His eyes turned to glittering black ice. 'You did fall for it,' he drawled, admitting her accusations, mocking her. 'I could have had you if that stupid boy hadn't come past here when he did! After all those years of waiting for Charles to finally notice that you're a woman, you're so frustrated that you fell into my hands like a ripe peach, and I didn't even have to try very hard.'

She hit out at him, he ducked and she hurt her hand on the edge of the shop window. Gasping in pain, she shed his evening jacket, let it fall to the floor, and as he bent to retrieve it Martine turned and ran, holding back tears, fighting not to give way to the waves of emotion swamping her. Two minutes later she was back in the hotel, in the safety of lights and other people. She didn't know whether Bruno followed her or not. The lift was standing open and she ran into it at once, pressed the floor button, the doors closed and she was taken up to her room.

Once she was in there, behind locked doors, she could start to cry.

CHAPTER THREE

MARTINE had her breakfast in her room: black coffee, orange juice, a couple of rolls with black cherry jam. She had slept badly but a careful make-up job hid most of the evidence of that and she deliberately picked out a smoothly tailored dark grey suit, short jacket, straight skirt, with a crisp white shirt under it, to make herself fade into the crowd, mostly men, in city suits, who would be attending the conference. Even her auburn hair was pulled back austerely from her face, but she could do little about her long legs in their sheer black stockings. Men always stared at them.

A car was coming at eight-twenty to take Bruno and herself to the Excelsior Hotel for the opening meeting of the conference. Martine left her room at eight-fifteen, and arrived down in the foyer exactly as the chauffeur-driven car arrived. Bruno appeared a moment later, elegant and formal in a dark city suit, red and white striped shirt with a stiff white collar and a sombre wine-red silk tie. Over the suit he wore a black cashmere overcoat, unbuttoned, thrown open.

She gave him a cool nod. 'Good morning,' she said for the benefit of the waiting driver.

Bruno's eyes were frozen wastes, and he answered her in a tone equally distant. 'Good morning.'

They drove side by side in the back of the car, each looking out into the crowded, noisy streets, neither speaking.

It was a short drive; the city lay around them like a living, breathing being. Everywhere they went Martine saw broken stone arches, columns of marble, great pillared churches; heard a continual sound of bells from steeples around the city, the clatter of pigeons in a square they drove through. She watched the birds rise up, wings iridescent against the blue of an autumn morning, heard the splash of fountains, some of them inhabited by magnificent statues, Neptune with a trident, cherubs, dolphins; and everywhere Martine saw flocks of priests in black and nuns with rosary beads rattling as they hurried along.

People said all cities looked alike these days—they couldn't include Rome. It was unlike any city Martine had ever seen.

She stared out at it from the car, feeling as if her every nerve-end had been intensely sensitised; each brief sensation she experienced was sending ripples of response throughout her nervous system.

Bruno leaned back in the corner beside her, his body swaying with the movement of the car. She fought not to look at him, but couldn't stop her eyes wandering sideways once, glimpsing his dark-clad, muscled thigh; one leg crossed over the other, his arm resting on his knee, his hand splayed, long, powerful fingers at ease.

Heat rose in her throat; she was remembering last night, that hand sliding intimately down inside her dress.

Swallowing, she looked away, her skin burning. The mere memory was enough to make her stomach churn. How could she have let him do that to her? Have wanted it? Because she had; she had been going crazy while he touched her, she couldn't deny it.

It was the wine, she told herself hurriedly. That was what had made her crazy: the wine. She wasn't used to drinking, and she certainly wasn't going to touch the stuff again.

It was a relief to reach the hotel. They had to go through Security first, hand over their identification and documents; be given an electronic pass with their name and country of origin, and the name of their bank, digitally recorded on tape on the surface.

'You must wear your pass at all times during the sessions,' they were informed. 'Or you will not be permitted into the conference hall.'

The proceedings began promptly at nine. There were hundreds of delegates seated in rows for this inaugural session, long addresses by very important people in international finance, from the dais; but after the coffee-break at half-past ten many people left for discussions in smaller groups in smaller rooms.

Martine stayed with the general session; Bruno left to take part in one of the groups who were discussing interest rates and the consequences of manipulating them. Martine listened to a series of speeches on market forces, third-world borrowing and debts, the dangers of over-lending.

Lunch was a buffet affair. You lined up to choose from an enormous range of cold or hot food and sat wherever you could find a place.

Carrying her plate of very attractively dressed salad towards a table which still had some empty seats, Martine found herself sitting next to someone she knew—Gerhard von Essenberg, an attractive man in his early thirties, an observer at the conference for the German Bundesbank.

'Lovely to see you, darling,' he said as he kissed her. His tones were those of someone who had spent a couple of years in the sixth form at Charterhouse, the English public school which turned out more city men than any other, before going to university in Germany and then on to MIT in the States for a year before taking up a career in banking. 'Is Charles here too?'

'No, he was to have been, but he has flu,' Martine told him.

'Oh, too bad. Poor Charles.'

They had met in London a year earlier at a reception at the German embassy in Belgrave Square. While he was in London Gerhard had dated Martine twice; they had seen a play together and gone ice-skating, at which Martine was hopeless but at which Gerhard was quite brilliant. He had skated as a child, on frozen lakes and rivers near his home in Germany, he said; she really should visit him there one day.

Charles knew all about him; he said he was a very rich young man from an old German family. Gerhard was fair, faintly cold, very clever. Theirs had been a brief relationship, they'd only known each other for a week; it had been an interlude; hardly a friendship, let alone a romance. But she was pleased to see him.

'We must try to sit together over dinner,' he said.

'We've been allocated seats,' she pointed out, but Gerhard shrugged.

'Oh, I'm sure we can change our seats if we ask. I'm bored by the people I'm with—frightful fellows who talk of nothing but money. Who are you sitting with? Do you know?'

She had been seated next to Bruno. 'A colleague,' she said offhandedly. 'I'd rather sit with you, if it's possible.'

'Anything is possible,' Gerhard said with the faint arrogance of his upbringing and class, and smiled at her with a charm that was entirely his own. 'Now, tell me all your news! Is there a man in your life?'

She shook her head. 'Not at the moment. Have you met the girl of your dreams yet?'

He laughed. 'I keep hoping, but so far no luck.'

'Maybe you're too difficult to please!'

'I've been brought up to expect the best,' he agreed with wry amusement. 'No doubt you're right, but never mind, I enjoy my life. I'm free, single and love to mingle, as they say on TV.'

She laughed. 'You still watch Sky MTV all the time?'

'All the time. When I work at home, I have the TV on with the music programme blaring out—it helps me think, keeps me awake during long night sessions.'

'I wonder how people managed before recorded music!' Martine said thoughtfully.

'My family had their own personal chamber orchestra in the eighteenth century,' Gerhard said casually.

'Good heavens!' Martine said, stunned.

'My father still loves that sort of music; he listens to Mozart, I listen to Guns 'n' Roses. The difference is, I like his music, too; but he hates mine.'

Martine ate her salad slowly, listening to him. She was just finishing her coffee when the delegates began to drift away; the conference was starting again in fifteen minutes. She looked at her watch and sighed.

'Time to get back. See you later.'

She got up and Gerhard rose, too. He bent and kissed her lightly on the mouth. 'Meet me for drinks before dinner in the bar, OK? Seven o'clock?'

She nodded. 'Seven. OK.'

As she turned to go she saw Bruno, at the next table, watching her with the cold eyes of an enemy.

Martine felt a leap of shock, the blood left her face. Pulling herself together, she walked away fast.

They were both in the main hall that afternoon, seated next to each other because the seats had been numbered in advance and one had to sit in the seat one was allocated. Martine tried to concentrate on the meeting, to ignore the fact that Bruno was so close, but she couldn't shut out her awareness of him.

Every time he shifted on his chair, every time he turned a page in his conference programme, every time he moved his head, Martine was deeply conscious of it. She even found herself listening to his breathing at one time, and was angry with herself.

Why was this happening to her? She had been working with him for months in London. She disliked, distrusted, suspected Bruno Falcucci—so why should she suddenly have become so intensely aware of him that she found it hard to think of anything else?

She was relieved when the business of the day finally ended and everyone began to filter towards the door to go back to their rooms.

'Our car will be waiting,' Bruno said offhandedly, and she nodded, following him towards the foyer. The porter went outside to whistle up their waiting vehicle, parked nearby, and Martine climbed into the back of it.

Bruno talked casually about the last discussion they had heard; Martine wondered when to tell him that she would be sitting with Gerhard for dinner.

When they reached their own hotel they took the lift upstairs. They were on the same floor, their rooms adjoining. As they approached the door of her room, Martine blurted out, 'By the way, I've been asked to join a friend for dinner tonight.'

Bruno halted outside her door, his face stiffening. 'The "friend" I saw you having lunch with?'

'Yes,' she said, defiance in her green eyes.

'You make friends quickly,' he said with cold derision.

'I've known Gerhard for ages,' she retorted. 'Charles introduced him to me last year, in London.'

Bruno's smile was sarcastic. 'Oh, well, if he's a friend of Charles's you must be nice to him, of course!'

She resented the emphasis. 'Charles would certainly expect me to be friendly to him. Gerhard is with the Bundesbank.'

'Would he expect you to sleep with him too?'

The words cut like a knife and Martine went red then white, so taken aback that for a minute she was simply dumb. She got out her key and turned to unlock her door, but Bruno hadn't finished yet.

'Because judging by the way he kept looking you over,' he threw at her back, 'that was what was on his mind as an after-dinner entertainment. From where I sat I could see him practically undressing you with his eyes.'

'You've got a one-track mind!' she angrily muttered, trying to get her key into the lock with trembling hands.

'It's a track most men follow, especially with someone who looks like you!'

At last she managed to turn the stiff key, pushed the door open, could finally escape from him. 'All men aren't like you, thank heavens!' she said over her shoulder.

'Well, don't say I didn't warn you,' Bruno grated.

He turned on his heel and walked away to his own room; she slammed her door, trembling with rage and agitation.

She had a long bath to unwind, determined to get herself into a mood to enjoy the evening. She had only brought two cocktail dresses, and one long evening dress for the formal ball which would wind up the conference. This evening she had intended to wear the dress she had worn the previous evening, since she would have to wear one short dress twice, but somehow she couldn't face putting the dark green velvet on again.

Every time she wore it in future she would be reminded of those moments in the dark shop doorway, of Bruno's mouth and hands, of the wild desire he had awakened in her.

She took out of the wardrobe a filmy black chiffon with a skirt that floated around her legs as she walked. Through the chiffon her throat and breasts took on a glimmering pallor; her dark auburn hair glowed with the colour of leaves in the autumn. She clasped a necklace of pearls round her throat, brushed glittery green shadow along her lids, painted her mouth a deep russet red, stood back from the mirror and contemplated her reflection uncertainly.

The dress was as sophisticated as the green velvet, but somehow... She broke off, frowning, biting her lip. Somehow sexier, she uneasily admitted. All that skin showing through the black gauzy material...maybe she should wear the green velvet?

No, she couldn't bear to. She turned away. She had to leave or she would be late. She didn't wait for Bruno; she took a taxi back to the conference hotel and found Gerhard waiting in the bar when she walked in, dead on seven.

His blue eyes skated over her as she walked towards him, and she remembered Bruno's accusation. He practically undresses you with his eyes, Bruno had said, and Gerhard was certainly staring, but Martine didn't find the way he looked at her offensive.

He stood up, kissed her on both cheeks gravely. 'Thank you for joining me. All the men are going to envy me tonight, having you for a partner. That dress is very sexy, and you look breathtaking in it.'

'Thank you, Gerhard,' she said, sitting down, brushing down her filmy skirts as they hissed silkily around her legs.

'What will you have to drink?' he asked, summoning a waiter.

Remembering what had happened with Bruno the previous evening, Martine ordered a mixture of orange juice and mineral water, and stayed off wine all evening.

The meal was superb, Gerhard kept her continuously amused and it would have been a wonderful evening if she hadn't been able to see Bruno from where she was sitting. By bad luck, however, he was seated facing her, on the next table; she had to avoid letting her eyes wander that way or she found herself all too often looking straight at him.

Every time it happened she felt a strange, dizzying lurch, as if her sense of balance had just gone and at any minute she might fall over.

It was disconcerting and disturbing. She became more and more afraid of the sensation. You would expect it to lessen after a while, as she kept seeing Bruno, but it didn't. On the contrary it was getting worse, the effect lasting longer. She would catch sight of him and feel the clutch of vertigo, her pulses hammering, her mouth dry, her head spinning. Hurriedly she would look away but the strange sensations went on and on, making it almost impossible to keep up a polite pretence of interest in what Gerhard was saying. She kept feeling she needed to hold on to something solid—the table, a chair, anything to give her some stability, stop this terrible whirling of the senses.

She was relieved when the meal was over and they all drifted out to the bar again. Martine let Gerhard find a table, agreed to have a crème de menthe liqueur, served on a pyramid of chipped ice; she sipped it slowly, through a straw, making it last half an hour. They had been joined by other Germans from Deutsche Bank, the biggest bank in Germany. They all knew Gerhard, who was a well-known sportsman and a leading light in the sporting activities of the Bundesbank when they played the other German banks at rugger and tennis and squash.

Martine was able to sink back into her chair and listen to them all, without needing to say a word, especially when they kept forgetting she was present and lapsed into German. She knew a little, but not enough to follow a rapid conversation, especially on international banking issues.

At eleven o'clock Bruno appeared beside their table. Martine stiffened as soon as she saw him. The Deutsche Bank people looked round, breaking into smiles and began chattering away to him in German in a way that made it clear they knew him. Martine picked up a phrase or two and realised they were asking him why he had left Switzerland to work in London. Bruno shrugged, replying in their language, and whatever he said made them all laugh.

He glanced coolly across their heads at her. 'Our car's here. Ready?'

Gerhard stirred, looking round at her. 'Darling, I can see you home in a taxi later—you don't want to leave yet, do you?'

Before she could say anything Bruno answered for her crisply. 'We all have to be up early; tomorrow is going to be a demanding day. Hurry up, Martine, we don't want to keep our driver waiting.'

She stumbled to her feet, very flushed, murmured something apologetic to Gerhard, who made a face, but bent to kiss her.

'Maybe he's right, your spoilsport friend? We have a lot to get through tomorrow. OK, sleep well, darling. I'll be seeing you at lunch, perhaps, if we are both free?'

She followed Bruno out of the hotel, got into the waiting car, secretly rather relieved to be leaving because she had been bored with all the banking talk, especially in a language she found it hard to follow, yet at the same time irritated because Bruno was ordering her about, making decisions for her, answering for her.

As they drove through the warm Rome night she muttered to him, 'Will you stop giving me orders as if I were here as your secretary? I'm Charles's private assistant, not yours. He never pushes me around, he treats me with respect, and I'd like you to do the same, please.'

'If I hadn't interrupted your little party you might have been there all night, and then you would have been in no shape to take part in the conference tomorrow,' he coldly said. 'I'm delivering Charles's speech, at eleven, remember; you ought to be there in case there are questions. I might need to consult you on what you think Charles's view might be on some issues. I'm simply his mouthpiece as far as the speech is concerned, and I may not know all the answers to the questions I'm asked, whereas I imagine you will. You make it your business to know everything there is to know about Charles and his opinions.'

'Don't use that sarcastic tone to me!' Martine broke out, her body tense, her face flushed.

'Merely stating the facts,' he drawled. 'If you don't like them it's because you prefer not to face up to the truth.'

The car pulled up outside the hotel. She climbed out, walked through the foyer, collected her key and went towards the lifts. Bruno caught up with her there; she ignored him, her head turned away.

The lift took them up to their floor, they walked to their rooms, Martine slightly ahead, Bruno strolling just behind her. She opened her door but before she could shut it Bruno's foot jammed it open. Tensing, Martine swung round to face him.

'What . . . ?'

'We need to talk, before the conference. I suggest we have breakfast together downstairs at a quarter to eight.'

'I prefer to breakfast in my room.'

His black eyes glittered angrily. 'A quarter to eight, downstairs,' he repeated. 'Be there.'

'Get your foot out of my door!'

'Are you trying to make me lose my temper?' Bruno ground out between his teeth.

'What happens if you do?' she mocked him scornfully. Did he think he could frighten her into obeying him? 'Do you turn green like the Incredible Hulk and burst out of your clothes?'

He wasn't amused, a dark colour in his face, his voice harsh. 'Very funny.'

She had a reckless impulse, and gave in to it, her head tossed back defiantly. 'And for the record you were wrong about Gerhard—he was an angel all evening, a perfect gentleman.'

Bruno laughed without humour. 'Because I came and got you before the evening ended!' His eyes flared, a sudden hard rage in them, and he deliberately looked her up and down, from her warm red mouth to her bared shoulders, down over the filmy black chiffon through which her pale flesh glowed like pearl. 'If you'd come back here with him in a taxi late at night, looking like that, he wouldn't just have seen you to your door and said goodnight. That dress is an invitation to do more than dance, and he would have expected to be asked to stay the night.'

His insulting stare had made her turn red, hating him. 'I ought to slap your face!'

'Try it,' he said, his teeth showing in a barbed smile. 'And by the way, I asked around about Gerhard von Essenberg. He's from an old German family, and he's tipped to climb in the Bundesbank, but he doesn't have the sort of money Charles Redmond has, so even if you do fancy von Essenberg I should go on hoping Charles will finally propose, if I were you. The other guy is closer to your age, but he hasn't got as much to offer.'

It was the final straw. Martine was tired, it had been a difficult day; she lost her temper. Her hand shot up towards his face, but Bruno was too quick for her. He caught her wrist, dragged her hand down again so hard that Martine fell forward.

She found her face buried in his shirt, her nostrils filling with the scent of his body, and went into mindless panic, making muffled sounds of fear, fighting to get away. Bruno took hold of her shoulders, she struggled, there was a tearing noise, and she felt the black chiffon over her shoulders ripping, and cried out wordlessly as one side of her dress tumbled down, leaving part of her breast naked.

Along the corridor a door opened, a face peered out, perhaps disturbed by the noise she was making, and Bruno quickly pushed Martine back into her room and followed, closing the door behind them.

'Get out!' she whispered hoarsely, holding her dress up, trembling violently.

'Martine——' he began, but she couldn't take any more.

'If you don't get out of here now I'll start to scream!'

'You're over-reacting,' he began again and Martine opened her mouth to scream.

Before she could get a sound out his hand was over her lips and he was pushing her backwards, away from the door. She hadn't yet put on the light, the room was pitch-black, she couldn't see him, but she fought him wildly, like a trapped animal.

Suddenly her foot caught the leg of a chair, she stumbled backwards and fell, unable to save herself. Bruno went with her. He landed heavily on top of her, on the carpet, knocking all the breath out of her.

Martine's auburn hair had fallen down, had tumbled over her face, long, silky strands blinding her. She was gasping, shaking, fiercely aware of Bruno's weight holding her down, of the power of that male body as it lay on her.

There was a thick silence; she looked through her hair and saw his face dimly, his black eyes staring down at her, glittering in the dark room like torch-light, setting her on fire.

He made a rough sound in his throat, then his head came down and his mouth was on hers, ruthlessly forcing her lips apart and invading between them, his hands clasping her face, holding her head so that she couldn't escape the probing intimacy of the kiss. Martine struggled helplessly, briefly, half fainting and feeling he would suffocate her at any moment. Her pulses were hammering at neck and wrist and between her breasts; she closed her eyes, a little moan escaping her as she stopped fighting.

Ever since they got to Rome she had been fighting an erotic awareness of him. She didn't understand it, but she couldn't silence it, this beating sensuality whenever Bruno came near her. Every time she saw him she caught herself staring; her mouth went dry; she was hot one minute, cold the next, locked in feverish response to him.

I don't like him; why do I feel like this? I don't trust him, I don't understand him, she told herself, and then, as his mouth slid hotly down her throat, making her shudder with aroused excitement, Oh, God, but I want him.

He pushed aside the torn fragments of her bodice and she groaned as he kissed her naked breast. Her hand went up to clasp the back of his head, and she twisted restlessly underneath him.

Bruno lifted his head, breathing raggedly, his fingers splayed warmly against her body. 'If you don't want this, say so now, while I can still stop,' he whispered in a voice so husky that she only just understood what he'd said.

At the same time his hand was softly moving up her thigh, the intimate brush of his skin on hers making her quiver in hungry response.

'Say something,' he murmured, even more husky, and she kept her eyes closed, groaning.

'Sssh...'

He made a sound like breathless laughter. 'Don't say I didn't give you a chance to say no,' he said, his hand slipping underneath her.

The zip of her dress smoothly ran down, then the silky folds of material slid down her body with a gentle murmur. She shivered in her bra and panties, starting to wake up from the overheated dream, beginning to realise what she was doing. Bruno was kicking off his trousers; he sat up to take off his shirt and she felt cold as the warmth of his body was taken away. Panic surged back into her.

'No,' she said, getting up, stumbling across the room, away from him. 'I must have been out of my mind... I can't...'

She made for the light switch but Bruno caught up with her before she reached it.

'Don't run away from it now, Martine, not now we've got this far,' he whispered in a smoky voice, his arms going round her from behind, pulling her back against his half-naked body, and she shuddered as their flesh touched, skin on skin, the roughness of his hair, the masculinity of bone and muscle imposing themselves, making her deeply conscious of her own femininity.

'I should never have let you touch me,' she said, as much to herself as him, hating herself because she felt the inexorable rise of desire again.

'You're not a virgin?' he murmured, kissing her neck, pressing himself against her.

'What's that got to do with it? I don't just sleep with anyone . . .'

'I never supposed you did. I wouldn't want you if I thought you had,' he said, and his hands covered her breasts, making her tremble with passion.

'But why . . . ?' she cried out, trying to think clearly, to work out what she really felt.

'Why do I want you?' He sighed, his long, naked thigh pushing softly against her, his hands wandering, exploring, making her so weak that she was shaking violently. 'You're beautiful. The minute I saw you I knew I had to have you.'

She had felt the same, she knew that at that instant. When they were jammed in that revolving door together she had felt his body against hers and a heat had begun deep inside her, a heat which had been growing ever since, and which just the sight of him could start into life.

She was torn between an aching need and fear. 'I...I haven't taken any precautions,' she muttered.

'Don't worry, I'll take care of that,' he said at once, and spun her round to face him, held her lightly by the hips, drawing her closer.

She gave a groan, stood on tiptoe and kissed him passionately, her arms going round his neck, her body yielding in boneless surrender.

Bruno lifted her off her feet and on to the bed. He didn't give her another chance to change her mind. While she was still catching her breath he entered her and she arched to take him, a wordless primitive cry coming from her throat.

For months desire had been driving her towards this instant. She had fought it, tried to pretend it wasn't happening to her, but it had been too strong, she had been helpless against it. She didn't know even now whether she was in love, or merely obsessed, she only knew she couldn't fight how she felt any more.

Last, night, when they had walked along the top of the Spanish Steps in the warm autumn night and she'd seen the young lovers in that shop doorway, that had been the moment when she'd known she wanted Bruno like that.

She had seen those two kissing, their bodies straining against each other, and suddenly she had felt heat sweep through her, her mouth had gone dry, and Bruno had looked at her with the same craving in his eyes.

She had wanted to go to bed with him then. If they had been up here, in her room, they would have made love. She had known it last night, she knew it now. If she hadn't slept with him now she would have, one day, sooner or later, because she couldn't stop thinking about it, day and night. The beat of that erotic desire drummed in her blood, in her ears; she had ached to touch him, to feel his hair under her hands, to hold his body as he moved in her, with her.

She cried out, her nails digging into his back, and Bruno groaned, head flung back in passionate pleasure.

His skin was red-hot, his breathing tortured; so was hers. She was caught up in the vortex of a whirlpool, irresistibly engulfed in a spiralling pleasure. She was deaf, dumb, blind to everything else in the world; entirely taken over by desire. She had shed all inhibitions; forgotten where they were, what room, in what city, in what country. There was only this bed, her body twisting and shuddering with his body driving into her.

She said his name, pleading, moaning. It seemed to be taking forever to reach the intense, dark heart of that feeling; she was going out of her mind, and she pushed her face into his warm, bare shoulder, kissed his perspiring skin, tasted the salt of his body on her tongue and grazed him with her teeth, bit him as the frenzy mounted, and then the aching tension broke and she gave a final long, moaning cry and began to fall down, down, out of all control.

It was like dying, her heart pounding, her lungs tortured, her limbs trembling violently.

She heard Bruno saying her name, his voice unrecognisable, gasping out in the same unbelievable ferocity; and then there was silence and she lay like someone who had drowned, her arms flung out on either side, her eyes closed, her lips apart, breathing in dragging anguish.

For minutes on end they just lay there, his body heavy on her, his head on her breast, the sweat running between them.

Then Bruno slowly slid off and lay beside her, his breathing gradually slowing. Martine was too exhausted to move. She couldn't even open her eyes.

He got up and went into her bathroom. She winced as light stabbed into the dark bedroom, put her arm across her face, and turned on to her side, her back to the light. He came back and got into bed again; by then she was half asleep and only stirred lightly as she felt his cooler flesh touch her when he curved his body round hers. He pulled a sheet over them both, but she hardly noticed. She was light as air, empty, drained. Moments later she was deeply asleep.

When she woke up in the morning he was gone.

CHAPTER FOUR

MARTINE might almost have thought she had dreamt the night before, except that as she sat up in bed she saw a note on the hotel's distinctive paper, lying on the pillow next to her, and recognised his bold and flowing handwriting.

The message was brief, almost curt. 'Breakfast 7.45 downstairs. B.' That was all it said. He didn't even say good morning. He hadn't even signed it with his name, just with an impersonal initial.

She ran a fingertip over the writing, as if she was touching him; felt her insides dissolve helplessly.

Bruno, she thought. Images of last night ran through her head and she trembled.

And then the phone rang shrilly, making her jump. She looked at it as if it was a snake and might bite. Then suddenly she thought: maybe it's him, ringing to say all the things he didn't put in that note?

A flush sprang into her face; she lifted the receiver, huskily said, 'Hello?'

'Good morning, this is your operator; it is seven-fifteen, *signorina*,' said the over-cheerful Italian voice.

'Oh . . . thank you . . .' Martine put the receiver back. She hadn't asked for a wake-up call; Bruno must have booked it.

Well, that had been thoughtful of him, and no doubt he had gone back to his own room very early, so that nobody should see him leaving hers, which was very considerate. Everyone on this floor was at the conference and some of them knew her; gossip could spread like wildfire at these events. She could remember at other conferences listening to gleeful talk of who was sleeping with whom; these things did happen when people were away from home and went in for long, long dinners with the wine flowing freely.

But her and Bruno... that was different! she thought with anguish. That hadn't just been a one-night stand at a conference, something to be forgotten about as soon as possible. Or... had it?

She sat very still on the edge of the bed, staring at that brief, cold, impersonal note. It was hardly a love-letter, was it?

He could have said something about last night, or at least signed his name. 'Love, Bruno' wouldn't have compromised him, would it?

Had last night meant anything to him, other than an easy conquest? He hadn't said he loved her; he hadn't made any promises. One minute they had been quarrelling at her door, the next they were on the floor, making love in a frenzy.

Her face burnt as she remembered those moments on the floor, on the bed; the intensity of passion they had shared.

Stricken, she screwed the note up and threw it across the room. What had she done? She'd never behaved that way before in her life, never been promiscuous, and now was a lousy time to start. She wished she could go back in time, turn back the clock, wipe out those moments in his arms.

She was twenty-seven, not inexperienced—she'd had a couple of serious relationships: one that had lasted for over a year before breaking up by mutual consent; the second the affair that had been so painful that she hadn't wanted to get involved with anybody else for a long, long time.

But no other man had made her feel the way she had last night. She hadn't even suspected that such incredible sensuality existed. It had been like flying; she had flung herself recklessly from a mountain peak and found to her astonished gratitude that she had wings, and she had been so sure he felt the same.

She shut her eyes, remembering his passion. That hadn't been faked! But maybe she had misunderstood—good sex didn't need emotion behind it. Had she forgotten that some men just liked sex, and could walk away afterwards without looking back, however good it had been?

Was Bruno like that? Oh, God, how was she going to face him this morning? The thought of breakfast made her want to throw up. Eating breakfast with him, having to look at him, remembering, knowing that he remembered.

She remembered her first impression of him. The good looks cloaked ruthless determination; he had killer's eyes, a mind like a computer. It made him good at his job, but a poor risk as a lover. That was the man who took you last night, she thought with a pang of stricken shame. As soon as he sensed that for some reason you were vulnerable to him, he took what he could, and then walked away.

How had he known he could do that? How had she betrayed herself? White, she felt her stomach heaving. A hand over her mouth, she ran into the bathroom and was violently sick.

She sat on the floor, sobbing, for minutes on end, a cold wet towel against her feverish face.

She couldn't stay there; she had to go down to breakfast, because he was capable of coming up here to get her. She didn't want him walking back into her bedroom. The very idea made her want to throw up again.

She showered and put on a dark grey pleated skirt, a lemon shirt, a grey waistcoat over that. She combed her auburn hair into an elegant French pleat and did her make-up, clipped neat silver ear-rings into her ears, then considered her reflection. She wanted to look businesslike, cool, remote.

Bruno Falcucci wasn't going to find any weaknesses in her today; never again, in fact.

She had lied to herself for too long; kept telling herself she hated him when she was secretly carrying a torch for him. Last night the torch had set her on fire, but it had burnt out now, all that was left was blackened earth and emptiness. Now she really did hate Bruno Falcucci. She would be armoured against him from now on.

She collected her conference briefcase, the notes, the folders, the printed material they kept being handed and never had time to read.

Head up, she took a deep breath and went down to the dining-room. She paused in the door, swallowing.

Yes. He was already there, sipping orange juice, turning the pink pages of a copy of the *Financial Times*, no doubt yesterday's paper. Today's issue would not have reached Rome yet.

This morning he looked grimly formidable in a dark suit, the jacket open to show his tight-fitting waistcoat, immaculate white shirt and dark blue silk tie. His face was closely shaven, unshadowed, his black hair sleek—he looked as if he had had a great night's sleep, damn him, unlike her. He must be as cold as ice. And last night she had been utterly convinced he wanted her as much as she wanted him.

She watched as he put his half-finished glass of juice down, his long fingers steady. Hard to believe those hands had taken her into heaven last night.

She flinched from the memory of his lovemaking; bit her lip and tasted the salt of her own blood in her mouth. Damn him. Damn him.

He closed his newspaper, glanced up, caught sight of her, his eyes narrowing, searching her face. What was he looking for? A sign of how much he had hurt her? She showed him a shuttered face; saw his brows flick together as if he was disappointed. If he thought he was having any more fun at her expense, he was mistaken, she thought grimly, walking towards him.

He rose to his feet. 'Good morning.' He came round to hold her chair for her, and she sat down, very conscious of him as he pushed her chair inwards again, unable to hide the flinch she gave as his hand brushed her shoulder.

Bruno gave her another of those piercing looks, his black eyes chilly. 'Did you sleep well?'

The bite in his tone didn't escape her. She wanted to yell, hit him, but she fought to keep her face as icy as his own.

'Yes, thank you. Did you?'

Before he could answer, the waiter arrived. She ordered coffee, orange juice, prunes with natural yoghurt, and toast.

When the waiter had gone, she asked Bruno stiffly, 'What did you want to talk about, anyway?'

'Your opinions on the conference discussions, obviously; or of what you'd heard so far,' he coolly said, as if they were mere acquaintances. 'You're making notes all the time in the conference hall, I noticed.'

He noticed everything, she thought. 'For Charles,' she said aloud.

His mouth twisted. 'Of course.' His eyes stabbed at her across the table suddenly. 'Did you make notes last night, for Charles?'

White, she whispered back, 'Shut up. Damn you. Shut up.'

The waiter came smilingly back with her orange juice and the prunes and yoghurt, poured her a large cup of fresh coffee, offered cream or hot milk.

'Black, thank you,' she said hoarsely, spooning the creamy white yoghurt over her prunes, feeling her stomach churn at the very idea of eating them, but forcing herself to do so.

She had to seem normal, calm, unworried; at all costs she mustn't let him guess how much damage he had done her.

The waiter refilled Bruno's cup. 'I'll bring your toast now.'

When he walked away, Bruno said in his remote, cool voice, 'May I read your notes, or are they only for Charles's eyes?'

Martine glanced at him secretly through her lowered lashes, hating him. 'You mean is there anything about you in them? No, there isn't, and there won't be, don't worry. I won't be telling Charles any private anecdotes.'

'I'm sure you won't,' he said, his voice stinging. 'Hasn't it occurred to you yet that I might?'

Her face grew taut, white as bone. She watched him with bitter contempt. 'Was that what it was all about? Was that your game plan? You got me into bed so you could tell Charles and wreck my...'

'Chance with him?' he drawled, mouth twisting.

'Reputation!' she said. 'I know how ambitious you are; I think you see me as some sort of threat to your plans. If I married Charles I'd stand in your way, wouldn't I? But I didn't think even you would sink to seducing me just so that you could run off and tell Charles about it!'

That got home. Dark red filled his face, and he looked at her savagely. 'And I wouldn't! I'm not the type to kiss and tell, you needn't worry.'

'Am I supposed to say thank you now?' she asked icily.

There was a barbed silence, then Bruno clipped out, 'What about your conference notes? Can I see them or not?'

'Oh, why not?' she wearily said. 'But they're in shorthand.'

'I can read shorthand.'

'I might have known you could,' Martine said bitterly. 'You're an expert at everything, aren't you?' Including seducing women. He was very good at that. He must have had a lot of practice to be that expert.

His black eyes glittered, but he answered flatly. 'I did a business course, before I went to university: shorthand, typing, computers. I've found it very useful.'

She tried to match his level tone. 'I use a rather scribbled shorthand of my own, though. Wouldn't you rather wait until the notes have been typed?'

'Not unless this is your roundabout way of refusing to let me see them.'

'Oh, very well,' she said, knowing he left her no choice, got out her notepad, and handed it to him.

'I'll read it some time today and let you have it back before we leave,' he said, putting it into his own briefcase.

The waiter arrived with their toast; Martine took one thin slice, spread it with black cherry jam, pretended to eat some. Bruno ate his with marmalade. They talked about the conference while they finished their breakfast, then Bruno looked at his watch.

'The car must be here by now, we'd better go.'

The drive to the Excelsior seemed endless, the car claustrophobic, stifling her and making her feel like screaming, shut up in it with Bruno, his body far too close, every movement he made tearing at her nerves and making her sweat.

She was so tense that as they got out of the car to go into the conference she caught her heel on the kerb. Bruno put an arm around her, to stop her falling, and as their bodies touched Martine had that familiar dizzying sense of the world spinning round her.

She pushed him away, trembling, and as she did so caught sight of a dark red graze on the side of his throat, just under his ear.

Heat enveloped her as she realised what it was. She had bitten him last night, in the last moments of their lovemaking. She hadn't realised she was leaving such obvious marks. What if someone noticed, made a joke about it? She would want to sink through the floor!

'Oh, for God's sake, stop looking at me like that!' Bruno snapped, his face icily hostile. 'You're as safe as houses with me after last night. I won't be trying my luck again. Charles is welcome to you.'

He turned on his heel and walked away and she slowly followed, fighting tears.

Bruno's delivery of Charles's speech was impressive; he had the full attention of the conference, and a number of questions were asked, all of which he was able to answer without needing to consult her.

There were a group of women from one of the big American merchant banks sitting behind Martine, who overheard their whispered comments.

'He's good, isn't he?' one of them said. 'I wonder what his view is on international intervention?'

'I wonder what he's like in bed,' one of the others said dreamily, and a little gale of laughter went up from them all.

Martine felt her face burning. She was glad nobody she knew was near enough to have overheard the conversation and notice her blush; they might have put two and two together.

The day dragged on; Gerhard was having lunch with some important members of the German banking fraternity and she only saw him briefly, in a corridor. Bruno was busy, too; at least she was spared the torture of his company that afternoon, and when their car arrived there was no sign of him so she went back to their hotel alone.

The ball was the final event of the conference, and Martine had been looking forward to it, but she could not face going, not after last night; on impulse she picked up the phone and rang the airport.

Yes, there was a plane for London that evening; yes, there was a free seat on it. Martine booked herself on the plane, then hurriedly packed her bags, wrote a note to Bruno, and went down to check out.

Two hours later she was in the air on the way home.

* * *

She woke up next morning with a splitting headache and a temperature, so that she didn't have to lie to Charles when she rang him at home.

'I flew home a night early; I'm coming down with flu, started throwing up, and it's so hateful being ill in hotels. I didn't miss any of the conference, though, except the ball. And Bruno is there, to cover anything that does happen.'

Charles was very sympathetic. 'Don't worry about it. I think you did the right thing, I hate being ill in hotels myself.'

'How are you? Feeling any better?' she asked, reminded that he had been ill before they left. In fact, that was why Bruno had gone at all. Charles should have been with her. She broke off a sigh, in case he heard it. If she had gone with Charles, how differently she would feel now!

'I'll be back at work on Monday—I'm fine,' he said. 'Maybe you've caught the same bug I had? I hope I didn't give it to you. Have you got a headache?'

'Frightful one.' But she suspected it wasn't flu that was making her head ache, although as she had been sick several times that day she knew now that it hadn't only been her shamed revulsion over letting Bruno make love to her that had made her throw up the morning she woke up to find him gone leaving just a curt note behind.

'High temperature? Thirsty? Shivery?'

'All that.'

'It sounds like what I had. Well, one comfort is, it doesn't last long. Stay in bed and call a doctor, and don't come back to work until you're one hundred per cent again.'

'I won't. Charles, I left my conference notes with Bruno, he'll give them to you if you want them urgently, but it would be easier for you to read them after they've been typed up.'

'Forget about work, Martine,' Charles told her firmly. 'Just concentrate on getting well.'

By that evening she felt terrible; it was definitely flu and she stayed in bed, shivering under a thick winter duvet, dosed herself with aspirin and drank a lot of squash and orange juice and water. She didn't eat at all, couldn't keep anything down.

When she went back to work she had lost weight and looked pale. Charles gave her a concerned look as she walked into his office.

'You have been ill! You look terrible.'

She laughed. 'Thank you, Charles, you're so flattering. Did Bruno give you my conference notes? Have they been typed up?'

'Yes, I've skimmed through them.' He talked about some of the topics which had been discussed at the conference, asked her some questions, then said, 'Guess who came into the office yesterday?'

Blankly, she said, 'Who?'

'Gerhard,' Charles said, laughing. 'He told me he'd run into you at the conference. He's in London with a team from Bundesbank to hold talks with the Bank of England. We're having lunch later this week—I told him I'd bring you along if you were back at work. Are you free on Thursday?'

'I think so. I'll have to check my diary, I'll let you know.'

She wasn't sure she wanted to see Gerhard again. Seeing him would always remind her now of what happened at the conference. Oh, that's so stupid, she thought! How could she forget any of it, when she still worked here, under the same roof as Bruno, and could hardly avoid seeing him every day?

And why on earth should she be so unfair towards Gerhard? It wasn't his fault, any of it. He didn't even know what had happened, nobody did. Red colour stained her face. She hoped nobody ever would.

She went to her own office to look at her diary and sat behind her desk, staring at nothing, wondering how she was going to feel when she finally saw Bruno again.

The phone rang; it was one of their investment managers, sounding gloomy. 'Martine, I'm having trouble with one of the clients—he's threatening to take his account away because he isn't satisfied with the way I'm managing his money. Could you talk to him? Have lunch with the two of us some time next week?'

She looked at her diary again, sighed. 'OK, Peter, Friday is free. Who is it?'

'His name's Weddon.'

'OK, send me his file down with all the details of the shares you've bought and how they're doing. I suppose we are making money for him?'

Peter droned apologetically, 'Well, I had one or two pieces of bad luck. You remember that big flotation we were handling in the spring—Brugell; I took up some of that for him. If you remember, we were all trying to talk clients into buying some.

And then, of course, it fell heavily not long afterwards.'

Martine's mouth indented. That had been one of their mistakes; they should never have got involved with that, but it had looked OK on the face of it.

'Why didn't you get rid of the shares for him? Switch into something else?'

'You know that's not our policy; Charles likes us to ride the ups and downs, not keep buying and selling. That was my instruction, and I stick to it.'

Martine made a face. 'Yes, Peter, but there are exceptions to that rule, and one of them is when a company is being run by crooks, and you know very well that Brugell's chairman has absconded with a lot of the company money. Well, I'll look at what you've been doing, and see if I can improve on our performance. Look, fix this lunch for next week, not this—that will give me more time to make some rearrangements.'

She rang off, and settled down to study the Japanese stock market, which was edgy at the moment, checking all the shares they held; comparing prices, the way the share had performed that year, on graphs held in their computer's memory. She had an appointment with a Japanese client that afternoon and wanted to be sure she knew what she was talking about.

It was lunchtime before she saw Bruno. She was walking out of the beautiful early-nineteenth-century building which housed the bank when Bruno strode towards her from a taxi which had just dropped him.

They met on the steps. Martine grasped the elegant ironwork railings for support, her heart lurching as she saw him.

His face was dark and cool; he nodded. 'Back at work, then?'

'Yes.'

'Charles said it was flu.' The sardonic tone said he didn't believe it.

She lifted her chin. 'Yes, that's right.' Her own tone told him she didn't care what he believed.

His mouth twisted cynically. 'But now you're back to normal.'

Anyone else overhearing them would have taken what he said at face value, but Martine heard the undertone, the sarcasm and distaste, and flinched from it.

'Yes,' she said, staring bitterly into his black eyes.

'I know you'll be pleased to hear that Charles kept saying how much he missed you,' he drawled. 'They say absence makes the heart grow fonder, don't they? So your bout of flu was brilliantly timed, obviously.'

She didn't answer, her face stiff, just walked away, blinded to the traffic and confusion of London through which she moved. She hadn't seen him for more than a week, but he had never been out of her mind all that time, and, just now, while they talked, she had kept looking at him, looking away, unable to stop looking back, swinging wildly all the time between extremes of feeling which left her giddy.

Absence had had a drastic effect on her heart, it seemed. She wished to God it hadn't.

That brief encounter on the steps outside the cream-washed façade of the bank would make it easier next time she saw him, though. She hoped.

In fact, she saw him again the following day, in Charles's office. There were several of the bank's directors there; Martine and Bruno were able to ignore each other most of the time without it seeming strange.

Nobody else seemed to notice the chill in the air whenever they spoke to each other, either, although it seemed so obvious to Martine. Only Charles picked up on it, and mentioned it later, in private, gently chiding her.

'What is it with you and Bruno? I hoped you two would get on better than you obviously do. Didn't you hit it off while you were in Rome? I thought that being thrown together like that might have broken the ice between you, but the way you talk to each other lately the ice seems thicker than ever.'

Flushed, and furious with herself for letting Charles glimpse her feelings she said huskily, 'I'm sorry if it's that obvious. I always try to be polite.'

'Oh, polite, yes. But I know you both, I don't need you to draw diagrams. Every time the two of you are in the same room the temperature goes down with a thump. You know my plans for him, Martine—one day he'll be sitting in my chair. Try to make friends with him.'

She forced a pretence of laughter. 'Good heavens, Charles, stop talking as if you're ninety-three! Unless you're planning to retire at fifty, Bruno isn't going to take over for a long, long time.'

Then their eyes met and she frowned, struck by a new idea.

'You aren't planning to retire, are you?' That prospect appalled her. Charles, gone. Bruno in his place? She would have to leave the bank!

'I'm certainly not planning anything of the kind, but you never know what the future holds, do you? So make friends with Bruno, Martine.'

It was too late for that, she thought grimly. She and Bruno were never going to be friends. They had briefly been lovers—now they were enemies.

CHAPTER FIVE

NOVEMBER was a grey and drizzly month; skeletal leaves blew along the windswept pavements and people looked fed up as they hurried in and out of offices and shops. Bruno jetted off to Australia and New Zealand on a fact-finding mission to have meetings with investment managers across the continent, clients of the bank who lived there, and to get an inside look at the Australian stock market, the major companies and growth areas. All world markets were volatile; the Australian one was no exception and you couldn't really get an idea of what was happening to it from this side of the globe.

Martine was working late the night before he left. Everyone else had gone home, but she had to finish some research on a new investment programme they were working out for a big pension fund.

She stopped to massage her eyes, Chinese style; her elbows on her desk and her palms pressed into her eyes, shutting out the light and easing the strain on the iris, at the same time letting her mind go blank. When she was very tired this often helped to revitalise her for a while.

She was totally unaware of Bruno's approach until he touched her shoulder.

Then she whirled round, green eyes wide in shock.

'Oh! It's you! Don't creep up on me like that, you nearly made my heart stop.'

'And we wouldn't want that, would we?' he said drily, and she felt herself flush. You had to be on your toes when you talked to him; he used double meanings like thorns under the skin. She let that one go by without comment.

'Why are you still working? You've got a long flight tomorrow, you should get an early night.'

'I shall,' he said. 'I'm just off, but I saw your light and came in to say goodbye. I'm sure you'll be relieved to see me go.'

She would, and yet she already felt a grey depression settling down over her like the mists of winter. She was going to miss him badly, but she wasn't admitting that to him.

One black brow curved sardonically. 'No comment? Well, none needed. But as I shall miss the Christmas office party and all the fun and games under the mistletoe which I understand goes on . . .' He bent very fast, before she had time to realise what he intended, and kissed her, his lips hot, compelling, waking the sleeping passion always coiled inside her body whenever he was near her.

It only lasted a moment, then he stood up, breathing thickly, darkly flushed, his eyes hostile.

'You can slap my face when I get back! Don't marry Charles while I'm away or you'll be very sorry you did,' he said, and walked out, leaving her trembling, frustrated, on the point of tears.

After he had gone it seemed to her to rain every day, and she couldn't get him out of her mind, especially at night, in her bed, when erotic fantasies about him kept her awake for hours.

'Lucky Bruno,' Charles said, looking out of the window one morning when the rain was beating down outside. 'If it weren't for the exhausting flight I'd have gone myself, but I couldn't face the journey.'

'I've never been to Australia,' she wistfully said.

'You should have said something! You could have gone with Bruno.'

'I didn't want to!' she erupted, caught Charles's eye and flushed. 'Well, you wouldn't want us both to be away at the same time, would you!'

Charles frowned. 'That's true. But, I've just realised—you can't stand him, can you? Odd; I find him likeable; a brilliant mind, too, very shrewd. I wonder why you don't like him?'

'I can't like everyone!' she protested, then tried to change the subject. 'Weather likes this makes you think of holidays somewhere hot and sunny, doesn't it? The Caribbean would be nice! Or Florida.'

'How about Germany?' Charles said wryly, and she gave him a startled look.

'Germany? That's not sunny! I remember Gerhard telling me about winters there when he was a child, how he skied to school and went skating on frozen lakes.'

'Yes, I know—but Gerhard did invite us to visit the Bundesbank and the diary is pretty empty for the start of December.'

Martine thought about it, chewing the end of a pen. 'Both of us?'

Charles looked mischievous. 'I think Gerhard would expect you to be there! Don't you?'

She grinned. 'I don't know what you mean!'

'Oh, yes, you do. He fancies you.' Charles lifted an eyebrow. 'Come on, you know you like him.'

'Of course I do.' And it was true that the first ten days of December was a blank space in her diary. Later there would be a lot of Christmas parties, both private ones and office parties.

'And while we're over there, we could do some Christmas shopping,' Charles said cheerfully. 'After we've had our discussions with Gerhard at the Bundesbank we could stay on for a couple of days and go to one of the wonderful Christmas fairs they have in Germany at this time of year.'

Her eyes lit up. 'Yes, that would be fun!'

'I suppose you'll be spending Christmas with your family as usual?'

'I'm not sure. I often do go home for Christmas, as well as for a week in the summer. It's much too far to go home at weekends, I'd no sooner get there than I'd have to drive back, so I like to have at least a week at home when I do go.'

'Do they come to London often? Where do they go for their holidays?' Charles was always interested in other people's lives; it was one of the things about him that made him a good boss and a good friend.

Martine sighed. 'My father hasn't had a day off in years. He's too bound up with life on the farm; he works three hundred and sixty-five days in the year, and so does my mother.'

Martine kept trying to persuade her parents to come to London, or to come away with her, on a foreign holiday in some exotic country, but it never happened.

The family hill farm, in the border lands between England and Scotland, made very little money, but her father loved it dearly. He was happy getting up before the sun broke through, looking after stock, mending dry stone walls, hedging and ditching, injecting sheep against the dozen or so diseases they were prone to, doing any of the hundreds of jobs which needed doing on the farm at any time of the year.

Joe Archer had been a big man in his youth; now he stooped but he was still tall, very wiry, with weathered brown skin, dark red hair thick with grey now, and brown eyes. His had been a hard life, but it was the life he had chosen for himself, and he never regretted it, never complained.

Martine's mother never complained, either, or gave any sign of resentment for the toughness of her daily life. She worked just as hard as her husband, indoors and out. She made the bread they ate, fed the hens and collected their eggs, killed them too, and cooked them. She washed the clothes and linen; she ironed and baked and scrubbed and cleaned.

There was never any money, and that had been a spur to Martine's own ambition. She had soon understood that if she wanted to get on in life she had to get good results at school. She had worked with intense concentration and got the results she needed. She had chosen banking as a career because she hadn't wanted to teach, enter the law, or any other possible profession, but her mother's brother had been a local bank manager and had told her banking was a good career for a girl these days.

So she had come down to London and got a first job here, in the bank, rising with surprising speed as she realised what an aptitude she had for the work. She found it all so fascinating: the big companies, share movements, commodity broking, the swings and roundabouts of money; the ups and downs of the dollar, the Deutschmark, the pound, the yen, the franc. She loved the speed of transactions, the electrifying nervous tension of the market on either good days or bad. Banking might sound dull to someone who only understood the day-to-day routine of a local bank, but to anyone working in a busy merchant bank it could be as exciting as love; as dangerous as piracy on the high seas, as nerve-racking as fighting to the death.

As the years went by she had grown away from her parents to some extent. She loved her father, but she had never felt able to relax with him. He had tunnel vision; only saw life from one point of view. She couldn't talk to him; he had no idea about the world she inhabited, the sort of life she led, and she was bored by talk of sheep disease, mineral deficiency in the grass, the price of lamb on the open market. They had nothing much in common any more, except shared blood.

He wouldn't even accept her offer to help financially when she knew times were hard for them. However much Martine assured them she could afford to send them money every month, her father refused to take it.

'You keep your money for yourself, girl!' was all he said. After years of living on a remote hill farm, where little from the outside world penetrated, he had a rigid, old-fashioned attitude to life. His pride wouldn't let him take money from his daughter. He might have taken it from a son, but never from a girl.

When Martine secretly sent money to her mother, Joe Archer made his wife send it back, and Marie Archer had written a short note with it asking Martine not to do that again.

Joe Archer lived by fixed ideas, fixed moral standards he had learnt in his youth. He read no newspapers, had no TV, rarely even listened to the radio. Martine knew that her parents lived in a sort of time-warp where nothing had altered since 1940; for instance, her father would be deeply shocked if he ever found out that she had slept with Bruno; he probably believed she was still a virgin at twenty-seven, waiting for the right man to come along before she married.

Her mother was a gentle, tolerant woman, but she had never supported Martine against her father in the past, and Martine didn't expect she ever would. Marie Archer was the sort of wife who said, 'My husband, right or wrong...' and stuck to it. Nearly sixty now, she looked older. The auburn hair she had passed on to her daughter had turned grey; her face had too many lines, and she always seemed tired.

Martine saw how the long hours of hard work were sapping her mother's strength, turning her old before her time, and each time she went home she had to bite her tongue not to say anything to her father, because her interference only upset her mother and never achieved anything. The truth was, her parents had shared everything, throughout their marriage; there was a deep, quiet love between them which had never altered, and never would.

So, it was better for her to go home very infrequently; she could hold her tongue if she rarely saw them.

'I've always thought I'd love to spend Christmas somewhere really romantic, like Vienna,' she idly said.

'We'll, why don't you?' said Charles. 'I'd like to go to Vienna for Christmas too. We could go together.'

She gave him a startled look, laughed. 'It would be magical, wouldn't it?' She didn't take him seriously; she thought that, like her, he was only fantasising, daydreaming. She had seen a programme on TV about Vienna the other day, had been enchanted by the wonderful architecture, the Belvedere Palace, the Schoenbrunn palace, Vienna cathedral, the State Opera House, and moved by the music that had surged behind the voice-over; Mozart, the waltzes of the Strauss family, but most of all by the sight of bell-decked horses pulling sleighs through the snowy Vienna woods on a winter's day.

'Let's do it,' Charles urged, and she suddenly realised he meant it.

He met her eyes, his face coaxing. 'I hate Christmas on my own. Friends invite me but family Christmas always makes me feel melancholy.

Staying in hotels is even worse, all that fake jollity and gaudy paper hats, waiters dressing up as Father Christmas! But you and me... we both know the score, we're just good friends, and no complications on either side. So, what do you say, Martine? Will you come?'

There was something so wistful about his tone; she hesitated, then threw caution to the winds and nodded recklessly. 'OK, let's do it.'

They sat and planned it there and then, and Martine went out to book the trip the following day. They would fly out three days before Christmas and come back a week later, stay in one of the best hotels in Vienna. They were both excited—it brightened the wintry days that followed, like candles burning in a dark place.

But that was before it dawned on her that she had missed two periods. She hadn't worried much about the lateness of the first one; she had never had regular periods. But she had never gone two months before, and as the days went by and nothing happened she began to be scared.

What if... but it couldn't be! Bruno had taken precautions; she couldn't be going to have his baby.

But if not, what was wrong with her? She was afraid to go to her doctor, a rather stuffy middle-aged man who didn't look as if he might be very sympathetic.

It would be so embarrassing to tell him she thought she might be pregnant; so she went to a chemist and bought a do-it-yourself pregnancy test. The instructions were very complicated and she hated having to go through the process; but she couldn't rest until she knew, so she did it at once that evening.

The result was positive. She sat looking at it with a white face and dark, shadowy eyes.

She was carrying Bruno's baby. Her stomach clenched in sick protest and dismay. Oh, why had she been so reckless and stupid? This was a consequence she hadn't been expecting. She had kept telling herself that, much as she bitterly regretted losing her head like that, at least she didn't have to worry about getting pregnant. How could she possibly have expected to be the one in a million for whom the precautions did not work?

In the first shock of the realisation she couldn't decide what to do. Her first thought was to have an abortion; the sooner the better. But she was afraid, and undecided. She couldn't make up her mind about something so drastic and terrifying in such a hurry. She needed time to think.

Should she have the child, but let it be adopted? Oh, but the very thought of going through a pregnancy, while working at the bank, and everyone knowing what was happening to her body, made her feel sick, especially because it would mean that Bruno would know.

She had no intention of telling him until she couldn't avoid it. This was her body; the decision had to be hers. He had no rights in the baby at all, she told herself bitterly, not after the way he had behaved.

While she was still trying to make up her mind what to do, she and Charles flew to Frankfurt late in November to have a series of meetings with

Gerhard and a handful of other top German bank executives. They had a heavy agenda; as usual the thorny topic of German interest rates and the European Common Market monetary practice was head of the list of subjects they discussed. There was no hope of changing German policy on that, but these inter-bank contacts were always useful in creating the right atmosphere for future development.

When the business of the day was over, though, Gerhard showed them Frankfurt's night life.

They were staying in the Frankfurter Hof, a grand hotel of the type Charles most enjoyed; each evening Gerhard arrived in a chauffeur-driven limousine to take them out to dinner and dance.

Charles tired early, and always suggested that Martine should stay on later, but she wouldn't hear of that. 'I have to get up early, too,' she would protest and go back to the hotel with him when he went. For Charles the best night was the one when Gerhard took them to the City Opera at the arts complex on Theaterplatz. Charles managed to stay awake for that, but on their last night in Frankfurt he went to bed early and didn't come out at all.

Gerhard took Martine to the latest disco to open in Frankfurt; they shouted at each other and danced in a darkness split every second by a revolving flash of coloured neon light, the heavy beat of the music raving around them.

Gerhard kissed her in the car on the way back to her hotel, and murmured huskily, 'Can I come in tonight?'

She had been expecting the question ever since they arrived, which was why she had always avoided being alone with him after Charles went to bed.

She stiffened in his arms, very flushed. 'I . . . I'm sorry, Gerhard . . . no.'

He looked down at her, his eyes intent. 'Do you mean not tonight? Or never, Martine?'

'I like you, Gerhard, you know that, I find you very attractive and charming, you've been a wonderful host, I've really enjoyed our visit here . . .'

'But . . . ?' he said drily.

She couldn't meet his eyes.

'There's someone else?' he asked and she hesitated, then nodded. 'I think I can guess,' Gerhard said.

Her green eyes lifted in shock.

Gerhard smiled crookedly at her. 'Bruno Falcucci, isn't it? I picked up vibes between the two of you in Rome.'

She flinched. Had it been so obvious?

'It was like being caught in an electrical storm; I almost ducked once or twice,' Gerhard drawled. 'But I wasn't sure whether you hated him or loved him, so I thought . . .' He shrugged with wry sophistication. 'What do you say in England . . . nothing venture, nothing gain? You're beautiful and clever, I rarely meet girls I find as attractive as I find you.'

She blushed and said shyly, 'Thank you, Gerhard. I like you, too, you know.'

'That's nice. I'll try to feel comforted by that thought,' he said wryly. 'Well, no hard feelings, Martine. I've really enjoyed showing you and

Charles around Frankfurt, I hope you come back soon, and I'll certainly be over in London some time in the new year. And who knows, if you and Bruno never get it together, there might still be a happy ending for me?'

Marten was shaken, staring at him. 'Gerhard, I don't know what to say.' She had been expecting him to make a pass, but she hadn't for an instant supposed he might be serious about her. Was he saying that he was?

He gave her one of his charming, dry smiles. 'Don't look at me like a wounded fawn, Martine. My heart isn't broken. I'll live.'

They arrived at the Frankfurter Hof and Gerhard kissed her hand lingeringly. 'It has been a magical interlude; thank you, Martine.'

For some stupid reason, tears filled her eyes. 'You're so kind, Gerhard, you've made our trip here so wonderful.' She hugged him, gave a husky sob, and ran into the hotel.

She lay awake half the night thinking that if she had never met Bruno she might have fallen in love with Gerhard and been very happy with him. It was another reason why she hated Bruno. He had blighted her life in so many ways.

She and Charles left for the airport early in the morning. Martine was pale and strained; she had a headache and felt queasy on the airport bus. She was afraid for a time that she was going to throw up. Charles kept looking at her anxiously as they waited in the check-in queue.

'Are you sure you aren't coming down with something? You look terrible, Martine.'

'Too many late nights,' she said lightly.

The queue seemed to be crawling along. They had been standing there for ten minutes; she wished she could sit down, she felt so strange.

'Martine...' she heard Charles say from far away and that was the moment when she realised she was going to faint.

She crumpled up without a sound, her auburn hair tumbling around her white face.

They called the airport doctor and Martine was taken, protesting, to a quiet room where the doctor examined her and asked her questions which Charles translated for her, then translating her replies.

After a few moments, Charles asked, 'He wants to know if there have been any other symptoms?'

Martine swallowed, biting her inner lip.

Her hesitation didn't escape the doctor, who asked Charles something sharply.

Charles gave her a quick, startled look, then said, 'He says... could you be pregnant?'

Martine didn't meet his eyes. She nodded.

Charles didn't have to translate that. The doctor smiled, said, 'Ah!' and added a flow of quick German which Charles, also, did not translate.

'He says that that is the probable explanation for the faint, then,' Charles quietly said. 'If you have any further problems you should see your own doctor as soon as you get home.'

They left the doctor and walked through the busy, echoing airport without speaking; bought newspapers, magazines, which they read while they waited to board their plane. On the flight Martine avoided meeting Charles's eyes, and he was grimly silent, his face absorbed.

It wasn't until they were back in London and driving back through the rainy city that Charles asked in a low voice, pitched so that the driver should not hear him, 'When is it due?'

She didn't want to answer, but after a pause she muttered, 'June.'

Charles was silent for a moment; she could almost hear him thinking, then he said, 'Have you made any plans yet? Will you marry the father?'

She shook her head, staring out of the window, her pale profile rigid.

She hoped Charles would stop asking questions, but he quietly went on, 'Wasn't it serious, Martine? Just a brief affair, was that it?'

She laughed, suddenly bitterly angry. 'Brief is the understatement of the year. It was one night, that's all, and this had to happen! Life is unfair!'

Charles looked stunned. No doubt he was shocked; he himself was not a man given to promiscuity and she sensed that he hadn't imagined she would be, either. Useless now to protest that it had been wildly out of character, that she had never intended it to happen, that she bitterly regretted it.

'Does the father know?' asked Charles and she shook her head. 'Will you tell him?' he asked and she shook her head again.

Another long silence, then, 'Do I know him?' Charles asked, and she hesitated a fraction of a second too long. 'I do,' Charles said before she could answer, then, too fast for her to see it coming, 'Is it Bruno?'

Her head swung, and she looked at him in white-faced disbelief. How had he leapt to that conclusion? She hadn't given him any clues that she could remember. First Gerhard had guessed, now Charles. Was she really so obvious?

Charles's mouth indented and he frowned. 'You were always a little too extreme in your reactions to him,' he explained his shrewd guesswork, on a sigh. 'I wondered what you really felt, and then, when you both came back from Rome there was something different between you—I knew something had happened there. The air turned glacial every time you were in the same room.'

She leaned back in the car, turning away to hide the gleam of tears in her eyes. Charles was so sensitive, so perceptive. Why couldn't Bruno be more like him?

When they reached her flat Charles said, 'I'll see you safely upstairs,' and murmured something to his driver in an aside too low for her to hear. As they entered the building, she heard the limousine drive off and looked round, looked up at Charles, frowning.

'Why have you sent your driver away?'

'I want to talk to you. I'll take a taxi home.'

Weariness in her voice, she said, 'Charles, please, I don't feel up to talking about this tonight. I'll sort my problem out and let you know what I plan to do, later this week.'

Charles ignored her protest, following her into her flat. 'Let me make you a hot drink—how about cocoa or hot milk?'

She put a hand to her mouth, nauseated by the mention of the drinks, ran to the bathroom.

When she came back she apologised. 'At the moment, anything seems to make me throw up.'

'You poor girl, sit down. I've made some tea,' Charles said. He had explored her kitchen and found some crackers too, and made her eat one. They sat and sipped their tea together in silence. It was very weak, a straw-coloured liquid.

'Have you decided yet whether you're going to have the baby or not?' asked Charles and she shook her head.

'I've been trying to make up my mind for weeks, ever since I found out.'

'Do you want to keep it? Will your family help you?'

She laughed grimly. 'I have no intention of telling them, even if I do keep it. My father would never speak to me again; he isn't broad-minded, he would be ashamed of me, he would be afraid everyone he knew would find out and gossip about me. He's lived in an isolated country area all his life; they don't even have a TV, I offered to give them one for Christmas one year and he refused, didn't like the idea. It was too new-fangled for him. He hasn't had a new idea in his head since he was in his teens, I suspect.'

Charles was fascinated. 'What about your mother?'

'She would never argue with my father. What he says goes, in our house. He's not a violent man, he never raised his hand to me, but he won't stand for being contradicted, especially by a woman.'

'He sounds monstrous,' Charles said, looking appalled.

She gave a little groan of bleak amusement. 'No, he's just a narrow-minded man who has never adjusted to changing morality. I shan't be asking my parents for any help or support.'

There was a long silence, then Charles said quietly, 'I've got news of my own for you, Martine. I'm under sentence of death.'

She almost dropped the cup she held. Her hand shaking, she carefully put the cup down, staring at him. 'What are you talking about?'

'I have a brain tumour,' he said in a casual, down-to-earth voice which made it even harder to take in what he was telling her. 'They say it's inoperable, and growing worse.'

Numbly, she kept her eyes fixed on his face, unable to believe it, yet reading the truth of it in every detail of the way he looked. Charles was so heartbreakingly thin now; his hair had no life in it, there were more silver strands every day and his skin was waxen, drawn too tightly across his fine bone-structure. He was beginning to look as skeletal as one of the leaves blowing through the London streets in the winter rain.

'Oh, Charles,' she whispered, her lips quivering.

'I could have six months, I could have six days,' he said calmly. 'They can't give me any definite answers. Now you see why I suddenly sent for Bruno and offered him a top job at the bank. I have no children, my wife and I never managed to have any before . . .' His voice wavered at last. 'Before she died.'

Hearing the pain in his voice, for his wife, which was not there for himself, tears welled up in Martine's eyes. 'Charles, darling Charles,' she said brokenly, and knelt down beside his chair, put her head on his lap, her arms around his waist, feeling as she held him how painfully thin he was, how frail and fleshless. She broke out angrily. 'Why is life so unfair? Why do these things happen?'

He stroked her rich auburn hair with a gentle hand. 'I asked myself those questions when I had that crash, and killed Elizabeth. I'd have given my own life to save hers, yet I was the one who killed her. It was such cruel irony. I never got an answer, and I still don't have one. These things do happen out of the blue to anyone, without rhyme or reason, and it's no use complaining that they're unfair.'

She was silent for a minute, then asked huskily, 'Are you absolutely sure there's no chance of an operation? Wouldn't it be worth taking a risk?'

Charles shrugged. 'They have told me frankly that there is almost no chance of them being able to remove the tumour without killing me. And I've been rushing ever since to put my affairs in order. If I had died a few months back, when they first suspected the tumour, I would have left chaos behind me. I hadn't made proper provision about anything; my wife's death invalidated my only will and I had some serious decisions to make. Now, I've tidied things up, and one of my decisions was to bring Bruno over to London and put him into a position at the bank where he could get to know the business before I died and he inherited all my shares.'

She frowned suddenly. 'Have you told him? Does Bruno know you're so ill?'

He shook his head. 'You're the only person I've told, apart from my specialists and my own doctor. Bruno has no idea.'

'But he does know you've made a will, leaving everything to him, all the shares in the bank?'

Charles shook his head again. 'No. And after what you've just told me I've had second thoughts. I need an heir to carry on at the bank after me, and you need a father for your baby. The child will have my blood in its veins, after all; it seems a very neat solution to both our problems, don't you agree? So, Martine, will you marry me?'

She almost thought for a minute that she hadn't heard him correctly, and she didn't answer, just looked blankly at him. He stared back, a half-smile curling his pale mouth, his blue eyes wry and gentle.

'Will you marry me, Martine?' he repeated then, watching the expressions flick across her incredulous white face. 'At once,' he added. 'And don't spend too long considering my proposal. There's no time to lose, for either of us.'

CHAPTER SIX

MARTINE didn't even need to think for a second. Shaking her head in utter disbelief, she whispered, 'Charles . . . thank you . . . you're the kindest man I know, and that's the most wonderful offer. . . you've taken my breath away, and I'll never forget that you asked me, but, you know, I couldn't possibly accept.'

'Why not?' He seemed taken aback, as if he had expected her to jump at his proposal.

She made a husky sound, half sob, half laughter. 'Dear Charles, I couldn't marry you for your money, even if it *was* all intended for my baby. I couldn't live with myself if I did. No, it's very sweet and thoughtful of you to want to help me, but money isn't really the answer to my problems. I earn enough to be able to take care of my baby myself, after all, and I have plenty of savings put by. I shall work something out after the birth, find someone to look after the baby while I work. Lots of other women find themselves in this predicament and manage to cope, I'm sure I shall, once I put my mind to it. And, as for you needing an heir with your family blood in his veins, well, I can't advise you on that, but Bruno is still your nearest relative and he understands merchant banking better than anyone I know apart from you.'

She got up, pushing back her slightly dishevelled auburn hair with both hands and Charles got to his feet too, frowning.

'I thought you hated him.'

She laughed. 'The way I feel about him doesn't stop me assessing his abilities honestly and recognising that the man is brilliant!'

'Yes, he is, isn't he?' Charles murmured, pushing his hands into his pockets and rocking on the balls of his feet. 'Brilliant, but amoral, it seems. I'm not sure that makes him a suitable candidate to take my chair at the bank, Martine. I'm not someone who believes you don't need a morality if you're in banking.'

'I'm sure Bruno has very high ethical standards where banking is concerned,' she drily told him, and Charles grinned at her, his face lightening.

'You can always make me laugh, even when I'm very down. And you're astonishingly fair-minded. I don't think many girls, in your shoes, would have been so strictly scrupulous where Bruno was concerned.'

She couldn't quite meet his eyes. In a low, muffled voice she said, 'He didn't force me to do anything I didn't want to do, you know.'

Charles was silent but he took her hand and held it tightly, comforting her without words.

'I may hate his guts,' she went on with bitter humour, 'but he didn't make me any promises, he didn't cheat me or lie to me. We didn't even have an affair; I think Gerhard put it in a nutshell . . .'

'Gerhard?' Charles repeated, looking astounded. 'He knows about the baby?'

'No, but he did guess that I'd been involved with Bruno. He said being with the two of us was like being caught in an electrical storm.'

Charles laughed. 'He hit the button there! I know exactly what he means.'

'Well, the one time we made love was like being hit by lightning, but getting up and walking away feeling dazed. I still don't know why I let it happen. But it's personal, Charles, just between me and Bruno. Don't let what happened between me and him make any difference to you. I'll admit, I never trusted Bruno, from the start, but if I'd known you were so ill I wouldn't have been quite so suspicious of him, I think. The point was, I thought you were being premature, sending for him to join the bank, talking of making him your heir. I thought you were much too young for all that, but that Bruno might take advantage of you. You were only running on one cylinder all these months, and Bruno was taking over right in front of my eyes. Now I understand what was behind your thinking and I have to admit, you've made the best possible choice, as far as the bank is concerned. He's streets ahead of any other candidates to take over from you.'

Charles listened carefully, nodding. 'I agree. He is. But it's very generous of you to say so, all the same. You're a remarkable woman, Martine. I should have thought of proposing to you long ago. I wonder what you would have said, if I had?'

There was a curious, questioning tone in his voice; she smiled at him affectionately. 'More or less what I said just now, Charles. I'm very fond of you and I admire you, but marriage should be based on something more substantial than that.'

'You're right, of course,' he said, his mouth rueful. 'That's why I never married until I met Elizabeth. It's true I was always busy, but even so I met enough women during those years, some of them very attractive. The fact was, I simply didn't meet anyone I wanted to spend my life with, and it bothered me for a long time. I thought I might be frigid, emotionally cold, incapable of loving anyone. Then I finally found Elizabeth and fell for her like a ton of bricks.' His eyes were full of pain. 'She was the most wonderful thing that ever happened to me, Martine; since I lost her I haven't really cared whether I lived or died.'

'Maybe that's why you...' Martine began then broke off.

He looked down at her, brows arching. 'Maybe why I what?'

'Got the tumour,' she whispered reluctantly, and Charles gave her a slightly irritated frown.

'You think I'm imagining it? I wish I were!'

'No, of course not,' she protested. 'But sometimes we can make ourselves ill when we're very unhappy.'

He thought about that. 'The tumour might be psychosomatic, you mean? I don't know, but it exists, Martine. I've seen the X-rays. Only a little of it is visible, the bulk of it is hidden, and inaccessible, they just know it's there; there's enough to see for the doctors to be certain it's large, and growing.'

'Charles, I'm sure the thing exists, but that's the whole point; the mind and the body are so closely entwined that they interact on each other all the time. Unhappiness can take strange forms, some of them actually physical.'

'I wouldn't wish myself a fatal brain tumour!' he said impatiently. 'I have such terrible headaches, and I'm having serious problems with my eyes—that's how they realised what was wrong, the eye problems. I began to think I was going blind; part of my field of vision had gone on my left side.'

She was aghast. 'You never said a word! How long has that been happening?'

'It's been gradual, and some days it's worse than others. Why do you think I've had so much time off work in the last few months? I stayed at home when it was really bad. Martine, nobody in their right minds would voluntarily go through what I have.'

'Charles, I'm so sorry,' she said, wrenched with sympathy. 'I wish you'd told me sooner; you shouldn't have coped with all this on your own!'

He shrugged, said wryly, 'You would have told me it was all psychological!'

Stricken, she broke out, 'That wasn't what I've been saying! Believe me, I wasn't implying that you knowingly wanted to have a brain tumour, but...you did just say that you didn't care whether you lived or died!'

His face changed, stiffened in a sort of shock. 'Yes, but . . .' He broke off, his eyes confused and troubled. 'My God, that never occurred to me. Do you really think I might have unconsciously invited it—that's what you're saying, isn't it? That my own mind has made this thing grow in my brain?'

'Not consciously, Charles,' she hurriedly said. 'Look, I can't understand why the hospital hasn't offered you counselling—you should be talking to someone about this, some sort of therapist who is used to dealing with these situations. Why don't you ask your doctor to recommend somebody?'

He shrugged. 'Oh, they suggested I saw someone like that, several times, but I couldn't see the point. I could accept death, I didn't need to be talked into accepting it.'

She was appalled. Her face urgent and distressed, she said, 'But don't you see, that's just the point? You accepted death too easily, you were half willing it. You need counselling badly, Charles. Please go and see someone at once, fix it up first thing tomorrow.'

He looked almost sulky. 'I still don't see that there's any point.'

'Of course there is,' she said, on the verge of tears again. 'I don't want you to die, Charles! I'd miss you terribly, we all would. You're far too young to give up on life like this.'

He looked touched. 'That's very sweet of you, Martine, but——'

'Don't say but!' She grabbed his shoulders and shook him. 'Charles, you must start fighting. You can't just let this horrible thing in your head win!'

He gave her a rueful look. 'You've always been a fighter, Martine. I spotted it in you the minute I met you, when you were as green as grass and just out of business college. I was a fighter, too, once. I don't know if I have the energy now.'

'Find some!' she told him fiercely. 'Charles, try anything, don't just sit around here waiting to die!'

He looked confused, his face full of shifting emotions, thoughts, uncertainties.

'When they first told me, I think I did just accept it,' he conceded at last. 'It seemed . . . like fate. I was too miserable to care. To be fair to them, there was talk of possible treatment, if an operation never became possible—they say that sometimes the tumour moves into a new area, where they can operate, and they're waiting to see if that happens. I asked them to give it to me straight, not wrap it up. I wanted to know what my chances were, and when they said I might only have a few weeks, or months, I told them I didn't want any of these new-fangled treatments that might not even work. They use lasers, I think. I didn't listen to any of that.'

'Well, go back and ask them to do something. Try any avenue, Charles—don't just give in!'

'It's probably too late now . . .'

She groaned, shaking him again. 'Don't be so defeatist! At least try!'

He looked down at her and gave that charming, boyish smile she had always loved. 'OK, OK, I'll ring tomorrow.' Then he said softly: 'Was I wrong, or have you definitely made up your mind to have this baby and keep it?'

She sighed. 'I don't know. At first, when I was in shock, I did think of an abortion, but I can't quite bring myself to do it.'

Charles listened without comment; she gave him a wry smile.

'You can't escape your upbringing, can you? My father brought me up to face my own responsibility for what I've done, not just get rid of the evidence and try to walk away as if nothing had happened. Abortion would be ducking out, wouldn't it?'

'It's your body—you're the one who has to decide. Women have abortions every day,' said Charles dispassionately.

'Yes, I know,' she said slowly. 'And I respect their reasons for coming to that decision; they have other circumstances to cope with, other backgrounds. I only know how I feel. I'm the one who has to live with the consequences, whichever way I take, all because I was reckless and stupid for just one night and went to bed with Bruno.'

'You see the baby as a punishment you deserve?' Charles thought aloud. 'What about the child, though? If you aren't going to want it, if you feel resentful, it seems a pretty grim outlook for the baby.'

Martine gave him a stricken stare. 'I hadn't thought about it from the baby's point of view! Oh, damn...why is everything so complicated? I'm only just beginning to come to terms with the idea that I'm pregnant, I'm still seeing everything from my own angle. Don't confuse me even more, Charles! Maybe we both need counselling!'

He laughed involuntarily. 'I think we do. Aren't we a pathetic pair? But you can always allow the child to be adopted, Martine, after the birth.'

She felt a strange, angry clutch in her stomach and her green eyes flashed. 'No, I shall keep it,' she said, realising that without being aware of the fact she had already decided on that.

'I suppose the maternal instinct is the basic female instinct!' Charles said in an approving voice, and she gave him a half-irritated look.

'Don't talk about instincts! It was a very basic instinct that got me into this mess in the first place!'

Charles laughed. 'Well, I think you'll make a good mother—you can be so calm and down-to-earth yet at the same time you're sympathetic and understanding. Lucky baby.'

Martine inwardly shivered. For the first time she actually wondered what the baby would be like if... when... it arrived; would it have her red hair and green eyes or would it inherit Bruno's colouring, black hair and eyes, an olive skin? And then she felt a stab of nervous tension and pushed the new ideas away. She didn't want to think that way. It made this baby too real, it made it harder for her to make a cool-headed, sensible decision about its future.

Charles glanced at his watch. 'I'd better be on my way, it's getting late. I'll pick up a taxi on the Embankment.' At the door, he paused. 'We are still going to Vienna, aren't we, Martine?'

She gave him a searching, uncertain look. 'Will you be well enough?'

His voice casual, he said, 'As long as this thing in my head doesn't suddenly start growing faster, I hope so. I'm living from day to day at the moment, but I really want to go, I'm looking forward to it enormously. It could be my last Christmas.'

She turned paler, flinched. 'Don't talk that way! Charles, you must stop being so negative; try to think positive thoughts.'

'Christmas in Vienna is a very positive thought,' he said, smiling at her. 'I have a feeling we will go! And I want it to be a very special time for both of us.' Then he paused, frowning, looked sharply at her. 'Unless you no longer want to go with me, now you know?' Dryness edged his tone. 'I shall understand if you feel you can't face the thought of spending a week on the edge of eternity.'

'Don't be silly, Charles! Of course I still want to go. I can't wait to see the Vienna woods in the snow,' she said at once, lightly, but after he had gone she felt her spirits sink, all her doubts and fears come back to haunt her.

That was yet another of her white nights. There had been so many nights like that lately, when she could not sleep, her mind going round and round, on the same old trails, like a mouse in a toy wheel. Tonight, though, she had something else to brood over. The bombshell of Charles's news was still reverberating inside her; the shock and grief kept growing, darkening, like a bruise which only came out on the skin as time went by.

What if he did die? She had worked with Charles ever since she came down to London from the North; she admired and loved him, she couldn't bear the thought of the bank without him.

She sat on her bed in white silk pyjamas, her knees up, her arms around them and her auburn head propped up, staring into the dark, hearing rain lash down the windows, the wind rattle a gate somewhere. Out in the London streets the traffic sounded like a distant roaring of animals, but Martine was unaware of it, too accustomed to the sound to hear it any more.

What Charles needed was to have some energy and drive put into him to help him fight this thing which was eating his brain away. Somehow she was going to have to talk him into exerting himself—saving his life, if he could. Charles must not simply give in to death without a whimper. She wouldn't let him.

Bruno returned from Australia a few days before Christmas, to a London which was colder than it had been so far that year. The thermometer had dropped, and people began hopefully talking about snow for Christmas.

Many of the offices in the bank were empty. One group of staff were going on a skiing trip to Switzerland organised by one of the young account managers. Around a dozen members of staff were going; mostly single, unattached people in their twenties looking to have a good time with no strings attached. Others were jetting off, singly, in pairs, or small groups, to sunnier places, the Caribbean, Florida, Tenerife; and Charles and Martine were leaving the following day for Vienna.

When Bruno walked in she was busy clearing her desk, making sure she had dealt with all correspondence, going through client files to make sure that everything was up to date before she left. It wasn't an easy task because the phone kept ringing, and she was the only one around to answer it. Her secretary had taken the morning off to do some Christmas shopping.

Charles had an appointment with a Harley Street specialist. He had taken her advice; this was a trial appointment with a therapist, and he was very nervous about it.

When her office door opened she looked around, unsuspectingly, thinking it might be Charles back early, then felt her heart thud as she looked into Bruno's face.

'Hello, how are you?' he said, strolling into her office, letting the door close behind him, leaning on it, his arms folded, his long, lean body casually at ease.

'You're back,' Martine stupidly managed in a dry voice.

'I can tell you're thrilled to see me,' he mocked.

She ignored that. 'Did you have a good trip?'

'I learnt a lot,' he said, then drawled, 'When I walked through the bank, I had the feeling I'd stepped on to the Mary Celeste; every office seemed to be empty. Where is everybody?'

'Mostly gone away for Christmas,' Martine huskily managed to answer, unable to take her eyes off him. Seeing him again after this long interval made her realise how deeply she was in love; she drank in the sight of him as a thirsty man in a desert soaked up water.

His weeks in the Antipodes had given him a deep golden tan and it suited him. Usually he wore a suit to the office, but this morning, no doubt because it was almost Christmas and he was not expected back at work until after the festive season, he was wearing a white polo-neck sweater, blue denim jeans, a heavy sheepskin jacket, which he had taken off and held over one arm, not needing it in the centrally heated building.

'Has Charles gone away too?' he asked.

'No, Charles is . . .' She broke off, looked down, realising she had almost betrayed Charles's confidence. 'Out,' she finished.

Bruno's black brows arched. 'Are you and Charles the only people at work today?'

'No, of course not. I expect a lot of staff are doing Christmas shopping in their lunch-hour. For most of us this is our last day. Charles decided to give most people two weeks off at Christmas, although there will be a skeleton staff on duty every day. We worked out the rota long ago, don't you remember? I don't know how the rota affects you. By the way, we had the office party yesterday; I'm afraid you missed it.'

'I expect I shall survive the crushing disappointment,' he drily said, moving away from the door with the cool prowl of an animal stealthily making its way through its own, familiar jungle. 'Was it a good party?' he enquired, picking up some telex messages from her desk. 'Lots of drink and a few crisps and things on cocktail sticks?'

'It was fun,' she said, prickling at the way he watched her out of the corner of his eye. 'Clients dropped in, brought bottles with them. We put on music and danced.'

'Magic,' he said. 'Who did you dance with, or can I guess? Did Charles make it a romantic evening for you? How lucky I was away, I might have spoilt the rosy glow.'

'I'm sure you'd have done your best!' she snapped.

He laughed coldly. 'You can bet on it. So, where do you spend your Christmas? Have you got a family to go home to?'

'Well, I have, and I usually do go home for Christmas . . .'

'Where do your family live?'

'In the North,' she said, remembering that although he had been at school here for several years, and had visited the country frequently, he didn't really know Britain all that well, outside London and the South of England. 'In the borders, between Scotland and England,' she expanded. 'My family have farmed there for generations; it's nothing grand, just a little hill farm, with a couple of hundred acres of scrubby moorland full of gorse and heather. My father runs sheep and keeps a few pigs, goats and hens.' She was talking quickly, nervously, to stop him asking more personal questions.

He watched her, lounging against a chair now. His jeans were tight, she tried to stop her eyes wandering down over them, noticing the smooth line from waist to hip, the tension where the denim stretched over his thigh.

'Do you have brothers or sisters?' he asked curiously, and she shook her head.

'I was an only child.'

'Are you driving up there or taking a train?'

She hesitated, then had to say it. 'I'm not going home this Christmas, actually.'

She felt his alertness. 'What are you doing, then? You're not spending it alone in London?'

'No, we're going to Vienna,' she said in an offhand voice.

There was a silence. She looked sideways, her nerves jumping, but he was still leaning against the chair. His body was no longer casually at ease, though; it had tightened up, every muscle seeming poised for violent action, like the body of a runner before the gun went off. Suddenly the room was full of nervous tension and Bruno's dark eyes were molten.

'We?' he repeated. 'Who is we?'

'Me and Charles.'

'You and Charles are going to Vienna?' he asked in a controlled and quiet voice which made the hair rise on the back of her neck.

'Yes.' No word had ever been so hard to say.

'Just the two of you?' The voice was like the edge of a sword blade on the back of the neck, now.

'That's what I said! Yes!' she burst out, so jittery that she was angry. How dared he walk in here and cross-examine her as if this was a courtroom? She wasn't putting up with being terrorised, in her own office. Especially by a man who had no right to look at her as if she had committed some crime!

'You're going there on bank business?' he bit out, and she raised her chin at him, her green eyes stormy.

'I told you, we're spending Christmas there, in a hotel.'

She heard him breathing, on the other side of the room. 'You're going away for Christmas with Charles,' he repeated in what still sounded like a calm, cool voice, as though the idea was too difficult for him to take it in all at once.

'Yes!' she almost yelled, then closed her mouth on the rage mounting inside her. She must not let him get to her. Not again. But she couldn't sit still, she was too restless. She got up with an armful of folders, and walked over to the filing cabinets on the other side of the room. But that was a mistake too because Bruno's black eyes observed her every step, staring fixedly at her smoothly brushed auburn hair, the white silk shirt which clung to her breasts, the straight black jersey skirt which was a little tight and emphasised the instinctive sway of her hips, the hemline quite high, leaving bare her knees, her lower thighs, the long, slender, black-stockinged legs.

Martine had never been so conscious of her own body. She was having difficulty moving, breathing, thinking. She leaned weakly on the filing cabinet and began putting files away with hands that trembled.

'You *have* been busy while I was Down Under,' Bruno bit out.

She pretended to believe he was referring to the bank. 'You heard what a success the Filby takeover was? There was no real fight in their management, most shareholders accepted the Datoon offer and it's all over bar the shouting. Datoon were very happy with the way we managed things, but

Charles will tell you all about it when you talk to him later.'

'Will he tell me all about you and him, too?'

Blindly she reached for another file to slide into place, and suddenly Bruno was standing next to her.

She jumped, looking up in alarm. His eyes were black coals, angrily smouldering.

'Are you sleeping with him?'

'If I am, it's none of your business!'

'Look at me when you tell me that!' His hand shot out, caught her by the upper arm and pulled her round to face him.

Her green eyes frightened, but defiant, she gave him one brief glance, then looked down quickly, unable to hold his brooding stare.

'Let go of my arm!'

His hard fingers relaxed their grip on her, but did not let go. Instead they began to slide slowly down her arm. She felt his warm skin through the thin silk of her sleeve, then his fingers touched her wrist, lightly caressing her pale skin, which was in such strong contrast to his own tanned body, making the very hairs on her flesh prickle and tremble in reaction to him.

'You aren't going away with him!' he said brusquely. 'I like Charles, I've become fond of him, and I realise you're fond of him, too, but you aren't in love with him, Martine, you never have been. For God's sake, the man's a burnt-out case. I'd say that ever since he crashed his car and killed his wife he's only been half alive. There's no vitality in him, and you're a very vital woman. You need a man to light your fire, not put it out.'

'You know nothing about what I need!' she muttered, her lids down, but unable to stop looking at him through her lashes.

'Oh, yes, I do, Martine, you know I do,' he said, his voice deep and hot with excitement, and she began quivering violently, her senses vibrating to the note in his voice.

From across the room she had felt the power of his body; at close quarters it drew her like a magnet, as the moon pulled the tides across the dark face of the globe.

She had a sudden vision of him naked, as he had been that night in Rome; the smooth cool skin of his muscled shoulders, the power of his chest, the way the rough dark hair curled down his body, his slim hips, the bush of black hair curling where his thighs began. A rush of hot desire rose inside her, drowning everything else in her mind.

It seemed an eternity since she had last seen him; he had never been out of her head all that time; she had dreamt about him, fantasised about him, day and night, and now he was here and she could touch him if she wanted to, but she wouldn't let herself be that crazy. She had surrendered to this sensual craving once, and regretted it ever since. She wouldn't do it again.

'Why don't you leave me alone?' she muttered, trying to slide past him, but then his hand closed on her wrist like an iron bracelet and jerked her towards him.

'Don't!' She fell against him, put her hands up to push him away; his arm came round her, making an unbreakable bar across her back, and her green eyes grew wide and desperate.

'I don't believe you've slept with Charles,' he said fiercely. 'You aren't in love with him—we proved that in Rome, didn't we? If you were in love with Charles you wouldn't want me!'

'I don't,' she hoarsely said.

'Do I have to prove it all over again?' His eyes were riveted on her parted, trembling mouth, and she felt her flesh burn under his stare, stared back at him like a rabbit at a snake hypnotising it.

'No,' she whispered, terrified.

'But I don't need to prove it, do I?' Bruno said. 'It shows in your face.' He put his head down suddenly, and she gave a strangled cry as she felt his mouth burn into her throat, making her pulses beat out of control. 'And I can feel it, here,' he whispered against her skin, and her eyes shut; she felt her legs give way under her. 'And here,' he said, his mouth silkily travelling up to kiss the pulse beating behind her ears. 'And here,' he said, his head descending again to the open lapels of her shirt, pushing between them to the pale cleft between her breasts, to track down the wild drumbeat of yet another pulse.

She gave a helpless cry of passion, her head falling back, her hands clutching at him to keep her upright.

'Charles will never make you feel like that,' he told her, and then lifted his head, and she opened her eyes to find his dark stare remorselessly observing what he had done to her, noting her hectic flush, the dazed brilliance of her eyes, her quick breathing.

Martine despised herself, and almost hated him for being able to reduce her to this slavish level in a moment. Bitterly she threw at him, 'But Charles makes me feel safe...'

There was another charged silence, then his hands bit into her arms and he shook her angrily.

'Safety? Is that what you've convinced yourself you need? Yes, I've no doubt Charles could give you all the security in the world, if it's money you're after, and I suppose that is what you want? Wealth, social position... is that what really turns you on, Martine?'

His harsh, contemptuous tone was like a slap round the face. She couldn't even answer him, she was so insulted.

'No answer?' Bruno snarled. 'Well, I can promise you, you'll never feel safe while I'm around, Martine, whether you marry Charles or not. I'll make sure of that.'

CHAPTER SEVEN

FLYING back from Vienna after Christmas, Martine felt her stomach cramp at the thought of seeing Bruno again. For her, the holiday had been haunted by the memory of the threat in Bruno's face, in his harsh voice, on the day before she and Charles left London.

She should have told him that she had no intention whatever of marrying Charles! But when his black eyes had blazed down at her with that look of contempt she had wanted to hit back at him somehow, anyhow. If he wanted to believe she was pursuing Charles, let him! she had thought, which had been stupid.

She'd known that, a few minutes later, but had been too proud to go after him and tell him the truth. Would he have listened anyway? Probably not.

Her mood shifted again; she scowled out of the plane window at the clouds through which they were descending. If he believed she was capable of marrying Charles for his money, nothing she could have said would have made any difference.

'Aren't you feeling well?' Charles asked, his voice anxious.

She turned, startled. 'What?'

'Your colour keeps coming and going and you're so tense!' He glanced down at the arms of her seat and she looked down, too, only then realising how she was gripping them, her knuckles white.

Hurriedly she relaxed her fingers. 'Landing always makes me nervous,' she lied.

'Nice to get back to London, though,' Charles said contentedly, stretching in his seat. 'Vienna was terrific, but I'm always glad to get back to London and work.'

'Vienna was a dream,' Martine said, closing her eyes to visualise it. Vienna in the snow was theatrical: a chandelier of a city, glittering and faintly unreal at times, the imperial palaces, the cathedrals and churches, like forgotten props, discarded scenery, for this was a city haunted by its Habsburg past, echoing with dead voices and living music.

Had Charles forgotten how much he'd seemed to be enjoying himself while he was there?

'I could spend a year here without getting bored,' he had said as they sat at a table in the window of a café near the Spanish Riding School, a baroque hall where the great white thoroughbred Lippizaner stallions with their uniformed riders performed to classical Viennese music twice a week during set times of the year. They had come at the wrong time of the year, but they had wanted to see the building, and then they had gone into the café to sip Einspanner, glasses of coffee which had towering alps of whipped cream capping them, and had eaten slices of Sachertorte, a rich chocolate gateau hiding a layer of delicious apricot jam under the icing.

'You might not get bored, but you'd get fat!' Martine had said, pushing away her cake, unfinished. 'Gorgeous, but too rich for me. Viennese cakes must be the best in the world. What are we going to do on our last day here?'

'We haven't had our ride through the Vienna woods yet,' Charles had pointed out. 'Let's do that tomorrow.'

'Yes, I'd love that, it's one of the things I was most looking forward to. I wonder if you can still ride in a sleigh?'

'No doubt at a price,' Charles had said drily. 'The woods will be deep with snow, of course.'

'Oh, wonderful! I'll wear my new red boots, and the cap and mittens I bought at the Christmas fair,' Martine had said.

'Any more shopping to do?'

'No, my suitcase is already packed with presents I'm taking back. I don't have any more room.'

Charles had looked at her wistfully. 'You aren't sorry you came, are you, Martine?'

'Of course not, I've had a wonderful time!'

It was the truth—and yet not quite true. Christmas had been fun, they had given each other presents, enjoyed Christmas lunch Viennese-style, goose stuffed with apples, onions, raisins and nuts, served with red cabbage and potato dumplings; Charles had drunk lots of Austrian beer. They had flung themselves into Christmas like children: pulled crackers, worn paper hats, waved streamers.

After dinner each night they'd waltzed to Strauss on the highly polished parquet floor of the ballroom, enjoyed the floor show, dancers, jugglers, mime artists, musicians, laughed and talked with other guests.

Yet Martine had felt melancholy; she didn't know quite why, perhaps because she kept remembering Bruno's angry eyes and wanting to cry; perhaps because she felt guilty at not having gone home, although her parents had said they understood why she wanted to do something different that year, and hadn't seemed hurt. They had always been self-sufficient, she didn't imagine her absence would spoil their usual quiet Christmas, yet she still felt guilty.

The hotel was exceptionally comfortable, the food excellent, the staff kind, but it was the strangest Christmas she had ever spent. Charles had seemed livelier than he had been for a long time; he threw himself into everything, determined to enjoy himself, so for his sake she was glad she had come. But, in the end, they had not got their ride through the Vienna woods in the snow.

Martine had felt too ill on their last day. The food in Austria was so rich; and since she'd got pregnant any unusual food made her queasy. The only cure was to rest, keep still, and be very careful what she ate and drank, and so she had stayed in the hotel, resting on her bed, all day, while Charles had amused himself taking a last look around the Kunsthistorisches, the Museum of Fine Arts, spending over an hour in the amazing room which held more than half the known works of art of Pieter Breughel the Elder. They had already seen them earlier, but Charles had wanted to see them again. 'Hunters in the Snow' and 'Peasant Wedding' were two of his favourite paintings. He sat in front of them for a long time, he said to her later, worshipping the genius of his favourite painter.

'There's such vibrant, earthy life in every brushstroke Breughel ever painted,' he said, as they landed at Heathrow, skidding slightly on the wet tarmac. 'You know, there was this woman in one canvas, very pregnant; I kept thinking of you. And I thought...you're going to have to tell Bruno about the baby sooner or later, you know, Martine?'

She turned her head to look at him, her face tense. 'I'm not going to! And you'd better not, Charles! I don't want him to know anything about the baby.'

'I understand you're angry with him, but...Martine, I'm sorry, but I have to say this. I think he has the right to know,' Charles said, sounding quite grave. 'I'd want to, if it was my baby.'

'You're not Bruno,' Martine said bitterly. 'You have a strong sense of personal responsibility. He has none at all. And, anyway, I'm the one having this baby, not him. It's nothing to do with him.'

Charles shifted restlessly, looking pugnacious. 'I thought you had more sense than to repeat all that claptrap about the woman being the only one with rights over a baby just because it happens to be carried inside her for nine months. Genetically, half the input of that baby came from Bruno, after all. Surely that gives him some rights? I'm sure he would agree to help you financially, and, even though you earn a very good salary a baby can be expensive, especially if you're going to have a full-time nanny.'

'I wouldn't take his money if I had to beg in the street instead!' she broke out, trembling violently.

Charles looked taken aback.

Martine saw she had shocked him again. Charles, like most men, had a strongly conservative streak; he was easily shocked by unconventional behaviour. She wanted to laugh and cry at the same time, but it was tears that won, aching behind her eyes. 'Charles, I don't walk to talk about this,' she said huskily, blinking the tears away. 'I'm too tired, I just want to get home and go to bed. My head aches, and I can't think straight. Can we leave this discussion until some other time?'

'I'm sorry, was I badgering you?' Charles said, sounding conscience-stricken. 'I won't say another word; why didn't you tell me you were so exhausted? Poor girl, you do look white. If you aren't better on Monday, take some time off. You ought to see your doctor, too, have a check-up—you might be anaemic or something. Isn't that quite common with pregnant women?'

She laughed helplessly. 'Oh, Charles, you're so sweet. Don't worry, my iron intake is fine. I'm sure I'll be back to normal on Monday. Flying always makes me feel tired.'

He dropped her off at her flat an hour after they landed, and she went straight to bed and slept like the dead.

Next morning she drove up to visit her parents and take them their Christmas presents. She did not tell them that she was going to have a baby, and so far there was nothing to betray the fact.

Nevertheless her mother picked up on her weariness and gave her an anxious look.

'Your holiday in Vienna doesn't seem to have done you much good; you seem very pale, love.'

'I'm fine, just tired after the drive up here.'

Her father gave a disapproving grunt. 'You do too much travelling—we keep getting these post-cards from you. Rome one minute, then you're in Germany, now Austria . . . it's a wonder you don't get giddy, flying around the world all the time. You'll be thirty before you know it, and still not married. And never will be, always going off on your travels! This boss of yours, is he a married man? What does his wife think about him going away with you all the time?'

'His wife was killed in a car crash, Dad,' her mother murmured uneasily. 'You remember, our Martine told us about it. Very sad, poor man. Is he getting over it yet?'

Martine shook her head. 'I doubt if he ever will.'

She left for London again the following afternoon and got back to her flat in a howling blizzard. She was exhausted, shivering violently; she ran a hot bath and stayed in it until the water began to cool, felt quite dizzy as she got out of it, and went to bed at once, with a hot water bottle and several duvets piled on top of her.

In the morning she couldn't get up. She felt feverish, her limbs ached, she had a headache. Not more flu! she thought gloomily, then rang Charles to explain, but he had already rung to say he would not be coming in to work either.

'We must both have the same bug!' she said to his secretary, who sniffed.

'I wonder where you both picked it up, then!' she said with a drop of acid in her voice.

Martine didn't reply, but after she'd rung off she lay in bed thinking grimly. Was there a lot of gossip going round the firm about her and Charles? Nobody had said anything in front of her, but she knew how the staff talked. Neither she nor Charles had mentioned to anyone that they were going on holiday together, but it might somehow have got out. What conclusion would they jump to? The same as Bruno? That she and Charles were having an affair?

She made an angry face. The gossip had to be stopped. But, how was she going to stop it? Maybe she should confide in someone, casually, make sure the truth circulated instead. Her own secretary? Her head hurt too much, she couldn't think clearly; she turned over and went to sleep.

Hours later, she was woken up by somebody ringing the front doorbell. She ignored it. It couldn't be anything important. Then it came again, louder; a sharp, insistent ringing she couldn't ignore.

She yawned, looked at the clock on her bedside table. Just gone midday. She dragged herself out of bed, put on a turquoise-blue velvet dressing-gown over her blue nightdress and wearily made it to the front door, keeping it on the chain as she opened it.

Through the crack Bruno's black eyes flashed over her. 'Oh, you *are* here!'

'Where did you think I'd be? The Sahara?' What was *he* doing here?

'As you and Charles both conveniently rang in to say you were taking sick leave, I did wonder if I'd find you sharing one bed!' he told her with dry sarcasm.

'Oh, go away, I'm too ill to cope with you,' she said, hating him. She tried to shut the door and found his foot in the way.

'Let me in,' he said.

Her green eyes glazed with tears because it made her heart ache just to see him and she was too ill to hide it.

'I'm not that crazy!' she bitterly said. 'Just go away, will you?'

He stared at her, grimly, walked away, and then, before she could shut the door, he came running back, full tilt, hit the door with a tremendous crash, and she felt the thin chain snap. The door swung open and Bruno came with it, almost knocking her off her feet.

As she stumbled backwards Bruno shut the front door behind him with a kick and caught her by the waist, almost in the same movement picking her up and carrying her into her bedroom. He sat down on her tumbled bed with her on his lap, both arms around her.

Her head whirling, she glared up at him. 'Who do you think you are? John Wayne? How dare you smash your way into my flat? Now I shall have to have a new chain fitted! I'll send you the bill. And let go of me, will you?'

He ignored her, pulled open the belt of her dressing-gown and began pushing it off her shoulders.

Her face burning, she slapped his hands away. 'What do you think you're doing? If you think for one moment that I'd let you touch me again, you're out of your skull! Even if you were the last man on earth! I'd rather die. Let go of me!'

He dropped her dressing-gown on the end of the bed, got up, letting her slide on to the bed. 'Get in between the sheets!'

'I'll scream the place down if you lay one finger on me!' she muttered, her head swimming.

'Don't be stupid, woman!' he growled, yanked back the duvets and the top sheet, smoothed down the bottom sheet deftly, as if accustomed to making his own bed, then turned, picked her up, kicking and fighting, and almost threw her down, her head tumbling on to the pillows. Then he pulled the bed-clothes back up over her, and she sagged, feeling too strange to argue any more, closed her eyes, a few weak tears trickling down her face.

'Bully.'

He bent down and talked close to her ear. She felt his warm breath on her lobe and shivered. 'Have you been taking anything? Any medicine? Have you seen a doctor?'

'No,' she said. 'Paracetamol. I don't need anything else. I've just got a touch of flu.'

'What's the name of your doctor?'

Panic streaked through her; her doctor might tell him that she was expecting a baby. She struggled up on one elbow, glaring at him through her tangled auburn hair.

'I don't want a doctor. Will you go away? Leave me alone! All I need is sleep.'

He stared down at her, blackly frowning; then he walked over to the windows and pulled the curtains together, plunging the room into shadow. Collapsing back on to her pillows, Martine watched him walk to the door.

'Goodbye,' she said to his back, and through her half-closed eyes stared hungrily at the long, graceful line of his spine as he moved, the elegant motion of the body under his smoothly tailored suit. Her mouth went dry at the memory. His black hair was dishevelled and windswept; it had looked like that while he was rising and falling above her; she had run her hands into it, clenching fingers in those strands.

She couldn't bear to remember it. Groaning, she shut her eyes.

He went out without a word, a backward look, closing the bedroom door behind him. She listened. Another door closed, sharply. The front door, she thought. He had gone. She shut her eyes, her lashes wet with tears; she wouldn't think about him. She sought refuge in sleep; her last resource.

Her dreams were feverish, troubled; she was perspiring heavily, her temperature must have broken and she was hallucinating. At one point she dreamt that Bruno was there, touching her, taking her nightdress off; she moaned in protest, so hot that it was as if she was on fire. He wiped her sweating face with a cool, damp sponge and she sighed gratefully. Then his hands gently began to stroke her body, sponging her breasts, her flat belly, her thighs. Another sort of heat began to burn in her and she groaned, putting her hand out, closing her fingers over his, holding his hand between her thighs.

'Bruno,' she whispered, shuddering, and heard his intake of breath.

For a second neither of them moved, and then he moved her hand aside without a word, began to pat her skin dry softly. The heat in her subsided. She felt cooler, her head was clearer. Bruno whispered, 'Go back to sleep now.'

But was she asleep, or dreaming? she thought dazedly, because it was so real; the desire had been so piercing she couldn't believe she had dreamt it. She forced her eyes open and looked around for him, but he wasn't there. Her bedroom was shadowy, but empty. She had been hallucinating, or dreaming, after all.

With a sigh she closed her eyes and went back to sleep, but now her sleep was deeper, less troubled, and she no longer sweated the way she had.

The next time she woke up the light had altered; it was dark. She had no idea what time it was; wasn't even sure what day it was. A second later she heard a sound that really woke her up. She couldn't think what it was at first, then she knew. Breathing. Someone was breathing. In the room, near her.

Nerves made her muscles tighten, her pulse-rate quicken. She carefully flicked her eyes around the shadowy room, without moving her head; and tensed as she saw a dark shape just a few feet from her.

Her nerves raw, she knew at once that it was a man, and fear made her sweat. Then she took another hurried, terrified look, and her heart turned over with a crash. Bruno! She looked again, to make certain; but it was him.

She had heard the front door close—how had he got back in here? Or hadn't he gone at all?

She tried to steady her pulse, calm down, before she spoke, but her voice still quivered when she broke out, 'What the hell are you doing in my bedroom?'

He gave an audible start, as if he had been half asleep too; then he leaned forward, switching on the lamp beside her bed. She blinked, half blinded by light, tried to see him through the dazzle. He was sitting in a small armchair he must have brought in here from her sitting-room. He was still wearing his immaculate Savile Row suit, but his shirt collar lay open, his tie was off and she could see the deep tan of his throat, a sprinkling of tiny dark hairs on his upper chest. She swallowed convulsively.

'How do you feel now?' he asked in a voice so casual that it made her mood shoot sky-high with rage.

'Never mind how I feel,' she retorted. 'Tell me why you're still here in my flat! I thought I heard you leave—didn't you go?'

He took a key out of his jacket pocket and laid it on the bedside table.

She stared at it, dumbfounded. 'That's...'

'Your front door key,' he agreed. 'You'd left it lying here, I saw it when I came at lunchtime, so I picked it up and used it to get back in later.'

'You had no right to do that!'

'No,' he admitted without seeming bothered by the admission. 'But I was worried about you.'

She bit her lip, disarmed. 'Oh. Well... that was kind, but, even so... you shouldn't have done it, all the same. I was fine. All I needed was sleep.'

He didn't comment on that, just stood up, dwarfing her, making her throat leap with a wild pulse. 'Can I get you anything? Food? A drink? You should be drinking plenty of liquids.'

There was a jug of lemon barley water and a glass on her bedside table. 'This is fine, and I can manage, thanks,' she said stiffly. 'It was kind of you to be concerned, but I think you should go now.'

'I think you should call a doctor—let me ring him...' he began and she interrupted crossly, face very flushed.

'No, thank you. I can ring him myself if I want him. I'd rather you left now, please.'

'I don't think you're in any condition to look after yourself; this is the second bout of flu you've had this winter. You must be run down, or under stress—isn't that what they say often causes illness?'

She didn't like the hidden insinuation. 'The only stress I'm suffering from is having to put up with you!' she told him coldly.

'That *was* what I meant,' he softly said, and her pulses went haywire again. To cover her confusion she snapped back at him.

'Look, I want to go to the bathroom, so will you get out of my flat?'

'What's the problem, Martine?' he drawled. 'I'm not going to turn dangerous at the sight of you in your nightie getting out of bed. We're way past that, you and I.'

She glared, then knew she could not wait any longer, she had to go to the lavatory. She slid out of bed, picked up her dressing-gown and put it on as she ran out of the room.

It was as she was cleaning her teeth a few moments later, staring at her reflection in the mirror above the sink, that she suddenly noticed her nightdress.

It was not the one she had put on first thing this morning. That had been white lawn, sprigged with blue violas; the one she was wearing now was crisp white cotton striped with yellow.

She stared, rigid with shock, rinsed her mouth and washed her face, dried it, moving like an automaton, her brain racing. She must be going crazy, she must have changed the nightdress during the day, and simply forgotten

She turned to leave the bathroom, and that was when she noticed the wicker laundry basket; the lid was slightly askew and she could see something blue inside. She lifted the lid with a shaky hand. The viola-sprigged nightdress lay on top of the clothes she had worn and discarded yesterday.

She closed her eyes, thinking of her hallucination, or dream: the fever making her sweat, her sheets burning, then Bruno coming, taking off her nightdress, the cool, moist sponge on her body, the clean nightdress going on.

She dropped the lid back on the basket as though it held a snake which might bite her, reached for the door and went out to confront him.

He was in her little kitchen cooking soup in a saucepan. Her nostrils quivered; she realised she was mildly hungry, but she was much too angry to stop and think of that. There was something much more important on her mind.

'You took my clothes off, while I was asleep, you bastard! Didn't you?' she accused hoarsely.

Bruno turned, eyes lazily mocking. 'You mean you only just remembered?'

'I thought I was dreaming,' she began and saw his eyes narrow, gleam.

'You have interesting dreams!' She felt the provoking drift of his eyes down over her body and pulled the lapels of her velvet dressing-gown closer together, but that only made him laugh.

'Look,' he said, 'I found you in a terrible state—your temperature had broken and you were bathed in sweat. You'd kicked your bedclothes off, your nightdress was saturated; the material was so thin it clung to you from your neck to your knees, like a second skin.' He paused, lowered his lashes, looked at her through them teasingly. 'A transparent skin, of course.'

'Oh, shut up, you're deliberately trying to wind me up!' she muttered.

Blandly, he said, 'Well, I couldn't leave you like that, could I? So I found a clean nightie for you, a towel and a sponge, and took care of you.'

'You should have woken me up!'

'I spoke to you, and when I started taking your nightie off to wash you you opened your eyes and looked at me.' His lashes lifted again, she saw his eyes, brilliant, black and hot, like the heart of a slow-burning fire, and trembled. 'Don't pretend you didn't know what I was doing, Martine,' he said huskily. 'You gave me a very tempting invitation...'

Scalding colour poured up her face as she remembered trapping his hand between her thighs, saying his name in a pleading voice. She had wanted him to make love to her, and he knew it. She couldn't bear to look at him.

'You were too ill or I would have had to get in bed with you,' he murmured. 'So I was the perfect gentleman, I let you go back to sleep, and then I sat here, going crazy with frustration.'

'I was hallucinating! Out of my head! I didn't know what I was doing!' she whispered, biting her lip.

'Oh, I think you did,' he whispered, and took a step towards her.

She shot back, agonised by the conflict in her between a wild temptation and a reluctance to get hurt again, throwing up her hands as a frail barrier. 'Don't! I couldn't bear it!'

He stopped dead at the anguish and fear in her voice, staring at her fixedly, his face hardening, darkening.

'That wasn't the impression I got a few hours ago!'

'I told you... I was out of my head, but now I'm not, and I don't want you to touch me.'

'Wrong wording, Martine,' he bit out, his face grimly contemptuous. 'You want me to touch you, but it's Charles you've decided to marry, isn't it? Your body wants one thing and your head wants another.' His voice thickened, roughened. 'Of course, I could force you to admit how you feel about me...'

She tensed, shaking, going white.

He laughed harshly, watching her with inexorable eyes. 'Oh, don't worry, I'm not going to! I realise it wouldn't make any difference, because I'm not telling you anything you don't know already, and haven't decided cold-bloodedly to ignore. We both knew in Rome, in the street, when we saw those two kids making out in a doorway, didn't we? I envied them like hell and so did you; it must have seemed so simple to them, at their age. They saw each other, wanted each other, took each other—they didn't let anything get in the way of what they desired, not even their own minds! They certainly wouldn't put a barrier up to shut out desire simply because of ambition, or some craving for security!'

'Maybe they wouldn't, but we're not teenagers,' she said quietly. 'We're both adults who know the score where life is concerned. Life isn't simple; and taking what you want without thinking about it can have disastrous consequences.' She took a deep breath, her chin lifted. 'As we're being so frank, I'll admit...you can turn me on.'

His eyes narrowed, brilliant, demanding.

She shook her head at him. 'But you're right, I do prefer to follow the dictates of my head, not my body. The body can betray you; it can lead you into a trap. I know, I've been in love before, and been betrayed.'

His brows jerked together. 'When was that?'

'Never mind; the point is, I learn from my mistakes.'

'Does he work at the bank?'

'Never mind about him...' she said irritably. 'Don't side-track me! He's not relevant.'

'He is to me,' Bruno said tersely. 'If he's one of the reasons why you're so determined to ruin your life, he's relevant.'

'Well, he didn't work at the bank, and you don't know him, but he was rather like you, in some ways.'

Bruno's face tightened.

She sighed. 'I seem to go for a type, and it's the wrong type for me. You are wrong for me, Bruno and I know how any affair I had with you would end in tears; so I'm not starting one. I have other plans for my future, so please, leave me alone from now on, find someone else to play your games with.'

'Your other plans do involve Charles, though, I may take it?' he harshly asked.

She nodded, her face tense and bleak. It was not quite a lie, since she certainly hoped that Charles would be around to run the bank and help her career, and she knew that she dared not tell Bruno the truth. She had to send him away, and she couldn't think of any other method of doing it.

He gave her a long, cold, deadly stare, his mouth twisting. 'Well, then, I won't waste any more of my time on you. I won't say I hope you'll be happy with Charles, because I know you won't be. He isn't the man for you, you're going to ruin his life as well as your own, and I hope you're as miserable as sin, because that's what you deserve.'

He turned on his heel and walked away; she heard the front door slam and the sound reverberated round her flat like the knell of doom.

CHAPTER EIGHT

WINTER seemed to drag on endlessly; January was icy, February it rained almost every day and during those grey, wet days it finally became impossible for Martine to hide the fact that she was going to have a baby.

She had been disguising it with loose tops or baggy sweaters over straight skirts with hidden elasticated waists, but the outline of the body under her loose clothes became all too apparent towards the end of February. By that time she was more than five months pregnant and, physically, feeling much better than she had for a long time. The first four months of her pregnancy had been fraught with sickness; her body hadn't reacted well to its new condition and she had had far too much time off work. Now suddenly she was blooming—skin clear, eyes bright, hair glossy—and was full of driving energy.

The whispers had begun though. First, people fell silent when they saw her, exchanged glances, whispered, covertly studied her changing figure. Martine flushed and tried to pretend not to be aware of the stares, but in the end decided it was time to confide in someone, so she picked Annie, the share analyst who was probably her closest female friend at the bank, and gave her an edited version of the truth.

Annie was a warm-hearted girl; she had a lively personality and men swarmed round her like flies round a honey pot, but she had been let down more than once by a guy she was really keen on. She sympathised at once with Martine's predicament.

'Men can be such rats! He dumped you as soon as he knew you were going to have a baby? Isn't that typical!'

'Well, no, he dumped me before I knew, actually,' Martine felt obliged to explain. Although why she should feel she had to defend Bruno like that she did not know, especially as she hadn't told Annie who the father was and it wouldn't enter Annie's head to suspect Bruno anyway, since Martine and Bruno had never been an item, publicly. Nobody had got an inkling that they had ever been involved with each other.

'Oh? Well, what did he say when you told him?' Annie asked.

'I haven't.'

Annie stared, openmouthed. 'But why not?'

'I don't see him any more; it's over, finished, I don't want him back.' That would make quite sure that nobody ever did suspect Bruno to be the father, she thought, if they believed the man was out of her life.

'I don't blame you, he sounds an absolute beast—but you ought to make him help out with money! I would. After all, it is his baby, too.' Annie's eyes rounded. 'Oh. Is he married? Couldn't he afford to help you because he has kids already?'

Martine almost nodded, then shook her head. 'But that isn't the point, I don't want his money!'

'Well, I jolly well would!' said Annie forthrightly. 'Or aren't you going to keep the baby?'

'Yes, but I can afford to take care of it without help from anybody,' Martine said, and Annie gave her an envious grin.

'On your salary, I suppose you can!' Annie did not earn anywhere near the same amount. 'Will you get a nanny?'

'For the first year, anyway, then I thought I might be able to get an au pair, or something of the sort.'

'Does Mr Redmond know?' Annie always blurted out her first thought; she had a naïve honesty which Martine liked. 'He's so conservative, isn't he? Downright stuffy sometimes! I bet he was shocked.'

'Charles is a darling,' Martine said, resenting the criticism of Charles, mild though it was.

Annie giggled. 'Oh, we all know you adore Charles—in fact a lot of people in the firm have been laying money on it that Charles is the baby's father, and I——' She broke off as someone walked into the room. Annie looked round, started to smile eagerly as she recognised Bruno, who was still her pin-up of the month, then stopped smiling as quickly, meeting a glare like black ice from him which sent her eyes skidding helplessly away.

'Nothing to do, Annie?' he bit out. 'The bank doesn't pay you for sitting around drinking coffee and gossiping.'

She scrambled down from her usual perch on Martine's desk and fled, for once totally wordless.

Martine looked at her computer screen, her mouth ash-dry with apprehension.

Bruno had been away for a fortnight, in Tokyo; this was his first day back and she knew at once that he had heard the gossip about her. She had been dreading this moment for a long time; the moment when Bruno first heard about the baby. Would he guess at once that it was his?

He closed the door and prowled across the room like a caged animal, making her nerve-ends raw, setting her heart thudding.

'Is it his baby?'

The question hit her like whiplash and her head jerked back in shock.

'I don't want to talk about it,' she whispered, her head turned away, her pale profile half veiled by the glowing dark red of her hair, which she was wearing loose these days because she had had it restyled, shorter, easier to do in the mornings. She had changed her whole image, for some reason she couldn't have explained—wearing softer colours, lipsticks, eye-shadow, a very light foundation. It wasn't just her pregnancy that had made her look so different; the change had begun in her mind.

Bruno's black eyes brooded on her. 'You were talking about it to that half-witted blonde just now. Why can't you talk to me?'

'Annie is a friend.'

He was suddenly rigid beside her. Out of the corner of her eye, she saw his hand clench, the knuckles showing white, and flinched, for a second afraid that he was actually going to hit her. The silence stretched between them like barbed wire; she heard him breathing, on his side of the wire;

dragging air into his lungs as if he was only just able to breathe.

'No,' he said at length, bitingly, 'I have no ambition to be one of your friends.'

That hurt. She wanted to yell back at him, but she mustn't let him see that he had hurt her. She managed somehow to keep all expression out of her face, her head held high.

Then the phone rang and she answered it quickly, grateful for the interruption, hoping he would go, but he didn't, he stood by the window, looking out into the chilly February sky, his shoulders back, his hands jammed into his trouser pockets, his black hair sleekly brushed back from his grim face.

The caller was a client, wanting to hear the latest news on a capitalisation scheme they were handling. Martine took her time explaining to him, but she couldn't keep the phone conversation going for ever, and the client finally rang off, thanking her.

She risked a glance at Bruno then and tensed up as she found him watching her with eyes like obsidian, glassy, black, volcanic.

'Did you do it deliberately?'

That question rocked her. 'Deliberately?'

'You know very well what I'm asking—did you get pregnant deliberately?' It seemed to make him even angrier that she was so bewildered. 'What were you trying to do? Force Charles's hand? Make him marry you? Was that your game plan?'

Darkly flushed, she stood up, turned on him, trembling, indignant. 'You've got a horrible mind! I'm not listening to any more of this, get out of here!'

'Not yet,' he said through his teeth. 'I want to know... did it work? Is he going to?'

'Go away!' She put her hands over her ears to shut out the relentless drill of his voice.

He took two strides closer; his hands closed over her wrists and yanked her hands down. The sudden contact sent fever through her veins; she swayed like grass in a high wind. Bruno bent towards her, muttered fiercely, 'He isn't, is he? I can tell from the way you're reacting. He still won't marry you. He may be fond of you, I think he is—he may fancy you, I imagine most men do. But marriage is something else again, and he probably knows why you want to marry him; he's no fool. It wouldn't be a love match, would it? Maybe Charles doesn't want to be married for his money, or for security, and you should have known he wouldn't sit still for this sort of blackmail, either.'

'Blackmail?' she repeated, stunned.

'What else do you call it? You're trying to force his hand and using this baby as a weapon. I call that blackmail, and you should have known it wouldn't work with Charles. You've worked with him for years, you should know him better than that. Charles may be a nice enough guy in private, but he has sabre-toothed tiger in his make-up or he wouldn't have been so successful heading this bank for years. You don't run a big City institution like this one without having predatory instincts.'

'You should know!' she bitterly said.

He gave her a cool look. 'So, if Charles refuses to marry you, what the hell are you going to do?

Will he acknowledge that he's the father, and make some sort of settlement on you and the child?'

'I have no intention of asking my child's father for money! And would you please let go of my wrists? You're hurting!'

He looked down, as if surprised he still held her, then unclenched his hands and let her go.

She looked at her wrists, the faint dark red line around them, where his fingers had gripped.

'I hope you're proud of yourself, leaving marks on me like that!'

'The marks you've left on me won't heal as fast!'

The snarl of the words made her flinch away in shock, feeling as if she had innocently opened the door of a house to find it was on fire when flames leapt out at her.

Bruno's skin had been a dark, angry red; now it was white and icy, like the face of a marble statue, and his eyes looked very black, impossible to fathom.

The silence between them was charged with electricity; she became terrified that he would touch her again, and send her emotional temperature sky-high.

'I told you that you were playing a dangerous game,' he said in a low, harsh voice, making her ears buzz with hypertension. 'I warned you, Martine. Sex is dynamite; you can't treat it with contempt, it's always likely to explode and blow you sky-high. You thought Charles would be easy to handle, as safe as houses—but, you see, you were wrong.'

Angrily she said, 'OK, I was wrong and you were right—there, does that make you feel happier? Is that what you were waiting for me to say? Consider it said. Now take your satisfied ego and get out of my office with it.'

Bruno stared at her, his face taut, then suddenly turned on his heel and strode out, slamming the door behind him; making her windows rattle and a glass on her desk vibrate noisily. Martine burst into tears, covering her face with her hands, put her head down on the desk and sobbed weakly until she managed to choke back her tears and pull herself together.

The next time she saw him Bruno totally ignored her, his eyes icy. He walked past her in the bank as if she were invisible; she felt as if he had slapped her face and had to bite her lip to stop herself betraying the pain she felt.

From then on, that was how it was between them. If nobody else was around he pretended not to see her. If there were others present he spoke to her, politely, coolly, but never quite met her eyes.

Martine kept out of his way as much as possible and fought to keep a calm look on her face whenever she did see him, but the ache inside her deepened day by day.

She was, however, seeing a great deal of Charles, out of working hours. One day every week he spent at a clinic having counselling and some sort of treatment about which he didn't like to talk. Martine had promised she would always be there for him when he needed her during this time. At first his treatment always left him grey and drained, but then he would recover a little; sometimes would take her out to dinner or to a play. It helped him keep his spirits up, especially the night before treatment, when he was obviously frightened and worried.

Gradually as the weeks went by he began to look more like his old self, to have some energy again, but above all to start enjoying life once more.

On a bright spring day in late April Martine went into his office with a pile of letters to discuss with him and he looked round at her with a spontaneous smile, full of warmth.

'Good morning, Martine! You know, being pregnant really suits you—you look lovelier than I've ever seen you.'

She put the letters on his desk, grimacing. 'Thanks, but I feel absolutely huge.'

'How much longer till the baby arrives?'

'It's due in five weeks.'

They both looked down at her bulge indulgently; and as they did she felt the fluttering little kick which kept coming these days, like an internal hiccup.

Charles gave a little gasp. 'I saw that! Your tummy sort of... rippled... what was it?'

'The baby, kicking, silly!' she said, grinning at him.

He gave her an uncertain look. 'Can I... would you mind if I...'

'What?' she asked, laughing.

'Feel it?' he said, a little pink.

She was slightly taken aback, but she was also touched by his fascination at the changes in her body during these months. In his mid-forties, having been married, and no doubt had other relationships too, over the years, Charles was still oddly innocent in some respects. He had missed out on children, didn't seem to know much about the process of having a baby and was constantly asking her questions about it; he had even read a book on it the other week. Sometimes she felt that he was having the baby with her, and she knew that his obvious interest had intensified the belief around the bank that Charles was the father.

'If you want to, of course,' she gently told him, and he gave her a shy smile, then tentatively laid his hand on the bulge under her black and white checked smock, but the baby had lapsed back into somnolence, and nothing happened.

Charles looked disappointed. 'It's stopped.'

'Yes, it only kicks when you don't want it to!'

'I bet it's female!' he teased, then hesitantly added, 'Would I be able to hear its heartbeat?'

Her green eyes smiled with affectionate amusement. 'If you want to listen, go ahead! Be my guest!'

Totally absorbed, he leaned his ear against her, his cheek laid along her tummy, and she looked down at his head, gleaming silver in the spring sunlight, with amusement, a smile curving her mouth.

His secretary had gone out a moment after Martine arrived, leaving his door slightly ajar. A movement in the corridor outside caught Martine's attention, she glanced that way and met the searing flash of black eyes.

Bruno was gone before she could react. White to her hairline, she closed her eyes, fighting not to let Charles see her pain.

'I can hear a sort of rustling noise,' he was saying, his cheek still pressing down against her. 'Like somebody crunching up paper, but rhythmic, too. Do you think that could be the baby's heart?'

She swallowed before she could answer. 'Probably.' Her voice sounded quiet, but surprisingly normal.

'Weren't you tempted, when they did the scan, to let them tell you what sex it was?' asked Charles. 'I would have been; I'm dying to know whether it's a girl or a boy.'

'I prefer to wait.'

'Not long now, it's growing every day,' Charles murmured dreamily. 'I can't wait to see it. I wonder what it will look like? You or Bruno? Will it be dark, or a redhead? Green eyes, or black? I can't wait to find out.'

In the beginning, when he had first known she was going to have a baby, he had once said, 'I won't be here to see it born.'

Now, she noted, with a glow of tears in her eyes he talked with certainty of being here to find out the answers to all his curiosity about the baby. There had been some deep change in Charles over the months of her pregnancy; he had turned again towards life, out from the shadows into the light.

She had a sudden strong instinct that he wasn't going to die. Her heart leapt like a salmon, but she resisted the temptation to tell him. At her suggestion they had not mentioned the word death since they came back from Vienna after Christmas. She had wanted Charles to stop dwelling on it, turn his mind to life; and she still did.

Charles suddenly sat up, leaned back in his chair, fiddled with a gold fountain pen on his desk, and without looking at her said, 'I wish it were my baby, you know. I wish you had married me, given me a right to help you, and the baby. We still could . . . Martine, I wish you'd change your mind, marry me at once, let me give the baby my name. It would make me very happy. Your baby has given me a reason for living.'

'Oh, Charles,' she said huskily, 'that's the loveliest thing anyone ever said to me, but life itself is the best reason for living.' She put her hand over his on the desk and smiled down at him. 'I have to say no again, but I am touched.'

He sighed. 'I can't persuade you to change your mind?'

'No. Charles, I wouldn't do that to you. Any day you might meet someone special and want to marry again—oh, I know there could never be another Elizabeth, but life is full of surprises. You're much too young to shut the door on love. You'll find it again, when you least expect it. Look at the change in you since Christmas—you look so well these days, you're a different man. You're putting on a little weight, your colour is good and your eyes are bright. What you need now is some outside interests—take up a hobby, painting, pottery, golf . . . anything to get you involved with people again.'

'Funny you should say that; my therapist has been saying something very similar,' Charles said. 'You aren't in a conspiracy with him, are you?'

She laughed. 'Of course not, it's just common sense.' She hesitated then took the risk of asking, 'When do you have your next series of tests?'

'In a few days. Keep your fingers crossed for me,' he said.

Martine was working in her own office later that day when Bruno walked in with a fat dossier on one of their new clients. He dropped it on her desk with a resounding clunk.

'You asked for that, I gather?'

She looked at the name on the outside of the box file. 'Oh, Klempto; yes. Thanks. It wasn't urgent, if you're still working on it.'

'No, I'm leaving early today,' he said curtly. 'You can send it back to my office when you've finished with it.'

'Of course.' She waited for him to leave, her eyes on the dossier cover, tracing the bold black handwriting she recognised at once as his.

He stood there, restlessly shifting his feet, then said in a tone etched with acid, 'Very touching sight, Charles leaning his head against you like that. I could almost hear the violins. The office grapevine tells me that he's become obsessed with this baby, and whenever I see him he can talk of nothing else; they all believe he's going to crack and marry you before it actually arrives in order to make sure it carries his name. Are they right? Are congratulations in order?'

She looked up at him, her green eyes dark with pain. 'No, they're not.'

His mouth was a hard, white line. 'Too bad,' he said, scarcely moving his lips, and then he was gone.

She sat for a long time staring at nothing, but she had grown accustomed to pain during these long months; she pushed the pain away and concentrated on her work. She would not let him keep hurting her the way he just had. One day she was going to wake up to find she was over him, that he no longer possessed her, body and soul, and she could start forgetting about him. She couldn't wait for the day.

That night as she was on her way home on the Underground, staring blankly into the dark windows through which one saw nothing but the walls of the tunnels, the train suddenly hit something with a tremendous crash and all the lights went out.

Martine was sitting down, but the carriage was full of people strap-hanging. Everyone standing up lurched violently, fell sideways; someone heavy fell on top of her, knocking all the breath out of her. She cried out in pain, heard other people screaming, the scrambling as they tried to get up, panic in the voices around her.

'What happened?'

'What's going on?'

'Did we crash?'

'Why don't they put the lights back on?'

'Got a match, someone? Anyone smoke? Got a lighter?'

Somebody struck a match; in the shadowy flare of it the man who had fallen on her struggled to his feet, muttering, 'Sorry...' and people straightened up, tried to get back to normal, then the match went out.

'I wonder if we'll get going again?' somebody whispered.

'If we don't... if we have to stay here... in this tunnel, in the dark, I shall go crazy,' a girl shakily said.

'Keep calm, Karen,' a boy's voice soothed. 'You aren't hurt; they'll get us out, don't worry. We can walk along the tracks to the nearest station, if the train doesn't start.'

'The rails are live!' she gasped.

'They turn them off if there's been an accident,' she was assured.

People began talking all round the compartment, in the dark, calming each other, reassuring, suggesting what might have happened, what might happen next.

It was fifteen minutes before the guard came along with a torch which he shone around the compartment to check that nobody was seriously injured.

'The train in front of us broke down,' he said. 'There was some sort of failure in the warning system, and we hit the back of the other train, but don't worry, nobody was seriously injured. Luckily, we weren't going fast—we got off lightly. Could have been worse. That's the good news. The bad news is that until they've cleared the previous train of passengers we'll have to stay put. But it shouldn't take long. Keep your spirits up and we'll have you all out of here as soon as humanly possible.'

A babble of voices answered him. One man claimed he had a weak heart, and had to be got out at once; someone else was feeling claustrophobic; a woman was sobbing noisily, begging to be allowed to get out at once.

'I hate the dark, I hate it, please, please, let me out of here...' she said.

The guard made soothing noises to them all, but could only repeat, 'We'll get you out as soon as humanly possible, I promise.'

Martine didn't say anything. She was in too much pain. Sweat dewed her face, and she was tense and shaking. Ever since the other passenger had fallen on her so heavily there had been a grinding pain in the small of her back. She had never felt it before, but she had read about it, she knew what it was.

The shock of the accident had sent her into premature labour. She had no way of knowing how quickly the process would move, and she was trapped here, without any medical help, in the hot, dark, overcrowded compartment where air was going to run short before too long.

I could lose my baby, she thought, biting her lips as another hard pain hit her. If I don't get help, everything might go wrong with the birth. When she'd first known she was pregnant she had been appalled, she had longed bitterly to turn back the clock, erase the baby from existence.

Now the thought of losing it was agonising.

CHAPTER NINE

THEY got her out of there two hours later, the longest two hours of her life. It was a nightmare trip along the tunnel to the station platform; there wasn't room for a stretcher for most of the way, and she had to walk, pausing every now and then as another pain started. An ambulance man was walking close behind her, encouraging her. 'Not far now, love. Keep going, we're nearly there.'

She didn't answer; she was too busy concentrating on riding the waves of pain; and even when the tunnel widened out and the ambulance men insisted on carrying her on a stretcher it was an uncomfortable ride, in the dark.

At one point she saw tiny points of light in a crevice in the dirt-grimed wall; little red eyes watching her. She screamed, and the ambulancemen stopped dead, peering at her through the half-gloom of the torches fixed on their safety helmets.

'Oh, my God, don't say it's coming!' one said, sounding panic-stricken.

'What is it, love?' said the older man, bending down to her.

'A...rat...I saw a r...rat...' Martine quavered, and there was a silence, then they laughed, half relieved, half disgusted.

'These tunnels are overrun with them; don't worry, they won't hurt you.'

She lay down again, closing her eyes, and minutes later they were in the next station and she was being carried up in a lift to the waiting ambulance.

Martine was admitted to the maternity wing of the hospital closest to her home an hour later, after she had been examined by a young registrar who said she was definitely in labour.

'If you had got here sooner, we might have been able to stop the pains, but I think it's gone too far,' he told her. 'Luckily we have an empty bed.'

She was given a hospital nightgown. 'Do you want to make a phone call? Tell someone you are in here? Make arrangements for a few things to be brought in later?' the ward sister asked, shrewdly noting the absence of a wedding-ring on her hand.

Martine flushed. 'I would like to make a call,' she stiffly said.

'Nurse will bring you a portable telephone.' Sister rustled away down the ward and the young nurse rushed off to obey her.

Charles was at home, luckily. Her news sent him into a tizzy. 'It's very early, is that a bad sign? What are they doing about it? What on earth made it start so early? I'll get a specialist to see you . . . you must have the best treatment . . . a private room, a consultant . . .'

'I'm fine where I am, I'm having the best of treatment, I don't want to be moved,' Martine said, impatiently because she knew another pain would start in a minute. 'Charles, listen, I haven't got much time . . . I'll need a few things from my flat. I'd already packed a case; they tell you to do that in advance. But it's in my flat. Do you think you can get it for me and bring it over here tomorrow?'

'Tomorrow nothing,' Charles said. 'I'm coming now. I want to be in on this. I've got a stake in this baby.'

She smiled faintly, didn't argue. 'It would be nice to have some company, although I don't know if they'll let you stay long.'

'Let them try and get me out!' Charles said belligerently. 'Now, how am I to get into your flat, that is the question.'

'Well, the girl who lives next door to me has got a spare key to my flat—she often takes in parcels and so on for me. Get her to come in with you and find the case—it's in my bedroom in the bottom of the wardrobe. Oh, and Charles, I'd like a few books to read—I have one on my bedside table that I'd like, and there's a bag of knitting on a table somewhere.'

'I'll find them all,' Charles promised. 'See you soon, don't have it until I get there.'

By the time he got there she had been in labour for over five hours and was beginning to tire. Charles was very excited; his eyes shone as he bent to kiss her.

'I talked to that doctor out there, the girl with the run in her stockings . . . she looks very young to be a doctor and bring babies into the world, don't you think so?'

Breathing rhythmically, Martine couldn't stop to answer him, so Charles plunged on, 'Anyway, she said you're doing fine and everything is OK, except that the baby is premature, but not dangerously so, and we're not to worry.'

'Who's worried?' Martine said, relaxing again as the pains stopped. 'Thanks for coming, Charles. Did you find my suitcase? The other things?'

'Everything,' he assured her. 'Your friend next door sent her love; she would have come too, but she's on night duty this week, she said to tell you.'

Martine nodded. 'I know.'

Charles gave her case to the nurse who put it away for the moment; he put some books and a Walkman with headphones and a few tapes into the locker beside her bed, then looked around the little room curiously.

'Is this where you'll have it?'

'No, they'll move me when I'm about to give birth,' she said, then clutched at his hand as another pang came.

Charles sat down beside the bed, holding her fingers tightly. He had discussed her antenatal exercises with her countless times over the past few months and was fascinated now by the real thing, although she caught a flicker of nervous apprehension in his eyes.

'Is it very painful, Martine?'

'I can bear it,' she said breathlessly, laughing, and he bent to kiss her cheek.

'You're so brave.'

A nurse starchily crackled into the room, paused, said rather tartly, 'You've got another visitor wanting to come in—do you want to see him?'

'Him?' Martine repeated, and had a flash of premonition. She looked accusingly at Charles. 'Did you tell Bruno?'

His face was startled but showed no sign of confusion or guilt. 'No, of course not! I didn't tell anyone except your next-door neighbour.'

Martine was in panic. 'Tell him to go away,' she said to the nurse, who turned to go.

'Wait a minute, Nurse,' Charles said. 'What does this man look like?' And then, aside, to Martine, added, 'It could be your father, after all!'

'Can't be,' said the nurse drily. 'He's not old enough. In his thirties, I'd say, tall, dark and sexy.'

Charles looked at Martine. 'It's Bruno, all right.'

'Tell him to go away,' Martine said, the nurse went out and then another pain hit, the strongest so far, and Martine had no time to think about Bruno. She gripped Charles's hand and he watched her anxiously.

A moment later she slackened again, Charles lent over her and wiped her perspiring face with a witch-hazel-drenched pad, from the tin of them which, in anticipation, she had packed in her suitcase.

'Charles, you're such a darling,' she whispered, smiling up at him.

At that moment loud voices made them both stiffen; the door slammed open and Bruno burst into the room, the nurse hanging on to his arm but unable to stop him any more than she could have halted a stampeding elephant.

'Do you want me to call Security?' she was yelling.

Bruno stopped at the bottom of the bed and looked at Martine, his black eyes fixed and grim in his pale face.

'They'll have to bring an army to throw me out of here before I'm ready to go!' he threatened.

Martine saw faces behind them, people in the outer ward, staring, all ears.

She couldn't bear a scene, not now. Wearily, she told the nurse: 'He might as well stay for a moment or two, it's OK.'

The nurse gave her an old-fashioned look. 'Well, make up your mind! And I hope one of them is the father, because our rule book says only one father to a bed.'

She stamped out and Bruno shut the door on the curious faces.

Charles got up and confronted Bruno. 'What on earth do you think you're doing? How did you find out she was here?'

Bruno gave him a deadly look, every bone in his face locked in bitter hostility. 'I wanted to talk to her so I went to her flat, I ran into her next-door neighbour on her way to work, and she told me Martine had gone into premature labour and that you had come for some things for her.'

'Yes, I did,' Charles said, frowning. 'Look, Bruno, you heard Martine—she doesn't want you here. I'm looking after her...'

'I know all about the way you've looked after her!' Bruno snarled and hit him.

Martine choked off an instinctive scream as Charles reeled backwards across the room and fell on to the end of her bed.

'Oh, my God,' she moaned, sitting up and scrambling towards him along the bed. 'Charles... You could kill him, hitting him like that... darling Charles...'

Bruno caught her shoulders and heaved her up towards him. 'You don't love him, you love me, however much you may wish you didn't,' he shouted at her, and as she looked at him, her auburn hair tangled and damp around her face, he groaned out, 'And I'm out of my mind over you, can't you see that? It's getting worse every day. I'm dying for you, Martine, I can't bear it any more—don't waste your life on a selfish swine who doesn't love you enough to marry you!'

'As it happens, I did ask her to marry me,' Charles said thickly, sitting up and massaging his jaw with a rueful expression on his face.

Bruno went white. He looked down into Martine's face, she heard the harsh drag of his breathing.

'And you accepted,' he said, rather than asked, then swallowed, and she saw his throat move convulsively.

'No, she turned me down flat,' Charles answered for her. 'Every time I propose she turns me down.'

Bruno's black eyes flashed to him, then back to Martine. 'What? I don't understand...'

She clenched up as the pain came again, stabbing, agonising; and Charles hurriedly pushed Bruno aside and came to help her to lie down, soothingly murmuring, 'You've forgotten your breathing, darling . . . breathe . . . count . . .'

The two men watched her raggedly breathing then the breathing slowing as the pain passed.

'But the baby,' Bruno said curtly. 'It's yours; she must have slept with you. Why would she do that and refuse to marry you?'

'No,' Charles said, giving him a dry look. 'I have never slept with Martine.'

'You haven't?' Bruno looked blankly at him.

'No, and the baby isn't mine.'

'It isn't?' Bruno seemed to be having difficulty understanding what Charles was telling him. Charles gave him a wryly amused look.

'No, it isn't; I wish it were.'

'But . . . if it isn't your baby, why did you ask her to marry you?'

Martine answered that. 'Because he was sorry for me, when he found out I was going to have this baby and had no father for it!'

Charles smiled down at her. 'And because I want this baby too,' he said. 'Having lived through this pregnancy with you right up till now, I feel as if I am the father.'

Bruno's face was rigid, his eyes riveted on Martine's face. 'If he's not the father . . . I am,' he said, intently watching the expression of her brilliant green eyes. 'I am, aren't I? That night in

Rome . . . but I was so careful! How could you have got pregnant?'

'*I* don't know! Obviously something went wrong; all I know is I ended up having a baby and I didn't sleep with any other man!'

'Why on earth didn't you tell me?' he demanded. 'Why let me think it was his? How could you do that? I don't understand you at all.'

'No, you don't,' she muttered. 'You were the one who decided Charles was the father...you were the one who kept insisting that I wanted to marry Charles . . . you wouldn't listen when I told you I didn't . . . you wanted to think the worst of me. I have my pride! I gave up trying to convince you and just let you think whatever you liked.'

His voice roughened by feeling, he whispered, 'You've tortured me all these months, put me into a hell of jealousy and misery, all out of pride!'

Her green eyes darkened. 'Do you think I was rapturously happy?' she said, and then another pain arrived and she stopped talking while she rode it.

'Here,' Charles told Bruno quietly, 'sit down on my chair, hold her hand, help her do her breathing, but stop shouting at her—she's in no fit state to go through an emotional scene just now, can't you see that? You can fight this out after your baby has been born.'

Bruno didn't even look at him, just slid into the chair and gripped Martine's hand.

A moment later when she shifted her head on the pillow, sighing in relief, she saw that Charles had gone and she was alone with Bruno.

Their eyes met, hers wavered, her lashes flicking down against her cheek, then she risked another look at him. 'I'm sorry, Bruno,' she whispered, aching with love.

He lifted her hand, his lips opened hotly against her palm and she trembled as she felt the intensity of the lingering kiss.

'I'm sorry, too,' he said huskily. 'I don't understand you, but I'm desperately in love with you. Don't ever send me away again.'

Their baby was born two hours later, and Bruno was with her throughout the birth, gowned and gloved, like one of the nurses; it was Bruno who laid their daughter on her breast, smiling as Martine gently touched the baby's damp black hair.

'What are you going to call her?' asked Charles two days later.

'Roma,' Martine said, laughing.

'You're kidding?'

She shook her head. 'I think it suits her; she has a distinct Roman nose.'

'Rubbish, poor baby,' said Charles, horrified. 'She's beautiful.'

'You should have seen her five minutes after she arrived—she was all wrinkles, red as a beetroot, and screaming her head off!'

'She looked gorgeous, I saw her as they wheeled her off to the nursery,' Charles said, indignantly, passing her grapes he had carefully peeled for her from a bowl beside her bed.

Martine did a double-take. 'You stayed until then?'

'I sat in the waiting-room with a pile of magazines and an endless supply of ghastly hospital tea to get me through it,' he said, grinning.

She was touched. 'Oh, Charles, that's so sweet . . . you should have gone home and rung up later to find out.'

'I wanted to be here, I wanted to see her arrive in this world,' he said. 'I am still going to be godfather, aren't I? You won't let Bruno change your mind.'

'He wouldn't try,' she said, and Charles gave her a dry look.

'He's so jealous he can hardly bear to look at me.'

She smiled secretly. 'Not any more, not now he realises he was wrong about us!'

Charles didn't look convinced. 'Are you going to marry him, Martine?'

'If he asks me,' she said, knowing he would—and that she was going to grab him with both hands.

Charles gave a gloomy sigh. 'I'm afraid he'll go back to Switzerland and take you and the baby with you, just to get you both away from me.'

'I didn't get the impression he wanted to leave the bank,' she said, startled. 'He loves living in London.'

Charles sighed. 'He's the type who'll want you to give up your job and settle down as a housewife and mother.'

She contemplated that. 'I think I would like to take a few months off, just while Roma is so small,' she tentatively said. 'I can get a nanny later and come back to work, if you want me back, that is.'

'Of course I want you back,' he said, as the door opened and Bruno walked into her room, stopping dead as he saw Charles, who gave him a defiant look. 'I was just going,' he said, getting up.

Bruno held the door open, face dangerous, full of narrow-eyed warning as he stared at Charles. Martine could have hit him.

Charles bent and kissed Martine's nose, pretending to be unaware of the menace behind his back. 'Give my goddaughter a kiss for me... oh, and tell her my latest test was very encouraging; they say there's been a striking improvement.'

Martine looked up, eyes glistening with tears. 'Oh, Charles, I'm so glad!' She put her arms round him and hugged him; he held her tightly for a moment, and she said, 'Come again, soon, tell me all about it next time.'

'Wild horses wouldn't keep me away,' he said, meaning that Bruno wouldn't.

Closing the door behind him Bruno asked Martine, 'What test? Improvement in what?'

She told him and Bruno drew a shocked and shaken breath. 'No! My God, no wonder he's looked so terrible at times. That explains a lot. Poor guy.' He frowned, staring at nothing. 'I wish I hadn't hit him. I might have hurt him badly. Why on earth didn't you tell me?'

'He didn't want anyone to know!'

Bruno nodded, mouth a white line. 'Do you think these treatments are genuinely having some effect? Might he recover completely?'

'I'm keeping my fingers crossed,' Martine said 'And, you know, I'm really hopeful.'

Bruno sat down on the edge of the bed beside her. 'It must have been very hard to refuse to marry him, after he'd told you he was going to die soon. You must have felt very guilty about that.'

She nodded, sighing. 'If he had said he loved me, I might have agreed, but we both knew there was nothing like that between us. We were friends, good friends, as close as brother and sister, I think. The only reason he proposed was so that the baby could inherit his estate, and I couldn't possibly marry him for a reason like that.' She gave him a sideways look. 'I know you thought I was chasing him for his money, but then you have a pretty cynical view of women.'

'Based on some I've known,' he said, grimacing. 'I can think of quite a few women I've met who were ready to marry for money.'

'Not me,' she crossly said. 'I'm not mercenary, even though you kept accusing me of it!'

'You deliberately let me think the worst,' he reminded her. 'You did a good job of fooling me, too. I was so jealous of Charles it's a wonder to me I managed to stop myself killing him.' He groaned. 'The worst of it is, I still am. You may have refused to marry him, you may never have been his lover, but the two of you are very close and he is obviously obsessed with the baby.'

She smiled tenderly. 'Yes, isn't he? I'm glad, because it was an obsession that helped him fight this tumour. In fact, I think the baby saved his life—as it grew inside me, I think the tumour shrank; the baby gave Charles a reason for staying alive.'

Bruno was frowning. 'Yet it isn't his—that's odd, isn't it?'

'Don't you believe me?' Martine felt sick at the prospect of dealing with this jealousy of his for ever, but Bruno at once shook his head.

'Of course I believe you, but I can't quite see why the baby should be so important in this.'

'I don't quite know why, either; but it worked that way, Bruno. Thinking about the baby stopped him brooding on the fact that he was driving when he had that crash and killed his wife, and that was what he needed. He was almost willing himself to die; he had to start willing himself to live. Focusing on my baby did that for him. The baby was a new life; it opened the future up for him again.'

Bruno watched her intently. 'What about us? Do we have a future, Martine?'

She took a deep breath, met his dark eyes, her own passionate, shy. 'I love you, Bruno,' she whispered, 'if that is what you're asking.'

'I was asking you to marry me,' he said in a low, husky voice. 'I already know you love me—that was what drove me crazy all through those months, knowing that you were mine, and yet having you refuse to let me near you.'

'I told you, I got badly hurt a few years ago, and I didn't want to risk getting involved again. The morning after we made love, in Rome, I woke up to find you gone...' Her voice broke and she closed her eyes, fighting remembered pain. 'Why did you do that? Why did you go, leaving just that curt note?'

He groaned. 'I wanted to write words that would burn the paper, but I didn't know how you would react to reading how I really felt. I sat there for minutes with a head full of passion, and in the end I just scribbled a brief note and crept out. I didn't want to wake you, you were sleeping so peacefully, but I couldn't stay with you in case somebody saw me in your room. I didn't want a lot of gossip about us spreading around the conference.'

She bit her lip, incredulous. 'But you were so cold when I came down to breakfast! You looked at me with total indifference.'

'That wasn't indifference, or coldness,' he said hoarsely. 'I was shaking like a leaf. I'd been there for half an hour, waiting for you, on tenterhooks, wondering how you would look at me, wondering what you would say...and then you walked in looking like an ice goddess, with that touch-me-not expression on your face, and I felt my insides cave in! The only way I could hide how I felt was to put on a mask, act offhand, pretend I didn't care.'

They stared at each other in silence, then Martine whispered, 'We've both been stupid.'

'Stupid doesn't cover it,' Bruno said. 'All these months, when I've been dying for you... If only you had given me a sign, the tiniest glimmer of hope, but every time I came near you you acted as if I was Public Enemy Number One.'

'I'm sorry, Bruno,' she huskily said. 'I didn't mean to hurt you . . .' Then she broke off, laughing unsteadily. 'That's a lie. I did want to hurt you; because you had hurt me so badly. I just didn't realise I had the power to hurt you.'

Bruno curved a hand around her flushed cheek, staring fixedly into her green eyes, moving nearer. 'You have the power to make my life a living hell,' he whispered. 'I'm so crazy about you; you've no idea what you've been doing to me in the past few months. I've lost a lot of sleep over you, and had some pretty hectic dreams.'

She felt her colour heat. 'So have I,' she whispered, her lashes falling over eyes full of confusion.

Bruno moved even nearer, and at that moment the nurse knocked on the door and came in with the baby cradled in her arms.

'Feeding time,' she announced. 'Are you ready for her, Mum?' She gave Bruno a sharp look. 'Not on the bed, please, Dad. We don't like that on our wards.'

Bruno got up and walked over to the window, stared out, with his back to them as the nurse helped Martine prepare to feed the baby. Once the little mouth was attached to one nipple the nurse marched out again. As soon as the door had shut Bruno came back to the bed and sat down again, in the same position, watching with fascination as his baby daughter took her meal.

'She's greedy, isn't she?'

'Little pig,' Martine fondly said, looking down at the round dark head absorbedly attacking her. The baby's small hand smacked rhythmically on Martine's warm, white breast while she sucked, and when Martine detached her after the requisite time and transferred her to the other breast the baby began at once to shriek, enraged at being taken away. She only shut up as the other nipple went into her mouth.

'I wonder what it tastes like,' Bruno said huskily.

Martine glanced up at the note in his voice, a new sensation beginning inside her.

Bruno slowly leaned forward; his eyes closing, he took her free nipple into his mouth softly and began to suck, a hand clasping her warm breast, stroking it seductively, coaxing the milk to flow again.

Martine drew a shaken breath, her face burning. 'The nurse will be back any minute, Bruno,' she muttered; yet the feel of his mouth around her nipple, the needle-like flow of the milk, was erotic, sensuous, and she didn't want him to stop. Her hand went out to stroke his warm, sleek hair, her skin prickling with awareness of him.

When he finally lifted his face, looking at her with languorous, passionate eyes, she felt the answering stab of desire deep inside her.

'How long do you go on breast-feeding for?' he whispered, still stroking her breast with one hand.

'Months,' she said.

'Good,' Bruno whispered and she couldn't help laughing, yet at the same time it sent a quiver of arousal through her.

'You're wicked,' she said.

He looked at her through half-closed eyes. 'You have no idea how wicked I can get, given half a chance. Martine, as soon as we can arrange it, we must get married, you must give up your flat and come to live with me, you and our baby. I don't want to miss another moment with you, either of you. Charles, damn him, stole months of our life together.'

She frowned. 'Don't be jealous of Charles.'

'I am jealous of Charles, I want you all to myself.'

'If he were my brother, would you be jealous?'

'He isn't your brother.'

'Not by blood, but in every other sense of the word. I love Charles, in a totally different way. I don't want him, he doesn't turn me on—but I am as fond of him as if he was my brother, and I don't want you to be jealous.'

He looked at her, his mouth crooked. 'I'll keep telling myself he's your brother-figure, but I warn you, Martine, I'm the possessive type. You're mine.'

'Body and soul,' she said, her eyes burning and intense.

She heard the fierce intake of his breath, then he said, 'Just make sure Charles understands that.'

'He understands,' she said, as the nurse arrived to take their baby away again.

She gave Bruno an affronted look. 'You're back on that bed again, Mr Falcucci. I hope I'm not going to have trouble with you. Now, sit on a chair, like everybody else, or leave my ward!'

Bruno sat on a chair until she had left and Martine's open-fronted nightdress had been buttoned up again, then as soon as the door was shut he slid over on to the bed and took her into his arms.

'Will she be back or can we have five uninterrupted minutes alone?' he asked her, his mouth moving against the smooth skin of her long neck.

'They never leave you alone for a whole five minutes!' groaned Martine. 'Bruno! Don't do that.'

His hands were busy, hurriedly undoing her nightgown again, freeing her breasts and stroking them, his fingers trembling slightly. He held her shoulders, pushed her gently backwards on to her pillows, coming down with her, lying half on top of her, his mouth searching for her breast.

She pushed his black head away, laughing huskily. 'No, Bruno—you can't, not here...' Yet she felt the drowning bliss of sensual pleasure even while she tried to stop him; he was making all her dreams come true, but this was not the time.

They both heard the door-handle turn. Bruno shot up and was on his feet before the door began to open. Martine feverishly did up her nightie again, pulling the sheet up to her shoulders.

'Time for Doctor's round, Mr Falcucci,' the ward sister said, looking suspiciously around the room as if picking up unwelcome vibrations from them both. Desire clouded the air with musky perfume. Sister did not like the scent of it, and her nostrils quivered. 'I'm afraid you'll have to go.' She walked over to the door and held it open pointedly.

Bruno came over to kiss Martine goodbye, and took the chance to whisper, 'Get out of this place as soon as you can and come home, my darling. We have a lot of lost time to make up for.'

Lynne Graham was born in Northern Ireland and has been a keen Mills & Boon® reader since her teens. She is very happily married with an understanding husband, who has learned to cook since she started to write! Her three children keep her on her toes. She has a very large old English sheepdog, which knocks everything over, and two cats. When time allows, Lynne is a keen gardener. She has been writing for Mills & Boon since 1987 and has published more than twenty books which have been translated into more than fifteen languages.

ANGEL OF DARKNESS

by

LYNNE GRAHAM

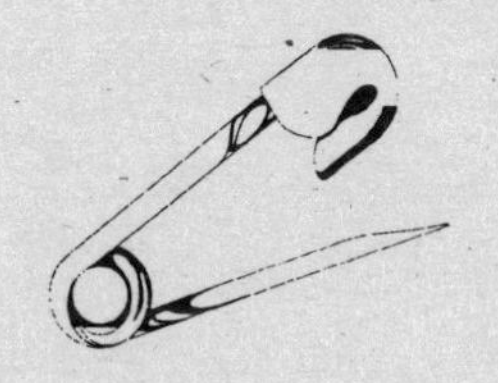

CHAPTER ONE

'I KNOW this is a shock for you,' Daisy Wyatt murmured uncomfortably, absorbing her daughter's stunned pallor. 'I would have told you ages ago but I was afraid you might be upset.'

'*Might be*?' Kelda raked her rippling Titian red hair back from her brow, a fiery mix of disbelief and temper leaping through her taut frame. 'For goodness' sake, you've been divorced from the man for over four years! Why on earth did you start seeing him again?'

Daisy looked uneasy. Small and blonde and barely into her forties, she was a very pretty woman but right now her face was strained. 'When I heard that Tomaso had had a heart attack, I... I—well...' She stumbled under fire from an outraged emerald-green stare of enquiry. 'I thought it was only decent to write with my good wishes for his recovery and Tomaso wrote me such a kind letter back asking me to visit... I didn't see how I could refuse——'

'But that was three months ago,' Kelda condemned in a shaken tone. 'You've been seeing him all this time and you *never* even dropped a hint!'

Daisy turned a guilty pink. 'At the start, it didn't seem worth mentioning. Just a few friendly visits to the hospital. Tomaso seemed so lonely. He didn't seem to have many visitors, apart...' She hesitated, assessing her daughter's vibrating tension and hurriedly averting her gaze before reluctantly continuing, 'Apart from Angelo, of course.'

That name struck Kelda like a stinging slap on the face. The fact that her sensitive mother wouldn't meet her eyes when she said it didn't help. Indeed, Daisy's visible embarrassment on Kelda's behalf merely piled on the agony. A moment out of time when she was eighteen. Inexplicable...inexcusable. Kelda blocked out the memories threatening her, refusing to recall that dreadful night and its appalling repercussions.

'And I suppose Angelo was as chillingly contemptuous as he was when Tomaso married you and polluted the Rossetti family with a lowly hairdresser!' Kelda snapped with ferocious bite. 'I wish I could believe you cut him dead but I bet you didn't!'

Daisy was studying her tightly linked hands. 'Tomaso and I should never have got married in such a hurry the first time. Angelo hadn't even met me...naturally, he was shocked.'

'Look, I'll make us a cup of tea.' Kelda was so furious, she had to get out of the room before she burst a blood-vessel and said what she really thought. How could her mother make excuses for Angelo? How could she *possibly* do that? When Tomaso Rossetti had married Daisy eleven years ago, his son Angelo had scorned her, snubbed her and treated her as though she was a scheming, common little gold-digger with a greedy eye to the main chance. Kelda's gentle, quiet mother had suffered agonies of discomfiture at Angelo's merciless hands!

Safe in her pine galley kitchen, Kelda snatched in air in heated gasps. Her memories of Daisy's short-lived second marriage were extremely painful. The discovery that Tomaso, for all his apparent devotion to her mother, was having an affair with another woman had shattered Kelda. The divorce had come as an incredible relief. It had freed her from the burden of a secret she had not dared to share with her vulnerable mother, and how could she tell Daisy the truth now? It wasn't even as if she had any concrete proof to offer...nothing more than the dismayed and embarrassed confirmation of a classmate.

There had been a piece about Tomaso in a newspaper. 'Looks as if butter wouldn't melt in his mouth, doesn't he?' Helena had giggled. 'He's had a mistress on the go for years, some blonde he takes to hideaway country pubs for dirty weekends. And even though he only got married recently, he's still seeing her...my father saw them all cosied up together in a dark corner only last week! Holding hands and kissing. Everybody's dying to meet his new wife and see what she's like——'

'She's my mother,' Kelda had said flatly.

Helena had looked aghast. 'Oh lord, I am sorry. I had no idea.'

Hell, why hadn't she told Daisy straight after the divorce? Well quite naturally she had believed the divorce was final. Most divorces were. 'We just weren't compatible,' Daisy had said sadly then, seemingly having no suspicion of Tomaso's infidelity. And now Tomaso had actually had the neck to pop the question a second time! How the heck could Kelda have foreseen that eventuality? And heaven knew, right at this minute, it was a problem she could have done without. She had quite enough problems of her own!

Determinedly, however, Kelda suppressed the bitter awareness that, thanks to all the bad publicity she had received of late, her career as a top model was over. There was no point in crying over spilt milk, she told herself and her poor mother's predicament was far more important.

Kelda had adored her own father, although her recollection of him was unhappily vague, built up on blurred impressions of a jovial, boisterous man, quick to temper, equally quick to laughter. She had only been five when her father began to spend long periods working abroad. She had only a couple of faded photographs of him when he was young and her mother had invariably resorted to tears whenever she tried to talk about him. But she still had every letter her father had ever written to her. The heart attack which had claimed his life in her twelfth year had seemed to devastate her mother at the time...

Yet four short months later Daisy had upped and married Tomaso Rossetti.

Her mother had been the manageress of a small hair salon, Tomaso, an extremely wealthy director in the Rossetti Industrial Bank. According to Daisy, she had been cutting Tomaso's hair for years but she had never once mentioned him to Kelda! Indeed, Kelda had not even had a chance to meet Tomaso before the wedding took place.

The first news she had had of the marriage had been in the headmistress's office at school. Called from class without any prior warning of what was coming, Kelda had been absolutely shattered when she was faced with a strange man with a proprietorial hand at her beaming mother's waist and told he was her stepfather. And she hadn't reacted exactly politely either. She had been appalled, resentful and alienated by the startling fact that the mother she loved could have kept so much from her. It had not been a promising start.

At the time, Kelda and her brother, Tim had been living with an elderly great-aunt in a quiet suburb of Liverpool, seeing their mother on only occasional weekends. Daisy had been unable to find a decent job outside London and her salary had not been enough to run to childcare outside school hours. She had refused to listen to Kelda when she argued that she was old enough to look after herself. Living as she then did in a far from salubrious inner city area, Daisy had been convinced that her children were far better off with their great-aunt.

'We'll all be together now!' Daisy had enthused. 'Tomaso wants us all to be one big happy family. He's bought us a beautiful house in Surrey.'

She could have coped with Tomaso with her hands tied behind her back. It had been Angelo she hadn't been able to handle. Angelo Cesare Rossetti. In the City, they called him the Angel of Darkness. It fitted him like a black velvet glove. Like an avenging dark angel, he destroyed anything and anybody foolish enough to get in his way. In comparison, his father was a positive pussy-cat, a gentleman of the old school, who treated women like creatures of spun-glass fragility in need of cherishing protection.

While Tomaso and Daisy had regularly scarpered abroad on what seemed to be one long impossibly extended honeymoon during the first years of their marriage, no doubt avoiding as best they could the poisonous atmosphere in their English home, Kelda had been left to Angelo's tender mercies. Angelo, the stepbrother from hell, who had loathed her on sight. Mind you, it had been mutual, she conceded grimly. Even now when she saw Angelo's name in a gossip column she still burned with an unholy, burning hatred that threatened to lick out of control.

As she slammed cups out on a tray, intelligence told her that she should be concentrating on Tomaso's sins, not those of his son. Tomaso, who had probably ordered all his business acquaintances to stay away from the hospital while he plucked violin strings and talked about the misery of his lonely life at the top. Daisy was an easy mark for a sob-story.

Well, never let it be said that Kelda didn't see her duty before her, even when it was unpleasant. The Rossettis had given her poor mother a very rough ride the first time around. Kelda intended to make sure that her mother thought twice, thrice and even more before she took the risk of marrying Tomaso again.

'So when did Tomaso pop the question?' she prompted with a brittle smile as she poured the tea.

'Last night over dinner.'

'He's out of hospital, then.' Kelda had had vague hopes that Tomaso had proposed from his sickbed. Her mother's dreamy expression might then have been excused as compassion.

'For ages. It wasn't a bad attack, more of a warning really,' Daisy shared. 'And Angelo has persuaded him to retire. He knows just how to talk to his father and he's been so kind——'

'Angelo? Kind?' Kelda echoed incredulously.

Her mother tensed. 'He sent a car to pick me up and take me home again every time I visited the hospital.'

'How many near-fatal collisions did it have?'

'Angelo really has been wonderful, Kelda,' Daisy murmured tautly. 'He...he even took me out to lunch. I find him rather overwhelming but he is trying to be friendly and considerate...'

Kelda wanted to laugh like a hyena. Angelo...kind, wonderful, considerate? Only her trusting mother could be so easily taken in. But on another level she was deeply hurt that so much had been happening behind her back. 'Does he know that his father's proposed again?'

Daisy nodded and smiled. Kelda ground her teeth together.

'Angelo even asked about you,' her mother advanced in a clear effort to impress. 'He was very sympathetic and understanding about...well, about that awful business in the papers.'

Kelda went white with rage and mortification and turned her head away. Of course, it had clearly been too much to hope that Angelo hadn't been laughing heartily over her recent sufferings. He never read the tabloids but she just bet that he had made an exception when the gutter Press were tearing her apart. Kelda still felt soiled and besmirched by the lies that had been written about her and the vicious quotes from ex-boyfriends who had jumped on the bandwagon in revenge.

'It's such a shame that you didn't let Danny Philips down more gently.' Daisy sighed regretfully.

'He was a married man!' Kelda reminded her acidly. 'Naturally, I got rid of him as soon as I found *that* out.'

'I expect he didn't mean to fall in love with you,' Daisy murmured sadly.

'He wasn't in love with me...he just wanted to get me into bed like all the rest!' Kelda fielded.

'But he must have been terribly hurt to take an overdose like that, and maybe if you'd gone to see him in hospital——'

'I'd have finished him off!' Kelda broke in rawly. 'He took an overdose because his wife found out he'd been seeing me. He took it to get back in with her and then he spilt his guts in that filthy newspaper to get his own back on me!'

'It was wicked of him to tell all those lies about you.' Daisy's large blue eyes were swimming with tears. 'I told Angelo that you'd never had an affair with anyone...'

'P-Pardon?'

Her mother reddened. 'I wanted Angelo to know that there wasn't a word of truth in any of it. You're not that sort of girl.'

Kelda was in agony. She adored her mother but she had never come closer to killing her! 'Kelda's saving herself for marriage.' She could just hear her mother saying it! And she could see Angelo, struggling not to choke on his wine, sardonically amused by her mother's blind faith in her daughter's virtue. Hellfire embarrassment scorched Kelda.

'Well...what do you think?' Daisy asked hesitantly.

'About what?'

'About me marrying Tomaso again?'

Kelda steeled herself. 'I think you'd be making the biggest mistake of your life. But of course...it's your decision.'

'I suppose the idea of us all being a f-family together is a little fanciful.' Looking stricken, Daisy was visibly swallowing back tears of disappointment.

Kelda felt torn apart by guilt but she reminded herself that it was for her mother's own good. 'Have you given him an answer yet?'

'No,' Daisy conceded tightly.

'If you do marry him, I'll hardly cut you off...I expect we can still meet for lunch occasionally...'

'Y-yes,' Daisy gulped, bending her head. 'But you and I are so close...what about weekends?'

'I will never cross the threshold of any house that harbours Angelo as a regular visitor,' Kelda stated without apology.

'You mean she just dropped it on you?' Her brother Tim burst out laughing. 'Isn't that just Daisy?'

It was the following day. They were lunching in a wine-bar round the corner from the insurance company where Tim worked.

'It wasn't funny! Why didn't you warn me?' Kelda snapped, throwing an icy glance of hauteur at the man at the next table, who had sat fixedly trying to catch her eye ever since she sat down.

Tim followed her gaze ruefully. 'The Iceberg buries another victim...'

'I loathe that stupid nickname!' She set her perfect white teeth into a celery stick and crunched. As she chewed, she flung her head back, her mane of entirely natural pre-Raphaelite curls rippling back over her slim shoulders in tongues of fire. 'Don't use it!'

'OK...OK!' Tim held up both hands in mock surrender.

'Why didn't you tell me she was seeing Tomaso again?'

His mobile features tensed. 'I guessed how you'd react.'

'I bet you said nothing, you lily-livered swine!' Kelda hissed across the table at him. 'You don't care if Tomaso runs around with other women behind her back!'

Tim had gone red. 'I don't think it's any of my business.'

'Oh, I'm all right, Jack!'

Tim grimaced. 'How much of the way you feel has to do with Angelo?'

Kelda froze. 'It's got nothing to do with him!'

Tim gave her an unimpressed glance.

'I can't stand him...that's true.' Her restive hands snapped a carrot stick in two but she held his gaze fiercely. 'But it's Mum's best interests that concern me.'

'You're terrified of Angelo.' Tim looked almost amused.

'Don't be ridiculous...I loathe and despise him...I'm certainly not afraid of him!'

Tim sipped his wine. 'Exactly what did happen the night of your eighteenth birthday bash? You know, I never did find out why Angelo had disappeared, Tomaso looked like thunder and Mum was on the brink of hysterics over breakfast the next morning...'

Every scrap of natural colour had drained from her complexion. 'I don't want to talk about it,' she said tightly.

Her stomach was churning sickly. She broke out in a cold sweat. If she lived to be a hundred, she would still relive that evening in her nightmares. Angelo had humiliated her. Angelo had destroyed her. At a most sensitive age, he had instilled in her an aversion to sexual intimacy that she had still to overcome. The Iceberg was dead from the neck down, she reflected with raw shame and bitterness. She couldn't bear a man to come too close. Her skin crawled when men got seductive and expectant. It made her feel soiled, cheap. Angelo had done that to her...with his scorn and revulsion.

'You're a promiscuous little tramp. It doesn't matter how much money my father spends on you...you will never climb out of the gutter!'

Kelda swallowed back nausea with difficulty. She was lost in the past, savaged by an indictment that had merely heightened the intense vulnerability she concealed from the world.

'Angelo seems to be encouraging Mum and Tomaso,' Tim remarked. 'If I were you, I wouldn't stick a spoke in his wheels.'

'You've seen him, haven't you?' Kelda demanded.

Tim didn't meet her eyes. 'He called into the office one day last week.' He cleared his throat awkwardly. 'Actually, he's offered to fix me up with a better job...'

'I can see I'm on my own,' Kelda breathed flatly.

Tim searched her vibrantly beautiful face anxiously. 'He's a vicious bastard when he's crossed, Kelda. Stay out of it. Mum's a big girl now. Let her make her own mistakes. And if Angelo's prepared to bury the hatchet——'

'I'll lift it out of the ground and bury it in his back,' Kelda slotted in with grim emphasis. 'I have no intention of interfering between Mum and Tomaso but neither have I any intention of being roped in to play happy families. I'm not eighteen any more. I have a life of my own.'

Tim groaned. 'You're not half as tough as you like to act. If you annoy him, Angelo won't just rock your boat, Kelda. He'll blow you out of the water.'

Her hand shook slightly as she raised her glass. Tim's imagery sent a chill snaking down her backbone.

'Any recovery on the career front?' Tim prompted abruptly.

She pulled a face. 'I'm trying to sell my apartment.'

'As bad as that?' Tim looked shaken.

'When the Fantasy campaign dropped me, I lost half my income...and other cancellations followed,' she spelt out tautly.

'But you'll make it up again...you're famous!'

'Notorious,' Kelda corrected with unconcealed bitterness. 'And that's not the sort of image that sells exclusive cosmetics and perfume. My contract with the agency is up in two months' time. I don't think it'll be renewed.'

Tim said something unrepeatable about Danny Philips. Then he smiled. 'You should marry Jeff. He's stood by you and he's got all his Daddy's hotels coming to him——'

Kelda concealed her distaste. She knew she would miss the luxuries her high earnings had brought her but she had no intention of marrying to maintain that lifestyle.

'I should have stopped seeing Jeff weeks ago,' she confided wryly,.

'I liked Jeff.' Tim frowned at her. 'Let him down gently.'

As she dressed for her dinner date that evening, she grimaced. She had already tried and failed twice to let Jeff down lightly. So much for her heartless bitch image! She liked Jeff but he was getting serious. He wasn't the Mr Right her daft mother liked to talk about. Kelda had decided a long time ago that Mr Right didn't exist. Not for her, anyway. She attracted all the wrong types.

The poseurs, the predators. To most men, she was a trophy to show off, a glorified sex object, whose greatest gift was the envious reactions she stirred up among their friends. Five feet nine in her bare feet, Kelda had the sleek slender lines of an elegant thoroughbred and a face that every camera loved. She had flawless skin, gorgeous hair and beautiful eyes. At sixteen she had suddenly blossomed from a gawky, flat-chested late developer into an eye-catching young woman, who turned heads wherever she went. The attention had been balm to a self-esteem continuously battered by Angelo's cruel tongue.

He had so very nearly prevented her from becoming a model. If it hadn't been for the divorce, she would have ended up resitting the final exams she had failed.

'You let her go to London, she'll go wild,' Angelo had forecast. 'She's too immature, too undisciplined and too volatile.'

Angelo had always taken great pleasure in ensuring that whatever she most wanted she didn't get and whatever she least wanted, she got in spades. But she hadn't gone wild, had she? She had clawed her way up the ladder to success and exulted in her first *Vogue* cover. Rather childishly, she recalled reluctantly, she had sent a copy of that edition to Angelo, desperately afraid that he mightn't have seen it. Very childish, she acknowledged. Then, Angelo had always brought out the worst in her character.

Jeff arrived with a massive bunch of red roses and her heart sank. Dinner at a candlelit restaurant followed. No matter how often she tried to tactfully change the subject, Jeff brought it back to marriage. He was like a terrier chasing a bone.

Her conscience smote her. Jeff had staunchly stood by her throughout the tabloid attacks. Other friends had deserted her like rats escaping a sinking ship. Jeff had had touching faith in her innocence. What a shame it was that you couldn't love to order, she thought ruefully. She valued Jeff's friendship but she was beginning to realise that no matter what she did, she was going to lose that as well.

'I'm really very fond of you,' Kelda stressed carefully.

'I don't want you to be bloody fond of me!' he muttered with unexpected heat. 'I want you to marry me.'

'I can't.'

For the remainder of the meal, he swung between arguing and a monolithic attack of the sulks. Kelda managed to charm him out of the worst of his mood but he was drinking too much. Unfortunately she had already agreed to join friends of his at a nightclub. Her attempt to pull out of the arrangement was badly received. Fearful of a public scene, she steeled herself to face what remained of a difficult evening. If it was at all possible, she didn't want to hurt Jeff's feelings.

Belatedly she realised that she had made the wrong decision. In the foyer of the club, Jeff suddenly attempted to drag her into his arms and Kelda slapped his hands away with the fury of a bristling tigress. Of all things, she hated being mauled in public.

'I'm absolutely crazy about you!' Jeff announced stridently. 'Doesn't that mean anything to you?'

'If you don't behave yourself, I'm going home!' she hissed at him in an undertone and turned on her heel, praying that he would cool off.

A split-second later, she stopped dead in her tracks, slaughtered by the sheer shock of finding Angelo less than six feet from her. He had the advantage, she registered. He had seen her first. At six feet four, he was one of the very few men capable of looking down on her even when she was wearing her highest heels.

She was paralysed, her heartbeat quickening, colour flooding her translucent skin and then slowly, painfully draining away again to leave her paper-white. Chillingly dark eyes cut into her like grappling hooks in search of choice and tender flesh. Every tiny muscle in her tensed body jerked tight as she braced herself for attack.

'I presume you do intend to speak, Kelda.' The smooth, cultured drawl sliced through the thickening atmosphere and clawed nasty vibrations of threat down her sensitive spine. He was like a sleek, terrifyingly dangerous black panther about to strike.

'Did you hear someone speak?' she asked Jeff, planting a trembling hand on his arm. 'I didn't.'

She swept past Angelo and his dainty little blonde sidekick with inches to spare and her classic nose as high in the air as she could hold it.

'Do you realise who that was?' Jeff bleated in her ear.

'Once upon a time, my mother was married to his father. That creep was my stepbrother. And we didn't part on such terms that I feel I have to notice him in public.'

'Why didn't you tell me that your mother had been married to Tomaso Rossetti?'

Jeff was so helplessly impressed by anyone whose bank balance was greater than his father's. 'It wasn't important.'

'You just cut Angelo Rossetti dead,' Jeff groaned. 'Are you out of your mind?'

Sitting down, Kelda fought to still the nervous tremors still rippling through her. 'He told me once that I had the manners of a slum child. He ought to be pleased to see how well I've turned out.'

Shock seemed to have sobered Jeff up. 'My father's into the Rossetti Bank to the tune of a million and we're looking for an extension on the loan. I was so shattered by what you did out there, I didn't speak either.' Abruptly, he bolted upright again. 'I'd better go and apologise.'

Her temples were throbbing. 'I'm sorry...I didn't intend to involve you——'

'My God, you must have a death wish!' Jeff muttered. 'Nobody treats Angelo Rossetti like that and gets away with it.'

'I think you'll find that I have,' Kelda asserted with more confidence than she actually felt.

She had gone too far. Temper and other emotions that she had no desire to examine had taken over. Did she never learn? Angelo taunted her and she still went for the bait. The teenage years might be behind her but evidently the responses weren't. Only she could know the depth of the bitter mortification which overwhelmed her in Angelo's radius. Nothing had changed.

Absolutely nothing had changed. In one glance she had learnt that. Angelo had stared her down with freezing hauteur and distaste. The dust beneath his feet would have inspired less repugnance. Of course he hadn't seen her since *that night*...not once, not even briefly. He had gone abroad and shortly after that their parents had parted. She shuddered under the onslaught of a mess of confused emotions, none of which was pleasant.

Tonight she had reacted in self-defence as she had so often in the past. 'Hit and run' best summed it up, she conceded shamefacedly. If she hadn't got away immediately, her control would have splintered and he would have seen that, caught unprepared, she was vulnerable. Naturally his hostility would be on a high again at the prospect of her re-entering the family circle with her slum-child manners and her legendary promiscuity.

But this time Angelo had been ahead of her. This time he was isolating her. She recognised the subtle brilliance of Angelo's manipulation of her mother and her brother. How come they didn't see it? Frankly, Tim was pleased at the idea of being part of the Rossetti clan again. Tim was always broke, always in debt. Tomaso was open-handed with money.

And Tim, like her mother, had always walked in awe of Angelo. Angelo was so clever that he had finished university in his teens. Angelo spoke half a dozen languages with the sort of fluency that made lesser mortals cringe. Angelo was so dazzlingly successful in the field of international finance that he was currently being tipped to become the youngest ever chief executive of Rossetti Industrial. Tongues that had dared to talk of nepotism had long since been silenced. Everything Angelo touched turned to gold. His opinions were quoted in the serious newspapers. Tomaso thought his son literally walked on water.

'I must say that he was very gracious about it.' Jeff reappeared, exuding an air of strong relief. 'He's asked us to join their table.'

Kelda went rigid. 'But what about your friends?'

Jeff grimaced. 'Don't be so naïve, Kelda. You get an invite like that from Angelo Rossetti and you grab it. He's got influence like you wouldn't believe in all sorts of powerful corners——'

'I'm sorry. I have a dreadful headache.' Kelda stood up, her face a mask of disdain. 'You can call a cab for me if you like——'

Slowly he shook his head. 'Kelda...'

She was immovable. Catch her falling for a trick like that? No way would she give Angelo the opportunity to put her down in front of an audience. He excelled in that direction. Time was when she wouldn't have had the wit to forestall him... time was when she would have waded in with both fists metaphorically flying, unconcerned by the presence of others. Suddenly she was unbelievably grateful to be a mature twenty-four, rather than an insecure, dreadfully unhappy teenager, trying to act older than she was.

Jeff was furious. She was wryly amused at the way the prospect of making an influential contact had cleared his wits and turned him off his previous insistence that he loved her and wanted to marry her. Insisting that he go and find his friends, she went home alone.

Switching on the lights in the lounge, she kicked off her shoes and switched on her answering machine. Nothing. Once there would have been at least a couple of messages. Not now...she was yesterday's news. The Iceberg, who drove innocent married men to suicide. Her apartment would sell for far less than she had paid for it. Her bank balance was at an all-time low. She had had insurance for accident or injury but nothing to cover what amounted to being virtually unemployable. The media had turned her into a figure of hate. There had been plenty of pictures of Danny's tear-stained, plain little wife. The wife that Kelda had not even known existed, living in the country as she did with their two young children while Danny had lived the life of a free and easy single man in the city during the week.

He had actually told Kelda that he went home most weekends to his elderly parents! With a sudden choked sound between a laugh and a sob, Kelda covered her working face with two unsteady hands. How could she have been so stupid? And how could Danny have told so many lies? For the money, she thought cynically. The true story would have made surpassingly unexciting reading. Danny had made her look like a vicious bitch, who used men up like tissues and threw them away when she got bored. And the truth...really the truth was far more pathetic, she reflected.

Here she was all dressed up in the proverbial sexy little black dress which showed off her perfect curves and endless legs and what *was* she, she asked herself painfully as she stared at her reflection in one of the mirrored wardrobes in her bedroom. A complete fraud! Less of a woman certainly than Danny's poor little wife, who loved him and had borne his children and who had apparently been willing to forgive and forget from the instant he landed in that hospital bed!

What did it feel like to love like that? She couldn't imagine it...she had never loved, only once experienced the devastation of desire...and *that* she never ever allowed herself to remember. It had hurt so much and so badly; she had been savaged by her own vulnerability. Deep down inside the pain was still there like an indoor alarm system. A man put his arms around her and if she felt anything at all, the alarm went off. *If he makes me want him... what then*? And she would go cold, inside and out.

The intercom buzzed beside the front door. It was two in the morning. With a crease between her brows, she pressed the button.

'Angelo here...'

Kelda's stomach clenched fearfully. She leapt back a step.

'Go away!' she shouted.

She heard muffled speech as if he had turned to speak to someone else.

'Calm down, *cara*,' Angelo purred.

Her lashes blinking in bemusement at the smooth endearment, Kelda let rip again, something terrifyingly akin to hysteria audible even to herself in her shrieked response. 'Leave me alone!'

She walked away from the front door, breathing fast, and backed into the lounge where she sat down on the sofa and wrapped both arms round herself tightly. She had had a lousy evening, a lousy week, a lousy month come to that. She was not in the mood for a fight with Angelo. Dimly she had known that it would come, but she hadn't been prepared for it to happen so soon.

It was with utter disbelief that she heard her front door open. She lurched bolt upright in genuine fear, cursing herself for not using the chain.

'Do you think I should call a doctor, Mr Rossetti?' a vaguely familiar male voice enquired. It was the night security guard.

'No... I don't think that will be necessary now that I am here. Thank you again.'

'It's a pleasure to be of service, Mr Rossetti.'

She heard the crackle of money changing hands and she still couldn't move or react. She couldn't believe that Angelo had somehow contrived to break into her very secure apartment with the assistance of the guard.

Angelo appeared in the doorway.

'If you don't g-get out, I'll call the police!' Kelda screeched at him.

CHAPTER TWO

KELDA had blocked Angelo out in the foyer of the nightclub. She had seen him and yet she hadn't seen him. Her eyes had skipped off him again double quick, discarding the imagery as if it burned. And it did... it did. Angelo was drop-dead gorgeous.

'My, but you're pretty,' she had trilled the very first time she met him at the age of thirteen, derisively scanning the near-classic perfection of his golden features and the lean, lithe perfectly balanced body that went with it. Amazingly, Tomaso had laughed. Angelo hadn't.

And then as now, Kelda had somehow found herself still staring, after the laughter had died away. He had the slashing cheekbones of a Tartar prince, long-lashed, brilliant dark eyes and a strong aristocratic nose. The whole effect was sexually devastating. She hadn't known what made him so disturbing when she was thirteen...but she did now.

Angelo was sinfully, scorchingly sexy. It hit the unwary like a forcefield of raw energy. The very air seemed to sizzle round Angelo and when you reached a certain age, she acknowledged, that certain age when you often embarrassed yourself with your own thoughts, you would look at a male like Angelo and find yourself quite unable to avoid wondering what he was like in bed...

A little voice inside Kelda's head cruelly reminded her that she was not entirely unaware of what Angelo was like in bed... and instantaneously a wave of mortified heat engulfed her translucent skin. It was hardly surprising that such painful imagery should visit her now. This was the first time they had stood face to face since that ghastly, unforgettable night over six years ago.

'The police,' Angelo reminded her with satire. 'Weren't you about to call them? Or have you decided that you really can't afford the publicity?'

As Kelda's teeth gritted, she made a swift recovery from her unfortunate loss of concentration. 'How did you persuade the guard to let you in here?

'I told him you were suicidal,' Angelo drawled softly. 'And you probably will be by the time I'm finished with you.'

'Get out!' Kelda gasped. 'Get out of my apartment!'

'It's not going to be your apartment for much longer.' Angelo cast her a veiled glance of cruel amusement. 'In the current market, I suspect you are about to suffer from a severe negative equity problem... the sale price is not going to wipe out the mortgage debt——'

'Damn, you to hell!' Kelda interrupted tremulously. 'I know what negative equity is. I'm not stupid——'

'You just didn't manage to pass a single exam in all those years of expensive education,' he inserted.

'I'm thick,' Kelda responded through clenched teeth, refusing to rise to the bait.

'Surpassingly so,' Angelo agreed. 'If you had listened to me, you could have had the modelling career *and* the education to fall back on. As it is, you have neither——'

'I can't believe you actually came here just to crow!' Kelda blistered back.

'I want you to understand your present position,' Angelo breathed almost conversationally. 'If you think that your future is on the skids now, you're wrong. Life could become so much more painful... with a little help from me.'

The assurance hung there in the pulsing air between them and her blood ran cold in her veins. She cleared her throat. 'Are you threatening me?'

'Surprised?' Angelo sank down with innate grace into a wing-backed armchair and surveyed her with total cool.

'I have no intention of allowing you to come between my father and your mother a second time...'

Her tongue snaked out to wet her dry lips. 'A second time?'

'You put considerable stress on their relationship six years ago——'

Rigid with incredulity, Kelda spat, 'That's a filthy thing to say!'

'But true, and this time matters were proceeding smoothly until once again you intervened——'

Kelda was shaking. 'I don't know what you're talking about!'

A satiric brow climbed. 'Last night, Daisy asked my father to give her more time to consider his proposal, and we both know why, don't we?'

Kelda thrust up her chin. 'Naturally she wants to think it over very carefully. You can't blame me for that. For goodness' sake, she divorced him five years ago!'

'You selfish little bitch,' Angelo murmured with a softness that was all the more chilling than a rise in volume. 'Daisy didn't have any reservations until *after* she saw you yesterday!'

Kelda stiffened, colour flying into her cheeks. Derisive dark eyes raked over her, absorbing her sudden tension.

'She's afraid of losing her daughter, would you believe?' Angelo drawled. 'Family ties are very important to Daisy. What the hell did you say to her?'

'Nothing that I wouldn't say again!' Kelda slung defiantly, although the ache of tears threatened behind her eyelids. 'And if she is having second thoughts, don't lay them all at my door. Your father wasn't exactly Mr Fidelity the first time around and maybe she suspects that!'

Angelo's striking bone-structure clenched hard. 'I told you that there was absolutely no truth in those allegations years ago,' he grated with savage emphasis. 'And if you have repeated those same lies to Daisy, I'll break every bone in your poisonously vindictive little body!'

Shocked by the depth of his anger, Kelda paled and drew back a step, but she was outraged by his treatment. No, she had no concrete proof to offer her mother on the subject of Tomaso's adulterous affair but, the year before their parents had separated, Kelda had flung that allegation at Angelo.

And for a fraction of a second Angelo's expression had one hundred percent convinced her that he knew exactly what she was talking about and that he was well aware of his father's extra-marital relationship with another woman. Kelda had taken him by surprise and his complete denial of that relationship had come just that little bit too late to be plausible.

Angelo had known all right. And no doubt, Angelo hadn't seen anything the slightest bit immoral in Tomaso's behaviour. In his world, married men with mistresses were far from unusual. But that same knowledge would have destroyed her mother. Now, Kelda found herself wondering if indeed her mother had at least suspected Tomaso of having another woman. It was quite possible that Daisy would have kept that information to herself, rather than share it with her teenage daughter.

'What did you tell her?' Angelo demanded ferociously.

'I told her nothing...not that that is any of your business,' Kelda stressed.

'When my father's happiness is at stake, it *is* my business.'

'I doubt if he'd thank you for your interference...and if my mother knew that you were here threatening me like this——'

'Are you planning to tell her?' Angelo had the stillness of a jungle cat about to spring.

Kelda wouldn't have dreamt of telling Daisy, but she was furiously angry and she lifted a bare pale shoulder in a deliberately provocative gesture. 'I might...on the other hand I might not,' she said sweetly, incandescent green eyes flaming at him. 'You'll just have to wait and see, won't you, Angelo?'

He had gone satisfyingly white beneath his bronzed skin, his facial bones harshly set. Kelda smiled, widely, brilliantly, smugly. It really had been very foolish of Angelo to come here and threaten her. Astoundingly foolish... astoundingly out of character for so noted a tactician. One lean brown hand was curled into his fist and without warning he stood up again.

'I came here tonight to appeal to your better nature——'

'I haven't got one, Angelo... not where you're concerned,' she said shakily but truthfully.

'I could break you with one hand,' Angelo savoured, eyes as treacherous as black ice on a wintry night, fixed to her with savage intensity. 'And I will... I don't mind waiting a little while... a very little while. And while I'm waiting, you'll be waiting too...'

Icy fingers were walking up her unbelievably taut backbone. Angelo hated her, he really did hate her. And she knew why. It lay unspoken between them, untouched but raw. She shivered, no longer able to meet that hard, dark scrutiny. Had she gone overboard? Should she for once have kept her mouth shut? But why should she stand and take abuse from Angelo?

Her front door shut with a soft click. Shaking all over now, released from the spell he always cast, Kelda collapsed down into the nearest seat. She felt sick. He had called her poisonous, vindictive, and yet all she wanted was her mother's happiness. Had it been selfish to make it clear that if Daisy married Tomaso again she was unlikely to see so much of her adored daughter?

But hadn't that only been the truth? She couldn't stand Angelo, and the savage hostility between them would be painfully obvious to both their parents. It would hardly add to connubial bliss, so naturally her contact with her mother would have to take place only when Angelo was elsewhere. Was that her fault? Was that so horribly selfish of her? Tears lashed her eyelids in a scorching surge. The memories were coming back...

Yes, she had bitterly resented her mother's remarriage all those years ago. Had she had a chance to get to know Tomaso in advance, had she even known of his existence, maybe she would have reacted differently.

The sudden material change in their lifestyle hadn't helped. Kelda had been parcelled off to an exclusive boarding school where her accent had provoked her classmates to pitying laughter. Her friends, her great-aunt, everything that had given her security had been wrenched away all at once. Instead of seeing more of her mother, she had actually seen less of her. Was it really any wonder that she had found it so hard to adapt?

The worst shock had been the discovery that, when their parents were abroad, Angelo was expected to take responsibility for her. Angelo ruled with an iron rod. When she was expelled from that first school for going 'over the wall' one night on a dare, it had been Angelo who took charge and reinstalled her in a convent day school with more rules and regulations than Holloway. It had been Angelo who took her apart when she failed her exams, Angelo who forced her to spend several fruitless vacations swotting with private tutors as bored and fed up as she was.

Tomaso had seemed to find his son's assumption of authority amusing. When he was around, which had been rarely, he hadn't interfered. Her mother had had a tendency to slip out of the room when Kelda appealed to her for back-up. Defying Angelo to her last gasp, Kelda had refused to work. She had frequently been in trouble at school but she hadn't cared because for the first time in her life she had been really popular.

At sixteen, Angelo had trailed her screeching out of her first boyfriend's car. She had sneaked out on the date, conscious that her mother would think that Josh at twenty-two was too old for her. The evening had been spent at a ten-pin bowling alley... nothing could have been more innocuous. Josh had parked his car a hundred yards before the entrance of the house on the way back. He had been on the brink of giving her a kiss... only on the brink, mind you, when all of a sudden the door was wrenched open and she was forcibly hauled out of Josh's reach by Angelo.

'Approach her again and I'll break every one of your fingers,' he had told Josh with a chilling smile. That had been the end of that, and the word had gone out on her locally. Josh had talked. Date Kelda and you tangled with Angelo Rossetti. Not surprisingly, it had destroyed her social life. Even her girlfriends had laughed and, not content with humiliating her, Angelo had told Tomaso and Daisy, ensuring that what little freedom she had had was even more severely curtailed. He had made Josh sound like a potential rapist.

Was it any wonder that she had hated Angelo? Even now, it still stuck in her throat that she had had to endure all those years of Angelo's moralising lectures. What about his own reputation?

From birth, he had made headlines. When Tomaso and his far richer Brazilian wife had split up, Angelo had been the most fought-over little boy in the Western world. Tomaso had lost, but when his ex-wife died he had fought for custody again, this time against Angelo's grandmother. Tomaso had won the final battle, but he hadn't managed to subdue the explosive temperament that powered his son.

Angelo's teenage exploits had shocked Europe. At the age of eighteen, he had inherited his late mother's millions, and for several years afterwards he had run wild. He had lived the self-indulgent life of the super-rich playboy. His insatiable appetite for beautiful women had been notorious. His sex-life might have become considerably more discreet over the last decade but husbands still paled in Angelo's vicinity.

As her mind threatened to leap forward to her eighteenth birthday, Kelda tensed and stopped her recollections stone dead in their tracks. She went to bed, suppressing all thoughts on the subject of Angelo's threats... after all, what could he possibly do to her?

Dawn was lightening the sky beyond the curtains when she woke up, shivering and perspiring, an hour later. She had been wrestling with the duvet, probably crying out. The fear was still with her even in the light of day. The nightmare had been so real.

Getting up, she poured herself a glass of mineral water in the kitchen. On wobbly legs, she sank down at the breakfast-bar and stared into space. She had been allowed to throw a party to celebrate her eighteenth birthday. Owing to her exams, the party had been held several months after her actual birthday. There had been two events to celebrate. Her birthday and the end of her schooldays. Daisy and Tomaso had gone out for the evening but naturally Angelo had had no such tact. Strange to think that some hours after that wretched party had started she had been desperately, pathetically grateful that Angelo had stayed home.

Before the party had started, Angelo had staggered her by complimenting her on her appearance. Ignoring her dropped jaw and looking oddly self-conscious, he had then taken himself off to his suite of rooms on the far side of the house. He had just come home after a long period working abroad and it must have been almost a year since she had seen him. After that astonishing compliment, she had actually wondered if her stormy relationship with Angelo was miraculously about to improve with his acceptance that she was now an adult.

She had promised that there would be no alcohol at the party but most of her guests had brought wine. Reluctant to be the odd one out, Kelda had had a couple of glasses. Half a dozen boys had shown up on the doorstep midway through the evening. One of them had been the brother of one of her best friends, so she had let them in.

It had happened in the library. Some people had drifted in there and she had had to shoo them frantically out again because the party had been getting rowdy and there were far too many valuable objects in that room. She should have called for Angelo's help then, because she had known that some people had had far too much to drink. But most of those people had been her friends.

She had been switching out a lamp when she was grabbed from behind. Having believed that she was alone in the room, she had screamed with fright. For a moment, she had assumed it was one of the boys she knew fooling around, but when she was dragged down on the carpet by bruising hands and a crude voice started telling her in the kind of language she had never heard before exactly what he was going to do to a 'snobby little cow' like her, she had been terrified out of her wits.

He had been so strong. Until that night she had never properly appreciated just how much stronger the average male was in comparison to a woman. She had gone wild, trying to kick, trying to claw with her nails while he yanked her dress up round her waist and bit horribly at the exposed slope of her breasts. He had hit her a stunning blow across the side of her head and then he had put his hand over her mouth, depriving her of the ability to scream. She'd been involved in a desperate struggle when the light went on and all of a sudden she was freed.

She had thrown up on the priceless Persian rug at Angelo's feet. Her assailant had taken immediate flight. She had not seen his face and, strangely, Angelo had made no attempt to stop him. He had simply swung on his heel and walked back out of the room to tell everyone that the party was over. At that point, she had been too hysterical to realise that Angelo had *not* understood what he had interrupted.

Stumbling and crying, she had fled upstairs to her bedroom. She had stripped and got into the shower, needing to wash away the taint of the hands that had touched her. There had been bruises on her breasts and a lump the size of a small egg on the side of her head where she had been struck. The attack had terrified her and she had been sitting still shaking on the side of her bed when Angelo knocked and entered.

'A promiscuous little tramp', he had called her and, still suffering from the effects of shock, Kelda had looked back at him numbly, unable even to credit that he could think she had been writhing about on the library floor in the dark out of choice.

'He attacked m-me!' she had gasped. 'He was trying to rape me...'

And she still remembered the way Angelo had looked at her. He had been so pale, so rigid with tension. She had recognised the seething anger he was struggling to restrain. It had glittered dangerously in his piercing dark eyes like a violent storm warning. For a foolish moment she had actually thought that he believed her and that he was angry with himself, angry that he had allowed her assailant to get away instead of calling the police to report an assault. But his next words had demolished that hope.

'You disgust me,' he had breathed in a savage undertone. 'I will never forget what I saw tonight.'

He had not even given her a fair hearing, had not hesitated in choosing to believe the very worst of her. His response, following so closely upon the attack she had endured had reduced her to stricken sobs. It had been some time before she pulled herself together again, and then the anger and the fear of what he would tell her mother and Tomaso had assailed her.

She hadn't thought about what she did next. Had she known what would happen, she would have stayed where she was, safe in her own room... but she had been distressed and frightened and helplessly determined that Angelo should hear her side of the story and believe her. She hadn't stopped even to put her dressing-gown on.

She had knocked on Angelo's door. Although she had been able to see faint light beneath the door, there had been no answer. She had crept in. The bedside lamp had cast a soft pool of light over Angelo. He had been asleep and about that point, her memory became confused between what she did recall and what, for a long time afterwards, she had refused to admit even to herself.

A white sheet had been riding dangerously low on one lean golden hip. He had been naked and she had been strangely hesitant about waking him. Indeed now, when she was of an age when she had learnt to be truthful at least with herself, she could admit that she had been mesmerised by his sheer masculine beauty. For the very first time, she had reacted to Angelo's physical allure. He had not been Tomaso's son, her hatefully arrogant stepbrother, who just so happened to be very good-looking. No, it had been much more personal, much more intimate than that, and the sensations Angelo had aroused in her had been painfully new to her experience.

He had opened his eyes, pools of passionate gold. He had not appeared to be still half asleep. But perhaps he had been. Something had flamed in that golden gaze that raked over her while she had hovered there in stupid paralysis and he had reached up with two very determined hands and pulled her down on to that bed with him.

'*Carissima... bella mia*,' he had breathed passionately against her lips in welcome, suggesting that he had inexplicably mistaken her for someone else. He could not possibly have been addressing those endearments to Kelda.

'Angelo!' she had gasped incredulously before he silenced her with the heat of his mouth.

It had not been to her credit that she had neither screamed nor raised a finger to fight him off. But the terrible truth was that she had had no thought of denying him. In fact she could not recall a single thought of anything passing through her blitzed mind during those fevered few minutes.

The explosion of desire, of need, of want had been instantaneous. The stab of his tongue into the moist interior of her mouth had drowned her in waves of intense physical pleasure. She had been reduced to mindless compliance within seconds. Angelo kissed with electrifying eroticism. She had wrapped her arms round him with shameless abandonment and the spell had only been broken when a thunderous male voice rudely interrupted them.

'You set me up!' Angelo had hissed incomprehensibly, staring down at her with cold, embittered fury.

Even six years after the event, Kelda still got hot and cold reliving that hideous moment when Angelo had released her and she had dazedly focused on Tomaso standing at the foot of the bed. Ignoring her, Tomaso had been ranting at his son in staccato Italian. Normally a mild-mannered man, Angelo's father had been shocked and completely enraged by the scene he had interrupted.

But then, oddly enough, Tomaso had briefly appeared to calm down. He had even managed a rather grim smile as he said something very clipped. Whatever Angelo had said in response had wiped that smile right back off his face again and two seconds later Tomaso had been ripping off his own jacket, draping it round Kelda's cowering shoulders and practically trailing her out of the room while throwing words that had sounded positively violent over his shoulder at his son. His precious, much beloved son...

Daisy had come to her bedroom. Kelda had striven to explain the inexplicable but tears had overwhelmed her. 'Just put it behind you, darling,' her mother had whispered, in sympathetic tears herself. 'I know you must feel very foolish but at your age one does do foolish things...that's a fact of life...and it's so hard to control your feelings but you'll get over him...'

Her mother had assumed that she had thrown herself at Angelo's head because she was infatuated with him, and Kelda had been too deeply ashamed of her behaviour and too desperately confused to protest. She hated Angelo and yet when he had touched her she had gone up in flames. It had not been the sort of self-discovery she could have shared with her mother.

Angelo had read her appearance by the side of his bed as a sexual invitation. Why he should have done so and why he should have acted on such an invitation, she had never understood. Angelo had never given her the remotest hint that he considered her even passably attractive. Could he *really* have mistaken her for another woman? She found that explanation unlikely. So why had he touched her? To humiliate...to hurt...and when had he planned to stop?

The next morning, Angelo had been gone. He had had an apartment in London. Her stepfather had heavily assured her that he attached absolutely no blame to her. She was innocent of all fault, he had stressed, making her feel guiltier than ever. She had felt so dreadful for causing a rift between father and son. When she had fought her embarrassment enough to mumble, 'Angelo didn't mean to——' Tomaso had grimly silenced her with the reminder that Angelo was eight years older.

Her mother had said later, 'I can't reason with Tomaso. He's very strict about some things and even though I assured him that it was only a few kisses, he won't listen to me. He said that he can no longer trust Angelo with you and he's very angry with him. I think he told Angelo to get out and that must have been devastating for both of them. Until now, they were so close...'

Angelo had accused her of setting him up. How, she had no idea, had never wanted to know, because frankly the way things had turned out afterwards she might as well have set him up. His father had told him to leave and she had been relieved of all responsibility for the episode. A couple of days later, she had travelled over to France with a girlfriend and her family for a month's holiday and while she had been away she had received a letter from her mother, telling her that she was separating from Tomaso.

Had that been her fault? She was much inclined to say no. In the months coming up to that fatal night, she had noticed that Daisy was far from her sunny self. There had been something wrong in that relationship then, some tension that had had nothing to do with what had later happened between Angelo and her.

Dear lord, she suddenly reflected, why had her mother had to get involved with Tomaso Rossetti again? And the second she thought that, she despised herself. How could she be so selfish? Had Tim been right to suggest that her hostility towards the idea of Tomaso and Daisy remarrying related more to her own hatred of Angelo than to any genuine concern for her mother's future happiness?

Mid-morning the next day, she received a call from Ella Donaldson, who ran the modelling agency she had been with since she was eighteen. 'I've got a last-minute booking for you...if you're not too proud to take it,' she announced.

Kelda bit at her lower lip, gathering that the assignment was downmarket and less lucrative than what had once been offered to her.

Ella didn't wait for her reply. 'A holiday brochure. A very upmarket company, mind you...St Saviour Villas. Mr St Saviour himself strolled in here not half an hour ago and made a personal request for you, and let me remind you,' Ella said drily, 'right now, personal requests for you are like snow in high summer.'

'I do appreciate that,' Kelda put in tightly. Her interview with Ella Donaldson a month ago had been very unpleasant. A tough, astute businesswoman, Ella didn't give two hoots about whether or not Danny Philips had been lying. Her sole angle had been Kelda's stupidity in leaving herself open to such damaging publicity. The agency had lost a big commission when Kelda was dropped from the Fantasy campaign.

'Good. Mr St Saviour thinks you're a very classy looking lady...' Ella told her. 'But he did beat me down on your usual fee——'

'Yes.'

'Someone else must have dropped out last minute,' Ella asserted. 'Otherwise he wouldn't be wanting you airborne by tomorrow afternoon——'

Kelda frowned. '*That* soon?'

'You're free until Monday,' Ella reminded her. 'The shoot is in Italy...you should be home by Saturday. They're using a photographer I've never heard of but you can't afford to quibble. The other models are Italian.'

Kelda replaced the phone after Ella had finished advancing flight details. Italy...tomorrow. She'd have gone for the cost of the flight, she acknowledged inwardly, just to get away for a while. The next morning, she tried to phone her mother but Daisy was out. She called Tim at work instead and told him where she would be.

It was late when her flight landed at Pisa. Her name was called out over the public address system and she was greeted at the desk by a morose little man, who merely verified her identity and his own before sweeping up her case and leaving her to follow him out to the taxi.

Their destination was a villa complex in the La Magra Valley, somewhat off the tourist track as befitted an exclusive development. Kelda had never been to Tuscany before in the past, she had had assignments in both Rome and Milan but, tightly scheduled as her timetable had been then, she had never had the opportunity to explore. Her expressive mouth tightened ruefully. It was a little late to wish that she had taken more time off at the height of her popularity. Now she no longer had the luxury of choice. She would have to take any work that came her way just to survive.

It was too dark for her to appreciate the scenery and she rested back her head and dozed, waking up with a start when the door beside her opened and cooler air brushed her face.

Her driver, surely the most unusually silent Italian male she had ever met, already had her case unloaded. Climbing out, Kelda stared up at the dim outline of what looked like a medieval wall towering above them. A huge studded oak door was set into the wall. Kelda frowned. The door looked more like it belonged to a convent than a hotel. Her driver tugged the old-fashioned bell and headed back to his car.

An old woman appeared in the dark doorway.

'Signorina Wyatt,' Kelda introduced herself.

'*Sorda*.' The woman smiled and touched one ear and shrugged. Then she pointed to herself and said, 'Stella.'

Did she mean that she was deaf? Grabbing her case up, Kelda followed her across a vast unlit courtyard. A huge building loomed on three sides. Her companion ushered her into a big tiled hall that looked mercifully more welcoming than what she had so far seen. No reception desk though... and it was so silent.

As she climbed a winding stone stair in the older woman's wake, she smiled to herself. For sheer character, this place beat all the luxury hotels she had ever stayed in! As for the silence, this was not high season and they were off the beaten track. It was also pretty late and the other models were undoubtedly in bed, preparing themselves for the shoot at some ungodly hour of the morning.

Stella showed her into a panelled room of such impressive antiquity and grandeur that Kelda hesitated on the threshold. A giant four-poster bed, festooned with fringed damask hangings, dominated the room. A door in the panelling was spread wide to display a bathroom of reassuringly modern fixtures. French-style windows opened out on to a stone balcony, furnished with a lounger and several urns of blossoming flowers.

The bathroom was hung with fresh fleecy towels, furnished with soap and an array of toiletries such as were the norm in any top-flight hotel. The sight was indefinably reassuring. Kelda found herself looking for the list of rules that every hotel had somewhere and, while she was glancing behind the bathroom door, Stella disappeared.

With a rueful laugh, Kelda frowned at the closed bedroom door through which Stella had wafted herself at supersonic, silent speed, and then her attention fell on the tray of hot coffee and sandwiches sitting on a cabinet beside the bed.

She didn't like to drink coffee last thing at night and she looked for a phone. There wasn't one. She went to the door and then hung back. Maybe it wouldn't be a good idea to go demanding mineral water to drink at this hour if Stella was the only member of staff on duty.

Undressing, she treated herself to a quick shower to freshen up. With a sigh, she allowed herself one sandwich and two sips of coffee before climbing into the gloriously comfortable bed. She thought it funny that nobody from the crew had come to greet her, not even the photographer, keen to issue instructions for the shoot in the morning. Maybe a taste of fame had made her too self-important, she scolded herself. And she certainly couldn't complain about the standard of accommodation allotted to her. Within minutes of switching out the light, she was fast asleep.

'*Buon giorno, signorina*...'

'*Buon* whatever,' Kelda mumbled, stretching sleepily and opening her eyes as the curtains were pulled back, flooding the dark room with brilliant sunshine. As she sat up, she registered that the voice had been male and hurriedly hauled the sheet higher, thinking that if someone had to come into her room when she was asleep, she would have infinitely preferred a maid to a waiter.

'*Giorno*,' he sounded out with syllabic thoroughness.

And a blasted irritating waiter come to that, set on educating her, she thought grumpily or maybe what was really irritating her was the fact that the unfortunate man sounded horrendously like Angelo. One of those growlingly sexy accents all Italian males were probably born with. Like a cut-throat razor wrapped up in smooth black velvet, contriving to be both riveting and unnerving simultaneously.

She shaded her eyes to focus on the offender and nearly dropped the sheet. Her emerald-green eyes incandescent with disbelief, she gasped, 'A-Angelo?'

CHAPTER THREE

'WELCOME to my lair in Tuscany.' Angelo uncoiled himself from his inexpressibly relaxed lounging stance against the French windows he had thrown wide and strolled to the foot of the bed.

Thinking she was in some impossibly realistic nightmare, Kelda didn't bother about proudly holding her ground. She jack-knifed back against the carved wooden headboard and simply gaped at the virile vision of masculinity her crazy mind had conjured up out of thin air. He looked good even in a nightmare, but for some reason he was dressed for riding. Long black boots, thigh-hugging breeches of positively indecently faithful fit and a black cotton sweater that lent him a devilish aspect. He wasn't real... he absolutely wasn't real, and if she shut her eyes again he would go away. She did so.

'Clearly you don't quite function at the speed of light when you wake up alone,' Angelo drawled in a tone that sent hideously responsive tremors down her rigid spine. 'I can change that. And from where I'm standing I'm very well satisfied. You look really hot mistress material. I thought you might look a little worn at this hour without the cosmetic tricks of the trade, *cara*...'

Kelda's long lashes swept up like fans. She swallowed hard.

Angelo was leaning in a very familiar way on the footboard, lustrous golden eyes wandering intently over every exposed inch of flesh above the sheet. 'All those lovers... all those different beds,' he extended. 'I was expecting to be just a tiny bit disappointed... but I'm not. You look all dewy and untouched... *Madre di Dio*, how do you do it? Not, you'll understand, that I am about to complain.'

Angelo...hot mistress material. Neither subject dovetailed. 'What are you d-doing in my hotel room?' she suddenly found the voice to demand explosively. 'How did you know that I would be here?'

'Ah, she speaks...shame,' Angelo sighed with mock regret. 'Now where do I start? This is not a hotel. It's a private house. It belongs to me. I came upon it three years ago when I was investing in Max's villa development. It was going to rack and ruin then but it was so totally private, I had to have it——'

'*Your house*?' Kelda repeated incredulously. 'This is your house? What the hell am I staying here for?'

'I brought you here,' Angelo said softly. 'It was astonishingly easy. Max St Saviour is a business acquaintance. He's very happily married and prone to romantic delusions. I had no problem persuading him to approach the Donaldson Agency on my behalf. He thought he was playing Cupid. Did you like the touch about the reduced fee? Now Max didn't like that bit but I felt it added a dash of authenticity...'

A slow, deep flush of almost uncontrollable rage was reddening Kelda's complexion. She couldn't even begin to believe what she was hearing, but there was something frighteningly sincere about the hard dark onslaught of Angelo's gaze. 'Are you telling me that there *is* no assignment...I don't believe you!' she snapped.

'Max couldn't afford you,' Angelo said with dulcet emphasis. 'But I can, and I don't need to know one end of a camera from another to know exactly what to do with you.'

Kelda's head was swimming with a mess of utterly bewildered thoughts. There *was* no assignment? Then why bring her here? Why would Angelo lure her to Tuscany? Why was Angelo surveying her as if she was a cream cake and he was starving for a bite to eat? Angelo had never looked at her like that before...and all the *double entendres*...what on earth was going on? Had Angelo gone insane? This was not Angelo as she knew him. This was another Angelo entirely.

'You really are the most spectacularly beautiful creature,' Angelo murmured in a thickened undertone. 'And if you stay in that bed much longer, I'm likely to join you.'

Kelda wrenched the sheet so high it came adrift from the foot of the mattress and exposed her bare feet, but she didn't notice. She couldn't take her eyes off Angelo's darkly handsome features. 'W-what are you talking about?' she demanded in a near shriek. 'Have you gone crazy?'

Angelo winced at the ear-splitting decibels. 'I wish I had volume control on your voice.'

'Y-you brought me here... all the way to Italy for an assignment that doesn't exist,' she recounted, spitting out each work with clarity. 'What I want to know is *why*?'

'I have this feeling that our mutual parents will get on much more happily with *you* out of the way,' Angelo drawled. 'I could quite happily have knocked you on the head and dragged you out of your apartment by the hair forty-eight hours ago. But that would have been foolish. And, *cara*, I am very rarely foolish——'

'You are right out of your tiny mind!' she launched at him in seething bewilderment.

'No. If you had simply disappeared, questions would have been asked,' he pointed out speciously. 'This way you're here on a perfectly respectable alibi——'

'But I won't be here for long! And you're going to pay for this!' Kelda spat.

'I have your passport, your money and your credit cards... not much use, those, are they?' Angelo remarked silkily. 'You're right up to your limit on all of them.'

'You have my passport... how do you *know* I'm up to my limit?' she suddenly heard herself demanding.

'I am completely conversant with your financial status,' Angelo admitted unashamedly. 'And I have to say, in my capacity as a banker, how did you get yourself in such a mess? You are in debt to the tune of thousands!'

Abruptly she turned her head away, utterly humiliated that Angelo of all people should know such things. She had been foolish with her money when she'd first started earning. But when Daisy had divorced Tomaso and had, inconceivably, refused to accept any alimony from him, Kelda had been determined to buy her mother a decent home to live in again.

She had bought Daisy a lovely little cottage not too far from London. It had not come cheap. She had sent her mother off on holiday several times. She had settled her brother's debts times without number, bought expensive presents for her family and friends. Her apartment had been the only major item she had ever bought for herself. It had never occurred to her that the gravy-train of her high income could come to a sudden frightening halt. But it had and she just hadn't been prepared for it.

'You really do *need* a rich patron, who can settle your debts and pick up the tab for your expensive tastes...someone who would never question the bills,' Angelo murmured with the soft, smooth delivery of a devil's advocate. 'I'm very generous with my lovers...I've never had a mistress before...you see, strange as it may seem to you *cara*...I've never had to buy a woman before. But the more I look at you in that bed and contemplate total possession and title, the more I see your investment potential...'

A steel band of tension was throbbing unbearably round her temples and it tightened another painful notch every time Angelo spoke. Perhaps she was very, very stupid but she just couldn't grasp why Angelo was behaving the way he was. 'I don't kn-know you like this,' she confided without meaning to.

Angelo vented a grim laugh that ironically made her feel much more at home with him. 'How could you? Much has changed over the past six years. Does it surprise you to learn that I deeply resented being forced to take responsibility for you when you became my stepsister?'

'Nobody asked you to take responsibility for me!' Kelda slung at him.

Angelo dealt her an assessing glance. 'But there was nobody else to do it. Our parents were abroad so much. And I know for a fact that my father was more than happy to leave you to me,' he continued drily. 'Daisy was such an adoring mother that he didn't want to get into trouble with her for disciplining you. And he would have done, make no mistake. Daisy's very protective of you. So I got landed with the job nobody else would touch!'

'How dare you say that?' Kelda threw at him fierily. 'How dare you?'

'And you were the most totally obnoxious teenager,' Angelo volunteered. 'You put me off having children for life.'

'If that means that there'll never be a junior edition of you running about making someone's life hell, I'm delighted to hear it!' But although the ready words flowed from her tongue, Kelda was dismayed to realise that she was deeply and genuinely hurt by what he had thrown at her. And she couldn't understand why. Hadn't she always known that Angelo hated her?

The difference was, she appreciated, that it had never once crossed her mind to wonder how Angelo felt about having the burden of a teenager thrust on him. She had not considered that aspect of those years before, had dimly imagined that Angelo had taken over simply to be officious and unpleasant. And why hadn't she thought more deeply... because to have reflected more deeply would have forced her to acknowledge the truth of what Angelo had said. Daisy and Tomaso had been abroad a great deal and Tim had been a quiet, self-contained boy, quite content to be sent off to boarding school and given plenty of pocket money in return for a lack of personal attention.

'I was only twenty-one,' Angelo pointed out, having ignored her childish response. 'And you were out of control. Between them your mother and your sweet old great-aunt had spoilt you rotten. Daisy, quite frankly, couldn't cope with you. You are very different from her in temperament.'

Kelda could feel tears burning behind her lowered eyelids. She had never hated Angelo so much and yet simultaneously, she had never felt so savaged. She found herself remembering the loneliness of those years and discovered that inexplicably, deep down inside, she must once have had the vague conviction that to take charge of her in the first place, Angelo must have had some slight affection for her. How she could have thought that and yet believed that he hated her at the same time was no more clear to her than anything else since she had arrived in Tuscany.

'I was more like your father than your stepbrother,' Angelo mused with an oddly chilling quality. 'You don't know me like this because in the past six years you have become an adult and I can now treat you as one. You wouldn't believe the pleasure that that freedom gives me.'

Kelda pressed both hands against her pale cheeks and forced herself to look at him over her straining fingers. 'Why did you bring me here?' she demanded in a shaken tone.

'Why?' Glittering dark eyes slid over the wild tangle of red-gold hair veiling her shoulders in a torrent of curls and lingered on the exquisite perfection of the triangular face pointed at him. 'Are you really that dumb? Six years ago you virtually destroyed my relationship with my father——'

'I...I didn't mean to——' Kelda was shocked and unprepared for the directness of that attack.

'The only woman ever to put one over on me was just eighteen,' Angelo spelt out. 'But no blushing virgin. You knew exactly what you were doing that night——'

'I *didn't*!' she protested.

'And it worked a treat,' Angelo breathed softly, black ice eyes holding distressed green with raw force of will. 'You waited until you heard Daisy and Tomaso come in and then you skipped into my room, knowing that they'd be surprised to find the party over and that Daisy's first stop would be your own bedroom. Finding you absent, my father was certain to come looking for me... and what did he discover?'

'It wasn't like that!' Kelda argued half an octave higher, appalled by what he was accusing her of. 'It wasn't planned!'

'On the contrary, it was beautifully plotted and carried out,' Angelo contradicted with satire. 'You had to keep me quiet about what I'd seen earlier in the evening, and what better way? You were paranoid, as it happens. I had no intention of sharing that sordid little scene with your mother.'

'If you hadn't touched me, nothing *could* have happened!' Kelda told him in a wild surge.

Angelo threw back his dark head and laughed with sardonic amusement. '*Cara*, this is Angelo you're talking to, not Daisy! You were standing over me in a minuscule see-through nightdress, eating me with your eyes. Up until that night, I was ashamed of the fact that I wanted you——'

'W-wanted me?' Her full attention pinned to him, Kelda sat up straighter again with a jerk that very nearly dislodged the sheet that was her only veil of modesty.

'You were like a thorn sinking deeper and deeper into my flesh.' Angelo angled a terrifyingly cold smile over her. 'Full marks for the pretence of innocence, but you knew, *cara*. In the cradle, you were as old as Eve. You knew that I wanted you and I've often wondered how it would have gone if I hadn't found you playing the whore so indiscreetly in the library that night. That really was remarkably careless of you——'

'Careless,' Kelda repeated, her mind fathoms deep in shock from what he was telling her, only he did not appear to accept that he was telling her anything she hadn't already known. But dear lord... dear lord, the past she had so recently recalled was assuming colours and depths and meanings that had previously been a mystery to her.

Angelo shot her a suspicious glance. Hard, narrowed, sharp. 'The only way I could have had you then was by marriage,' he delivered silkily. 'That was the price and it would have been one hell of a price to get you flat on your back on the nearest available bed... but I damned near paid it. I was prepared to wait for you to grow up. Now that is a surprise to you, isn't it?'

'Y-yes.' She was incapable of saying anything else.

'And the reason I'm telling you that six years after the event is that I don't want you to waste your time plotting and planning how to turn this little sojourn abroad into a trip to the nearest church,' he spelt out flatly. 'I will *never* marry you.'

'N-no,' Kelda agreed, feeling like someone taking part in a Salvador Dali dream sequence of spectacular complexity. Marriage and Angelo. She could truly put her hand on her heart and swear that such a prospect had never crossed her mind in her wildest imaginings.

'But I will make love to you as no man ever has before,' Angelo swore in a sizzling undertone that purred along her sensitive nerve-endings like bittersweet chocolate, inflaming her in all sorts of intimate places she had never dreamt were so susceptible. She couldn't take her eyes off him. She was magnetised by the most extraordinary excitement. It came from somewhere deep and dark inside her, some secret place, until that moment undiscovered even by herself.

'I have had six long years to think about how I intend to entertain you,' Angelo savoured with unrestrained eroticism. 'And I knew that this moment would come. When you sent me that *Vogue* cover, I knew that we were playing the same waiting game. There you were wearing a string of priceless emeralds and nothing else——'

'It only looked that w-way!' Kelda heard herself stammer.

He dug a lean brown hand into the pocket of his riding pants and tossed something almost negligently on the white sheet. 'They came from Cartier... I bought them.'

Her long, luxuriant lashes lifted and dropped again but the glorious string of matched emeralds separated by diamonds still lay like a river of glittering fire in the strong sunlight flooding through the windows. She could not resist touching them with a tremulous finger. She had not seen them in six years.

Angelo laughed, softly, lazily and with immense and unconcealed satisfaction, rampantly amused by her state of dazed, unspeaking paralysis. He strolled confidently round to the side of the bed, scooped up the necklace and sank down on the edge of the bed. He smoothed her torrent of hair gently out of his path and she felt the cool touch of his fingers at her nape, then the weight of the jewels at her throat, and she couldn't breathe, couldn't move, couldn't speak...

His breath fanned her cheek and her heartbeat thundered in her eardrums and still she couldn't move. He rearranged her hair with the intimacy of a lover, trailed a caressing forefinger down her knotted spine. 'So tense I could almost believe you were terrified,' he teased and then he pressed his mouth briefly, hungrily, agonisingly to an incredibly sensitive spot just below her right ear and she could feel every bone melt, every muscle give way in surrender.

'Tonight,' he breathed huskily, and vaulted gracefully upright again.

She began to shiver, suddenly cold, shock giving way to wave upon wave of after-shock.

'Do you want to come riding with me?' He was already at the door in two long, elegant strides. 'No? I'll meet you for breakfast in an hour in the courtyard.'

And then he was gone. Kelda slid bonelessly down the bed. She was in Tuscany with Angelo. Angelo wanted her. Angelo had apparently been lusting after her for years. Angelo was prepared to deck her in emeralds and diamonds before breakfast. Angelo was asking her...no, expecting her to become his mistress. Hot mistress material. And when he had touched her, it had been like coming alive in paradise...she had felt...she had felt wildly immoral and wonderfully sensual for the very first time in her chequered and, until now, not that exciting existence.

So much, for not being a *real* woman, she tasted. Angelo had actually admitted that he would have married her six years ago purely to satisfy his hunger for her. *Hunger*—she savoured the concept shamelessly. All this time and she hadn't known, hadn't even suspected that Angelo desired her. She rolled over on her stomach and stretched, conscious of every individual skin cell in her body. She felt incredibly powerful for several more minutes...this was Angelo where she had always wanted him...on his knees.

And then common sense began to assert itself. It was an uphill battle but it got there in the end, hacking a passage through the layers of sublime contentment that she was suddenly quite unable to reasonably explain. Did she like Angelo wanting her? Oh, yes. It was retribution for all he had put her through in the past.

But that was her teenage self talking, not the adult she was supposed to be. It was impossible to explain the fact that she had allowed him to festoon her in emeralds and diamonds unchecked. She put both hands to her throat in sudden anger and attempted to remove the necklace. Five fruitless minutes later, when she was afraid of breaking the wretched thing, she gave up and leapt off the bed, wide awake but still...she just couldn't help it...still not thinking straight.

Of course, she was going home on the first available plane. He had her passport but he would hardly insist on keeping it...would he? Dear heaven, he had virtually kidnapped her! He had lured her here with the intent of seduction. Such an old-fashioned word and quite inappropriate. The sole seduction Angelo intended to employ was his immense wealth.

You arrogant, conceited swine, she suddenly thought, livid. Angelo actually believed that all he had to do was flash extravagant jewellery at her and she would fall down gratefully at his feet. He had reminded her how broke she was. He was willing to strew the passage to his bed with emeralds, diamonds and cold, hard cash. Angelo might find her incredibly desirable and she really couldn't restrain the flush of heat that enveloped her at that repeated reflection but his confession had not been coined to flatter her. Angelo was treating her like a high-class whore.

What the hell sort of a spell had he cast, that she had lain there and simply listened without rearranging his features for him? Men had insulted her before, but leave it to Angelo to fathom out the grossest possible insult! He assumed that all he had to do was ask and he would receive...he really did think that! Abruptly, hot moisture flooded her eyes and she was shocked at herself.

She didn't know why she was crying. She ought to be laughing her head off. Angelo had miscalculated and made an ass of himself. She was not for sale, she was not tempted, and if she lusted after being badly treated and abused she would find a street corner to haunt faster than she would sink to the depravity of allowing Angelo Rossetti to lay one arrogant finger on her!

Six years...six years, though, he had waited for her, wanting her, thinking about her, presumably noticing her every time she appeared in the newspapers and on advertising hoardings and in glossy magazines. Six years—she just couldn't get that out of her mind. Six years . . . good to know that she hadn't been the only one scanning boring newsprint, gossip columns, tuning in to BBC 2 when there was a stock-market crisis, just *knowing* he'd be interviewed . . .

And why had she done that, she asked herself in sudden stricken dismay? A sliver of conversation she had had recently with Tim returned to her.

'Did you see Angelo holding forth on TV last night?' she had mocked.

'I don't watch that sort of stuff.' Tim had dismissed. 'Sometimes I think you're obsessed with Angelo . . .'

'Because I hate him,' she had responded drily.

Was that a kind of obsession too? Was hatred so all-encompassing? And, if she hated him, why hadn't she broken out into a rash of revulsion when he'd pressed his mouth to the pulse beneath her ear?

She turned the shower on full blast on cold. Go on admit it, she scorned with throbbing self-disgust. Ever since that night, Angelo has fascinated you. He had taught her the meaning of desire. A terrifying devastation of the senses. After that night, she had decided she was a slut in the making, all rampant hormones and no self-control. She had imagined that Angelo would recall her response to him with cruel amusement.

She had cringed from the memory. She had hidden from the fact that even though hours earlier she had been subjected to a brutal assault of a very sexual nature, she had still contrived to melt into Angelo's arms without a shred of fear. He had stolen her peace of mind forever. He had shown her how frail she was under fire of her own sensuality. But only with him . . . only with him, a little voice whispered inside her head. Only with Angelo.

Admit it: *you want him too*. Incredibly bad taste, she told herself. It was purely physical chemistry, the sort of thing she had no control over. But of course, she would have complete control of that weakness now because she had freely admitted it to herself. As an arrangement of flesh, muscle and bones, Angelo was indisputably very nicely arranged. However, that was *all* it was, just a stupid, mindless physical thing.

Having placed Angelo exactly where he belonged, Kelda got dressed in a pair of matador-style high waisted cotton trousers and a sheer lace shirt. Combing out her towel-dried hair, she didn't even bother to reach for her cosmetics case. After all, she didn't want Angelo imagining that she was making an effort for his benefit! Poor Angelo, she reflected, feeling much more like herself. This time, he really had gone in over his head!

'My passport, please,' she rehearsed in front of the mirror, and laughed.

There was no sign of breakfast in the courtyard she had entered the night before. She trekked back through the echoing hall, glancing into rooms on her passage past, her feet moving more and more slowly. Fabulous house, she found herself thinking, more of a *palazzo* than a mere dwelling. Trust Angelo to have found it, she thought. Probably picked it up for a song and then spent millions on it which he could well afford, she conceded darkly, absently fingering the emeralds still at her throat. But where, oh, where were the serfs to people his feudal kingdom in the Tuscan hills...impossible to imagine Angelo 'doing' for himself!

There was a little inner courtyard. There he was, bathed in a pool of golden sunshine that glinted off his ebony-dark hair, accentuated his strong profile and turned his gorgeous eyes to honey-gold. Something went hip-hippety-hop behind her breastbone and she momentarily froze on the threshold. All of a sudden, as he looked at her, it was so incredibly hard to breathe. It was intimidating.

He slid upright. Superb manners, she absently recalled. Angelo was the only male she had ever met capable of opening a door and standing back politely for you to precede him even in the middle of a violent argument.

'I want my passport,' she announced.

'Have some cappuccino,' Angelo suggested smoothly.

She planted both hands on her slim hips. 'Look, the comedy is over, Angelo. I want my passport.'

'No.'

Kelda waited. 'Is that it? Is that all you think you have to say? *No*? And the little woman says sorry for asking!'

'You signed the usual contract with St Saviour Villas?'

Kelda frowned. It had come over by special messenger within hours of Ella's call. 'Yes, but the contract was a blind——'

'I can assure you that Max will stand by it if I ask him to,' Angelo murmured softly. 'It would be your word against his that there was never an assignment in the first place. I would ensure that he sued you for breaking the contract. He would say that you had walked out. Can you afford to be sued for default right now?'

Her lips had parted in disbelief. 'You couldn't do that!'

'I never threaten what I can't deliver. Think about it...you return to London, inform the agency that you were—what?'

'Blasted well lured out here by a crackpot and his accomplice in crime!' Kelda shot at him in outrage.

'I do believe my reputation and my influence would upstage yours, *cara*. Who would believe such a thing of me?'

Kelda couldn't credit what she was hearing. 'I would believe it!' she shrieked tempestuously.

'But it is scarcely credible that I, Angelo Rossetti, would go to such lengths to entrap a woman——' he countered with silky emphasis.

Kelda stared at him with wide furiously frustrated eyes. She wanted so badly to hit him, she didn't trust herself to get any closer. Her nails dug into her palms.

'You see *cara*...my reputation is considerably more...shall we say...clean than yours?' Angelo added in offensive addition.

'You lousy, rotten, calculating bastard!' she hissed.

He offered her a fresh roll as she collapsed down into a seat opposite him. Her knees had given way. She took a deep breath. 'Angelo, you wouldn't do that——'

'But I wouldn't be doing it. I would be safely behind the scenes, quietly pulling the strings,' he responded gently. 'Did you really think that I brought you here without covering myself on all fronts?'

Half an hour ago, she had felt rather like a fluffy lamb gambolling on a deep, lush and grassy meadow. It had been a game. All of it. A glorious and exciting game that challenged her. But now, she was feeling sick and shaky. Angelo was making it indisputably clear that the kind of game he liked to play had suicidally high stakes.

'This...this Max St Saviour,' she framed, 'why would he lie for you?'

A hint of a smile curved his ruthlessly sensual mouth. 'He couldn't afford not to lie if I told him to——'

'Hell's teeth!' Kelda exclaimed in horror. 'You don't mean that you would put pressure on the poor man simply to punish me!'

Angelo sipped at his coffee with inhuman calm. 'I should dislike the necessity,' he conceded very softly. 'But to cover my own back? Yes, I would do it. In a tight corner I always come out fighting. One cannot be sentimental about the weapons one employs.'

'I'll go to my mother, tell her everything!' Kelda threatened wildly.

'And she'll think you've suffered a resurgence of your infatuation with me and been cruelly rejected,' Angelo inputted sardonically. 'And she will be terribly, terribly upset on your behalf——'

'My m-mother knows me better than that!' Kelda swore, her cheeks flaming with outraged colour. 'I was never infatuated with you!'

'We know that,' he said lazily. 'But does she?

Kelda tugged with shaking fingers at the clasp of the necklace. Suddenly it felt like it was strangling her. 'Take this bloody thing off me *now*!' she demanded.

'It has a trick fastening for security.'

'I'll break it!'

'You value beauty too much to destroy it.' Angelo lifted a careless hand and stroked an amused forefinger along the tremulous line of her generous mouth. 'And so do I,' he murmured in a wine dark undertone of intimacy. 'You really must stop underestimating me, *cara*. It's such a waste of your energies.'

Kelda jerked violently away from the taunting caress and left the table.

CHAPTER FOUR

STANDING on the stone balcony, Kelda drained her cup of cappuccino and moodily surveyed the incredibly beautiful countryside spread out like a picturesque map. When Angelo had said 'totally private', he had not been joking. A patchwork of wheat and barley fields, grape and olive groves and copses of trees was interrupted by the sienna walls and terracotta roofs of occasional farmhouses. There was no town anywhere that she could see within walking distance.

And what would she do even if there was a town? Offer herself up to the local policeman? Refusing to give up her passport had to be a crime, but did she really want to try to prove such a claim against a native Italian like Angelo, who was undoubtedly a major landowner in the locality and probably held in considerable respect? She would end up with egg on her face.

She could not risk being sued for defaulting on her contract. Her relations with Ella Donaldson were poor right now. If she was sued, she would get the name of being unreliable as well as being notorious, she reflected grimly, and she might never work again. Photographic modelling was a tough business and behind her, ready to walk over her and take her place, were countless beautiful, ambitious teenage girls eager for their chance of success. Tim had called her famous but she was not in the super-model bracket, although her career had been heading that way before Danny Philips had tripped her up.

Like it or not, Angelo had her trapped. She could hitch her passage to the nearest embassy and say she had lost her passport but she would be in breach of contract if she walked out. Ella wouldn't be a sympathetic listener to some far-fetched story about Max St Saviour and Angelo Rossetti.

She was here for only two days... what could happen in two days? Angelo was enjoying wielding power over her. Well, let him, she urged herself. Up to a point, anyway. Angelo wanted revenge for that night six years ago. This was it. Now that she was prepared, she could take Angelo in her stride, couldn't she? Beyond keeping her here as an unwilling guest, he couldn't force her to do anything that she didn't want to do.

He had had breakfast sent up to her on a tray. It had been delivered by not one but two giggling maids, intent on getting a good look at Angelo's latest bit of fluff. Her chin came up. Why should she care about what the staff thought? Nobody else was ever likely to know that she had even been here.

She strolled downstairs and paused in the doorway of the room Angelo evidently used as an office. It was so painfully well-organised and tidy, it screamed Angelo, and unexpectedly she found herself smiling, imagining him seated behind that exquisitely polished desk. Angelo *wanted* her. Imagine that... Angelo, sitting back to wait for her to stumble and fall into his ruthless hands. Angelo, who had probably never had to wait for any woman and who would, sadly for him, still be waiting for her on Judgement Day!

'You look very pleased with yourself.'

Kelda spun and very nearly tripped on the corner of a rug. Angelo raised his hands to steady her, long brown fingers curving round her forearms. Without warning, he was much too close for comfort. 'You can let me go now,' she said breathlessly. 'I'm not liable to fall at your feet——'

'Ever?' Lustrous eyes of gold challenged her with assurance. 'Don't be so sure, *cara*.'

'Of that I am very sure.' But her breath shortened in her throat as his scrutiny wandered at an outrageously leisurely pace over her, lingering unashamedly on the proud swell of her breasts. In shocking betrayal, her nipples tightened and thrust forward against the fine lace fabric, heat pooling between her thighs.

Kelda pulled back, crossing her arms protectively over herself. She couldn't believe that he could make her react like that without even touching her. Her body trembled, taut and sensitive, on the brink of arousal. And it had happened so fast. She was shattered by the discovery that her body had a life of its own in Angelo's vicinity.

A slow, sensual smile tilted his beautiful mouth but surprisingly he said nothing. He hadn't noticed, she told herself in relief.

'Would you like to go out to lunch?'

'I'm allowed out?' she prompted in astonishment.

'You're not in a prison cell... or a cage,' he added with something less than his usual cool, and she noticed the strangest thing. Dark colour had overlaid his tautened cheekbones when he made that crack about a cell.

A slight pleat formed between her brows, for she had no idea why he had suddenly tensed. 'I'd love to go out,' she murmured truthfully.

'So tell me about Jeff Maitland,' Angelo invited as he raked the Porsche down the dusty hillside. 'I hear that he wants to marry you.'

'Surprised?' Kelda tossed back, eyeing him from behind her sunglasses.

'Not at all, *cara*. But I suspect his father might have something to say about it...' Angelo drawled and then continued speciously, 'Of course, perhaps you've already met Maitland Senior?'

Kelda compressed her lips, stayed silent.

'He's a narrow-minded prig,' Angelo proffered smoothly. 'And he's been telling anyone willing to listen recently that he wants you out of his son's life.'

Hot pink flamed in her cheeks.

'Now, I am not a narrow-minded prig,' Angelo divulged softly. 'I can live with absolutely *anything* that you might choose to tell me about your past.'

Her teeth clenched but she turned her head and cast him a glimmering smile. 'I don't kiss and tell, *caro*.'

'But your lovers do,' Angelo inputted flatly.

Kelda stiffened. 'I bet you devoured every word!' she condemned.

'Yes but I don't say that I believed every word of it,' he pointed out drily. 'Of course, if you want me to tie you up and cover you with whipped cream, I'm more than willing...but on a first date?'

'I *love* strawberries and cream,' Kelda asserted, aggressively determined not to plead her innocence on any count.

'Cream is so messy...I prefer champagne,' Angelo countered huskily, rather taking the wind out of her sails. 'Now, the black leather and the riding crop. I didn't credit that. That made me laugh, most inconveniently in the middle of a very boring meeting. You are not a sadist——'

'But I feel very sadistic around you, Angelo,' Kelda told him, her eyes glittering furiously at him.

'You'll purr like a cat in my bed,' Angelo murmured silkily. 'And you won't need black leather, zebra skins or jacuzzis to enliven the experience.'

'Dream on,' Kelda spelt out shakily. 'I will never get into your bed!'

'You are more likely not to want to get out of it again.'

'You don't suffer much in the way of humility, do you, Angelo?'

'Not in the bedroom, no,' he conceded silkily.

Kelda took a deep breath. 'And the idea that I have had dozens of lovers doesn't even bother you?'

'It might if I believed that...but I don't.'

Kelda was sharply disconcerted. 'You don't?'

'A woman who has had dozens of sexual partners wouldn't get all hot and bothered talking about sex. She wouldn't blush when I looked at her breasts, either,' Angelo delineated with immense calm, and then shot her a nakedly amused glance that sent her pulse racing. 'In the space of a couple of hours, I've learnt more about you by observation than you could begin to imagine.'

'Really?' she endeavoured to sound bored but deep down inside she was churning up with dismay.

'Really,' Angelo confirmed lazily.

He took her to a tiny sleepy village on a hill. It was entirely enclosed by pale thirteenth-century walls and half a dozen lookout towers. The restaurant was in a former monastery and they chose to dine outside below the spreading shade of a giant chestnut tree. Kelda accepted a glass of wine and stood at the wall, taking in the spectacular view of the wooded valley far below. It was a truly glorious day and the world seemed to be drowsing in the noon day heat. Behind her, Angelo was choosing their meal with the sort of serious selectivity that made her smile.

'You know,' she heard herself saying without really thinking about it, 'I wasn't going to interfere between my mother and your father.'

'But you already have,' Angelo countered drily.

'I was asked for my opinion and I gave it.' Kelda shrugged. 'What was wrong with that?'

'Apart from the fact that Daisy is highly suggestible and very much afraid of damaging her relationship with you, what makes you think that your opinion was worth hearing?' Angelo murmured very quietly. 'You have all the sensitivity of a steel butterfly in your own relationships with men——'

'I beg your pardon?' Kelda demanded hotly.

'And you've never been with any man longer than about six weeks. I would say you were uniquely unqualified to offer advice on affairs of the heart——'

'A steel butterfly?' she queried acidly.

'I both heard and saw you in action with young Maitland.'

'He was being difficult,' she parried uncomfortably.

'So you went home alone and left him drowning his sorrows. Your heart really bleeds, *cara*,' Angelo mocked.

'He wants to marry me and I don't want to marry him. A bleeding heart would have been out of place.' Kelda held his lustrous dark gold eyes in angry challenge. 'How do you dump your women when you're finished with them, Angelo?'

'Not in a public place,' he parried quietly. 'And they invariably see the writing on the wall in advance and extract themselves with dignity.'

Kelda flushed, uneasily aware that she had been clumsy with Jeff. Her mouth tightened. Just like old times. Angelo criticising her, implying that she did not have a great deal of class. It was a relief to see the waiter approaching them across the cobbles.

The meal began with a salad of young turkey and grapefruit and was followed by rosettes of veal with artichoke sauce. She refused the saffron rice with quail and drank glass after glass of wine in a vain attempt to cool down in the heat before falling victim to the *spongata*, a very rich pastry filled with walnuts, almonds, pine nuts and raisins mixed with cognac and honey.

'I do believe I have found food I would kill for,' she sighed, blissfully stuffed as she rested back in her chair.

'I didn't think you would eat most of it,' Angelo confided.

'I lost so much weight last month, I can afford to indulge a little.' Pleasantly relaxed, Kelda asked him a question that had been bothering her for several days. 'Tell me, when did you change your mind about my mother? What makes you so keen for her to marry your father again?'

'He hasn't been happy since the divorce. He was working too hard... in spite of medical advice. Hence the heart attack,' Angelo divulged unemotionally. 'He still loves your mother. To be brutally honest, even if she was the money-grabbing blonde I once thought she was, I'd still encourage the marriage. He needs her. I accidentally walked in on them the first time she came to the hospital and there she was, fluffing up his pillows, hanging on his every word, generally looking at him as if he was a god come down from Olympus——'

Kelda could not avoid wincing at the description of her mother's behaviour around Tomaso. 'I bet he loved it——'

'Fifteen minutes of Daisy and he was itching to get out of that bed,' Angelo said wryly. 'She made him feel like a man again. She did more for him than all the specialists I had flown in to try and cheer him up about his future prospects.'

Kelda chewed at her lower lip. 'Mum can't help being like that round a man,' she muttered defensively. 'She's the nurturing, cherishing type.'

'I have to admit that when I first saw her in action years ago, I thought it was all an act.' Angelo topped up her empty glass and sent her a shimmering smile that made her feel oddly dizzy. 'Of course, it wasn't. It was just Daisy. I know that now. She's one of that rare breed, loving and giving...no greed, no calculation. Eleven years ago, I should have had greater faith in my father's judgement. He's no fool.'

Kelda's entire attention was intently pinned to him. A glorious smile spontaneously curved her full mouth. The free admission that he had entirely misjudged her mother, followed by such generous praise of Daisy's nature, soothed once raw loyalties and delighted her no end. In response to her smile, Angelo's intense charm blazed forth, catching her unawares.

Feeling scorched, her heart leaping behind her breastbone in a sudden onrush of excitement, she lowered her lashes and struggled to think of something to say but Angelo got in first.

'What was your father like?'

Bemusedly, she repeated, 'My *father*?' She was so unused to anyone mentioning her father and then once more, she smiled. 'He was really wonderful,' she said softly.

Dense ebony lashes dropped low on Angelo's intent gaze. 'Tell me about him,' he encouraged very quietly.

'I get my height and my colouring from him,' Kelda shared with unhidden pride. 'He was hot-tempered but he had a terrific sense of humour and he was marvellous with kids. I remember the way he used to play with us when we were very young. He was like a child himself sometimes.' She laughed. 'We moved house a lot. He was very restless, or maybe it was Mum who was restless. He started working abroad when I was five... it really broke my heart——'

Angelo seemed strangely preoccupied with the contents of his glass. 'Where abroad?' he cut in.

'He was an oil worker with a big company in Jordan.'

'Jordan?' Angelo repeated softly. 'Did he come home very often after he started working in... Jordan?'

She frowned. 'It cost so much, you see. He came back a couple of times but we really kept in touch by letter. I have every letter that he ever wrote to me. He used to tell me terrific stories about the desert. Savage Arabs and crazy camels. He had a great imagination... I dare say he made up half of it to amuse me——'

'Possibly,' Angelo murmured in a curiously flat tone.

Kelda didn't notice. 'It's silly, but I always used to wish that he would write direct to me instead of just enclosing his letter to me in with one to Mum. She used to bring them to Liverpool when she came, and she never brought the envelopes with the foreign stamps and I always wanted those to show off to my friends!'

Silence had fallen. A bee buzzed languorously over to the acacia blossoms by the side of the wall. Kelda was feeling wonderfully relaxed. 'What hurt most,' she sighed, 'was only finding out that he had died *after* the funeral! Mum thought we were too young to handle it but I was thirteen and I still remember her coming up to Liverpool to tell us. I was so angry with her for not telling me immediately.'

'She was trying to protect you.' Angelo rose with that lethal elegance of movement that was so characteristic of him. 'I think it's time to go.'

Kelda reddened. 'You should have said that you were bored.' She was furious with herself for rabbiting on as she had. Why had she done that? She had never discussed her father with anybody before.

'You never bore me, *cara*.'

As she clashed with his brilliant dark eyes, she felt oddly naked, horribly vulnerable all of a sudden. Abruptly, she stood up and their surroundings swam dizzily around them. She had had far too much wine. Alcohol loosened the tongue, she reflected ruefully. Angelo closed a large hand over her smaller one and silently guided her down the steep steps to the car.

Her stupid fingers were clumsy with the seatbelt. Brushing them away, Angelo did it up for her. 'Do you still think of me as a slum chid?' she heard herself ask without forethought.

Lean fingers curved to her delicate jawbone, inexorably forcing her to turn her head towards him. 'Shut up,' he said softly, not unkindly.

'I did grow up on a council estate——' she began sharply.

'I told you to shut up.' His brown fingers moved caressingly over her taut cheekbone and then he leant down, deftly winding his other hand into her hair and let the tip of his tongue slowly and smoothly trace the tremulous line of her lower lip.

Her breath escaped with a tiny gasp and her heart thudded like that of a wild bird in a cage. She wanted his mouth so badly she burned, every sense pitched to an unbearable high as he toyed expertly with the sensitive fullness he had discovered. Her eyes slid shut, her long throat arching as she bent back her head instinctively.

Angelo set her back from him and fired the engine of the car. Her lashes swept up on glazed green eyes, her whole body throbbing with an intensity that was pure pain.

A blunt forefinger raked down the slender length of her thigh. 'I know,' Angelo breathed thickly.

Kelda looked out of the side window, fighting for composure. She saw two elderly women, dressed in black, crossing the empty square towards the tiny church. But they didn't seem real. The only reality she could currently register was the seething sexual vibrations in the atmosphere.

And she couldn't handle the silence that lay between them. Deliberately she rested her head back on the restraint and pretended to doze. The second the Porsche raked to a halt in the courtyard, she leapt out of it. She couldn't get away from him quickly enough.

'Kelda.'

Involuntarily, she found herself glancing back. 'I'm going for a walk.'

'Fine.' Angelo held her strained scrutiny with unnerving ease and tenacity. He was in control. The raw masculine power of him sprang out at her. Angelo, a predator and a sensualist combined. She had let her guard down over lunch and it had not only been the wine. Angelo had drawn her out with subtle skill and she had fallen for it, talking her foolish head off about her father. A man, who had been little more than an unskilled labourer on an oil site, a man in whom Angelo could not have the slightest genuine interest, though he had admirably concealed the fact, she conceded bitterly.

He strolled over to her. 'The gardens are rather wild——'

'I don't mind.'

'But beautiful in an informal style,' he completed.

She abandoned hope of shaking him off.

'You're like a fox waiting for the hounds to come in for the kill,' Angelo remarked silkily as they descended the terrace steps, passing beds blazing with a mixture of perennials and wild flowers.

It wasn't a bad comparison, but that he should openly make it outraged her pride. She snatched in air headily weighted with the scent of flowers and moved on in the direction of a rioting shrubbery.

'You invite only weak, inadequate men to your bed,' Angelo drawled. 'That way you stay in control, and that's very important to you, Kelda. Isn't it?'

'I find you incredibly offensive!' she flared incredulously.

'If you haven't had much loyalty from your lovers, you can only blame yourself.' Angelo dealt her furious hectically flushed face a chillingly amused glance. 'Inadequate men boast and tell whoppers in news-print——'

'Or sore losers!' Kelda threw back, still walking at top speed, but the ground was descending steeply now and she was forced to slow down.

'If it's not too rude a question,' Angelo murmured smoothly, 'how many of them *were* losers?'

She whirled round and just exploded. Lifting her hand, she slapped him so hard across one hard cheekbone that her whole arm went numb, and then the pain came. She had hurt her wrist and she bent over, pressing it into her stomach, sucking in oxygen in a strangled gasp.

'I *could* say it served you right.' Angelo reached out for her arm and cradled her wrist between surprisingly gentle hands. His fingers explored her fine bones. She didn't look at him, she stared fixedly at the grass until it blurred. 'You've wrenched it, that's all. Relax, *cara*...I'm not about to hit you back but I should warn you that I have a very hot temper. I lose it rarely but, when I do, sensible individuals dive for the nearest shelter.'

He released her hand. Her throat was closing over. Tears were threatening. Her emotions were storming about in all directions. 'You can dump the Mr Nice Guy routine!' she advised unsteadily. 'I hate you, Angelo. I have always hated you. That's what makes your ambition to seduce me into your bed so *laughable*!'

'I could have screwed you in the Porsche with an audience of shocked pensioners, and all without one word of seduction,' Angelo delivered with brutal candour.

Kelda jerked and flinched as though he had punched her in the stomach. She forced her head up, was literally nailed to the spot by the fierce anger flaming in his golden eyes. 'No...' she whispered in feverish, desperate denial.

'And what does seduce mean?' Angelo wasn't finished with her yet. 'To deceive? I have been totally honest with you. To corrupt? The days of your innocence are long gone. Once I would have put a wedding-ring on your finger before I touched you. I would have treated you with honour and respect——'

'Stop it!' She fled into the orchard of peach and cherry trees, frantic to escape that mercilessly cruel tongue.

She didn't get very far before a powerful hand closed over one slim shoulder and yanked her back. He spun her round with frightening strength. 'Look at me!' he demanded with inborn arrogance, glittering dark eyes scanning her pale, distraught face. 'Your freedom is gone, and not only now, *cara*. It's gone for as long as I want you. I will keep you and I will clothe you and you will not make a single move that you haven't cleared with me first. You are *mine* and you had better start adjusting to that idea fast. I am not the most patient of men.'

Shaking all over, Kelda sucked in great gulps of oxygen. She was devastated by what he had said. Every lancing syllable rang with savage confidence. 'You can't take my freedom a-away——'

'But I already have,' he reminded her. 'And this is only the beginning.'

'You can do nothing to m-me,' she persisted, fighting sheer cold threat to the last bastion of her strength. 'Talk's cheap!'

He stared down at her and then released his breath in a slow hiss. 'It doesn't have to be like this *cara*. You can't fight me and win. Surrender would be so much sweeter for both of us. Capitulate with grace and you will discover how generous I can be——'

'I can live without emeralds and d-diamonds from Cartier,' she had to force the assurance past her convulsed throat.

'But I don't think you can live without me.' Angelo said with velvet clarity.

Kelda went white and then red, functioning on the most basic of responses. What she felt was pretty much what she thought. And what she felt was cold, hard fear followed by a sudden flaring surge of sexual awareness so intense that her whole body heated.

'You need me——'

'No,' she argued fierily, 'never. I have never needed any man.'

Angelo was unimpressed. He curved a lean hand almost negligently to her taut spinal cord. 'Until me,' he countered thickly, his lean, lithe body tensing against hers as her tongue snaked out to moisten her dry lips. 'And I haven't even kissed you yet...'

'Let go, Angelo,' she said breathlessly.

'I think I will.' His stunning eyes skimmed with hungry sensuality over her and then he drew her close with controlled power and took her mouth with slow, drugging intensity.

She was a good strong swimmer but she drowned in Angelo's arms. Six years melted away and she was back, back where her body told her she belonged, back where the world contracted into the crazy thunder of her heart and the mad race of the hot blood in her veins. A sensation akin to a hot wire being jerked tight knifed through her stomach, and with a stifled moan she arched her back in response to a pleasure than was close to pain.

Angelo said something rough in Italian and he was tugging her down in the lush meadow grass. The two buttons on her back that secured her top came adrift, fabric drifting down her arms over her wrists in a soft whisper, and all the time he was making love to her mouth with a naked and devouring passion that excited her to the brink of madness. Her fingers were dug deep in the springy depths of his hair, tracing the shape of his head, luxuriating in the silky strands, holding him to her.

He pulled her hands away and lifted his mouth from hers and then he just looked at her, a feverish flush of colour accentuating his striking cheekbones, his breathing pattern audibly fractured.

Her breasts were small, high and perfectly formed. Her nipples were shamelessly distended rose-pink buds. Angelo released his breath in a long, sighing groan as though he was afraid to touch her. She knelt there in front of him, quivering all over, every heated inch of her flesh ready to take fire.

The silence was electric. A voracious hunger vibrated like a physical aura between them. 'If I touch you...do you vanish?' Angelo whispered unsteadily.

'Do you?' Without any need for thought to precipitate the action, she leant forward and all fingers and thumbs embarked on unbuttoning his silk shirt. When it was open, he trailed it off with scant ceremony.

She looked at him exactly as he looked at her: with a driven, utterly consuming absorption. She dragged passion-glazed eyes possessively over the bronzed breadth of his muscular chest. A tangle of rough dark curls clung damply to his golden skin, arrowing down into a silky furrow over his flat, hard stomach.

She couldn't swallow, she couldn't move, but she had never wanted so badly to touch another human being.

It was a fire in her blood more potent and more powerful than any fever. Angelo reached for her in the same moment that she was about to reach for him. He hauled her on to his hard thighs and shaped her breasts with his hands. A stifled cry was dredged from her as he caught her nipples between thumb and forefinger and gently pulled on them.

She had not known that she would be so incredibly sensitive there that one touch and her whole body would become one gigantic yearning ache. But Angelo must have known by instinct.

'You are so glorious,' Angelo murmured against the corner of her lips. 'So perfect... *bella, mia cara*.'

His passionate mouth took hers and she shuddered with excitement as his clever fingers toyed with her swollen flesh. Nothing existed but the urgent, increasingly desperate hunger of her body to be submerged in his. He lifted her up as though she was a doll, unzipped her trousers, effortlessly peeled them away. Then he closed his hands over the ripe swell of her hips and buried his mouth hotly against her breasts.

It was electrifying. Her fingernails dug unwittingly into his broad shoulders as he licked and stroked and tantalised her to the edge of insanity. His hand cupped the apex of her thighs, his fingers splaying firmly against the damp scrap of silk and lace that was all that separated him from her.

'You are mine,' Angelo told her, lowering her into the grass with raw determination. 'Tell me that, before I bury myself in that exquisite body...'

Her lashes lifted. She focused on blazing golden eyes and melted to the consistency of honey all in one go. 'Yours,' she framed in a whisper of sound torn from the very depths of her.

'Always,' Angelo attached with savage emphasis.

Her desire for him was so powerful, he could have made her say anything, do anything in that instant but then the outside world intervened. She heard the low mutter of male voices, a soft burst of laughter and she went rigid.

'Gently, *cara*,' Angelo soothed. 'We're behind a twenty-foot wall.'

Shaken up, Kelda stared up at him in sudden torment. Beyond him she saw the peach and cherry trees, and mental awareness returned. For a split-second, still agonisingly controlled by her aching body, she wished it away again. She wanted him so much, she wanted to die if she couldn't have him. And she knew then without any helpful prompting from him what feeling suicidal felt like.

She knew then why she had always been afraid of Angelo. Why Angelo, alone of all men, threatened her peace of mind. You took fascination and obsession and a devastating physical desire and whatever the recipe produced, it was *not* hatred.

Through heavily lidded eyes Angelo dealt her an oblique look, the hard planes of his strong features shuttered. He reached for her discarded top and was smoothly feeding her arms into it before she grasped that, while she had been wildly out of control and lost to all reason, Angelo had never planned, it seemed, to consummate his desire for her in a peach and cherry orchard.

Had it been a punishment for calling that desire *laughable*? She turned cold and shivered. In anguish, she relived the torrid abandonment of her response to him. She didn't feel like laughing. Fear fluttered in her throat and churned in her stomach. She was not as tough as she had thought she was. Angelo had shot down that illusion in flames.

With supreme self-assurance, Angelo reached down a lean hand and hauled her upright. Kelda trailed her fingers free in violent rejection. Her brain was working now at a furious rate. Nothing that Angelo had so far threatened her with was worth this humiliation! Tonight, somehow, some way, no matter what it took, she was leaving...

CHAPTER FIVE

KELDA had only brought one dress, fashionably floral, ankle-length and buttoned from scoop neckline to hem. She had packed it because it was casual and uncrushable. Her fingers fluttered tautly towards the glittering jewels still encircling her throat. People put collars on dogs to control them, and after the collar came the lead... it was all part of the training. Pure rage glittered in her emerald-green eyes. Later she would break the necklace. It certainly wasn't going with her!

The high of fury and self-loathing powering her had yet to dissipate. She had degraded herself. She had been a fully participating partner in Angelo's arms. Her skin burned as she recalled how he had made her feel, how she had behaved. There was no excuse. She was not a teenager at the mercy of rampaging hormones. She was a grown woman, supposedly in control of her own responses.

Dear heaven, she had *actually* thought that she had a fairly low sex drive. So many men had tried and failed to rouse her to passion. Her distaste for intimacy had been intense. She had blamed Angelo for her apparent frigidity. He had treated her appallingly that night six years ago. She had been at a very sensitive age when Angelo had contrived to combine sex, shame and sleaze all into one uneasy package inside her impressionable mind.

But what infuriated her most of all was that none of those inhibitions had prevented her from responding wildly to Angelo. It was sexual infatuation... what else could it be? A raw physical attraction of the lowest order. That Angelo had known that he could exercise such power over her, long before she herself even suspected it, was doubly humiliating. On that level, her own lack of experience made her a pitifully easy target and no way...absolutely no way was she sticking around for any further demonstrations!

Angelo was in the drawing-room when she came downstairs. Golden eyes gleamed beneath dense ebony lashes, a faintly sardonic curve hardening his eloquent mouth as he returned her perusal. Her chest tightened. She felt as if she had gone down in a lift too fast. And the spacious room suddenly felt claustrophobic.

'What would you like to drink?' he drawled smoothly.

He handed her the glass of pure orange with an edged smile of amusement that made her fingernails bite into the palm of her free hand.

'You weren't drunk on anything but desire this afternoon but I salute your choice,' he murmured lazily. 'Alcohol dulls all sensations.'

Her nails inflicted purple crescents on her palm. Her teeth ground together. She lifted her fiery head high. 'Don't you think this farce has gone far enough?'

'Farce is comedy. I notice that you're not laughing.'

'Few people laugh at threats, grotesque or otherwise,' Kelda countered fiercely.

A maid came in to announce dinner. Kelda sank down rigid-backed in a heavily carved chair in the dining-room. As soon as the main course had been served, she thrust up her chin. 'I did nothing to be ashamed of six years ago! You have no right to threaten me and no excuse to keep me here!' she told him angrily.

'*Nothing*?' Angelo repeated drily.

'Nothing,' Kelda reiterated with conviction. 'And the way you treated me was absolutely unforgivable! When you came into the library that night, that boy was trying to rape me——'

Angelo quirked a satiric ebony brow. 'Still tossing that old chestnut on the fire? Really *cara*...if you're in search of an extenuating circumstance for what you did that night, can't you do better than cry rape? In the light of your hot-blooded nature, I find it excessively hard to believe that rape would have been necessary.'

Furious colour flooded her cheeks, highlighting the brilliance of her green eyes. 'I was switching out the lamps,' she persisted doggedly. 'I thought I was alone. He came up behind me and forced me down on to the floor. He hit me...' her voice trailed away, her facial muscles tightening as she forced herself to continue '...he b-bit my breasts and he hurt me...'

What shattered her was Angelo's raw burst of laughter. She had had to steel herself hard to describe that assault and she had been prepared to counter disbelief, but not the sheer earthy amusement raking through Angelo's lean, muscular frame.

'Love-bites,' he breathed in a sizzling undertone that somehow contrived to combine the lingering remnants of his amusement with complete disdain. 'I did notice them.'

'I am telling you the truth!' Kelda spat back at him tightly, painfully, outraged by his response. 'I was terrified...if you hadn't interrupted him, he would have got what he wanted!'

'You're not even a good liar,' Angelo whipped back with derision. 'The facts don't fit. You were in a dark room behind a firmly closed door. You didn't scream, you didn't demand that I call the police, nor did you come up with the attempted rape story until that boy was safely out of the house.'

Her stomach was churning with nausea. She could have explained all those things but why should she humiliate herself by persisting? Describing that assault even briefly had brought it alive again. The sensation of sick terror, overwhelming relief and shock had flooded back in a debilitating surge. Angelo's laughter and derision had been brutally inappropriate. Trying to defend herself was a waste of time.

Loathing was rippling through her in violent waves now. How dared he dismiss her story out of hand? How dared he talk as though she had been a promiscuous little slut at eighteen? The truth lay at the other extreme. Compared with her considerably more experienced friends, she had been almost laughably innocent. But what was that saying about one picture being worth a thousand words? Angelo had *seen* her in a compromising position and had chosen to see only what fitted his own interpretation of her character.

In the electric silence she stared down at the plate in front of her without appetite and with sudden decision, she stood up, emerald eyes flashing like polished gemstones in the pale, taut stillness of her face. 'I'm not hungry and I'm tired,' she said shortly.

'*Madre di Dio*...' Angelo breathed with driven impatience. 'You still sulk like a child!'

In the doorway, Kelda whirled round to face him again, all pale dignity banished by blazing anger. 'You hateful bastard...somehow, some day, I'll make you pay for bringing me here!'

As she strode through the hall, she paused beside an ornate marble and gilded side table. Angelo had tossed his car keys there earlier and they were still there, she noted with relief. She took the stairs two at a time, rage still storming through her veins in an energising tidal wave. Discarding the floral dress, she put on a pair of black leggings and a sweatshirt top before packing the remainder of her possessions. That small task taken care of, she sat down to wait for the rest of the household to go to bed.

It was one in the morning before Angelo retired for the night. She heard him passing by her room and froze for a second, but he didn't even hesitate at her door. To be safe, she waited for another forty minutes and then her heart thumping unnaturally loudly in her eardrums, she grabbed up her bag, opened her door as quietly as a mouse and crept downstairs. With her breath in her mouth, she slowly lifted his car keys off the side table before tip-toeing down to the room Angelo employed as an office.

She needed her passport and her money. No doubt she would eventually get home without the passport but it would be a lot easier if she could simply step right on to the first available flight. Afraid to turn on the desk lamp in case someone saw it shining out into the courtyard, she had to make do with the moonlight.

Her passport would be in his desk. It was the obvious place. She rummaged frantically through the drawers, only one of which was locked and that she left to the last. Biting her lip in frustration, she looked round for a suitable weapon to employ. She swooped on a paper knife and tried, nervous perspiration beading her brow, to force the lock. The knife scraped incredibly loudly across the wood when she failed.

It was an antique desk, built to last. She hacked with increasing desperation at the recalcitrant drawer, her nervous tension escalating by the minute. Finally, she acknowledged defeat. May you rot in hell, Angelo, she thought furiously. The window was not locked and it opened with the minimum of noise. She was halfway over the sill when she remembered the necklace.

With a curse, she wrenched at it and all but strangled herself! Using both hands, she attempted to pull it into breaking without lacerating her own throat. It was a considerably more difficult feat than she had imagined. Her neck bruised and sore, she gave up, and all the time her rage was building even higher. Hacking at Angelo's desk had made her feel like a criminal. She slid the rest of the way out the window and hurried across to the Porsche.

Angelo hadn't got all of her money. She had had some tucked for emergencies in her case. It would be sufficient to cover petrol if she needed any, at least one night's accommodation somewhere and telephone calls to arrange sufficient funds to travel home on. She would abandon the car in Pisa and head for the tourist office to ask what she had to do about her 'lost' passport.

Taking a deep breath, she started up the Porsche. It fired with a low growl and she filtered it slowly down towards the gates. Damn, they were shut! Leaping out, she opened them, dived back into the car and took off down the hill like a bullet.

Kelda was a confident driver but she had no map. She had driven quite a few miles before she came on a small town. There she slowed down in search of a signpost. A car came up close behind her and flashed its lights. Ignorant pig, she thought, so I'm not going fast enough! When a police siren went off, that same car overtook her at speed and pulled across the road in front of her, forcing her to a halt. She was thunderstruck.

She was arrested. The policeman spoke even less English than she spoke Italian but there were sufficient similarities between the languages for her to grasp with a sinking heart that she was being accused of stealing the car. Dear God, Angelo had reported the Porsche stolen! Her inability to produce her passport only exacerbated the situation.

Within half an hour, Kelda was in a police cell. It was a small town, an even smaller station and it was the middle of the night. Clearly there was nobody available to question her in English.

'*Domani*...' the policeman said in receipt of her shattered protests. Tomorrow. Tomorrow, it would be sorted out.

Kelda was in a blind panic by then. It had finally dawned on her that she *had* stolen Angelo's Porsche and that if he wanted to proceed with such a charge, he was probably well within his rights. She curled up on a bed with all the comfort of a funeral slab and burst into floods of tears. She was terrified. How was she going to explain what she had done?

It was dawn when the cell door was unlocked and she was taken into what appeared to be an interview room.

The policeman went out again and reappeared with Angelo.

Kelda took one paralysed look at him, flew out of her chair and threw herself at him. 'Angelo, get me out of here... please!' she sobbed.

He went rigid for a split second and then he closed his arms round her and said something in his own language to the policeman. Somebody else started talking. She took a deep shuddering breath and fought for self-control but she really was at the end of her tether.

Angelo guided her back out to the Porsche. 'How the hell could you be so stupid?' he raked at her as he pushed her into the passenger seat.

'How could you report your car stolen?' she gasped strickenly. '*How could you do that to me*?'

Angelo drove off at a mercilessly controlled speed. His profile was set like granite, tension emanating from him in waves. 'I did not report my car stolen. Stella saw it being driven off and got one of the maids to ring the police immediately. As it happens,' he shared with grating emphasis, 'they were already on their way. When you climbed out of the window of my study, you activated an alarm at the police station——'

'An alarm?' she echoed.

'A highly sophisticated security system installed to repel intruders,' Angelo spelt out fiercely. 'If it's activated and I don't call to say it was a mistake, naturally the police take it seriously. By the time I got out of bed, they were on the doorstep. When I saw the open window and the mess you've made of my desk, it did not instantly occur to me that *you* were the culprit——'

'Well, it should have done!' she raged at him with a sob tearing at her shaking voice.

'Do forgive me if I am not accustomed to a guest under my roof sneaking out of a window in the middle of the night and stealing my car!' Angelo flashed back at her with savage impatience.

'I was not stealing your car... I was b-borrowing it!' she blistered back hotly.

'You took my car without permission.'

'Oh, shut up about your bloody car!' Kelda shrieked at him. 'You took my passport and my money away! I was a prisoner! Of course I tried to escape... I'll never forgive you for what you've done to me tonight! Do you hear me?'

'*Sta zitto*!' Angelo bit out wrathfully.

'No, I will not keep quiet. Why sh-should I?' she sobbed furiously at him. 'I was locked up like a common criminal——'

'You were arrested because you were driving a car that had been reported stolen. It was a misunderstanding and you are fortunate that the police, who drove me here to pick you up, were willing to be so helpful. You could have been locked up for the rest of the night.'

'I hate you so much I could kill you,' Kelda threw at him bitterly. 'What did you tell the police?'

'That we had had a lovers' tiff,' Angelo drawled silkily as he filtered the car to a halt in the courtyard. 'What else? Italian men understand and appreciate women of volatile temperament.'

'I *hate* you,' she said again, unable to think of anything more vicious to say in the state she was in.

'*Say that just one more time*,' Angelo bit out in a sizzling undertone across the bonnet of the Porsche.

'And you'll what?' she shouted back with seething contempt as she strode into the house. 'I hate you... I hate you... I hate you!'

A powerful hand caught her wrist and yanked her round in the hall.

Her teeth grinding together, Kelda collided with incandescent golden eyes. It was like falling on an electric fence. 'Let go of me!' she hissed. 'Or, so help me, I'll scream the place down!'

'Go ahead,' Angelo invited, hauling her roughly up against him. 'Scream.'

Kelda was in the grip of such fury that she took full advantage of the invitation. In a passion, she threw her head back and screamed so loudly she hurt her throat and choked. She waited in the simmering silence. Nobody came running. Her lashes fluttered in bemusement.

Before she could part her lips again, Angelo literally grabbed her off her feet. One minute she was standing on solid ground, the next she was airborne and on the way up the stairs. 'Put me down!' she screeched.

He kicked her bedroom door wide, kicked it shut again and dropped her down on the bed. 'Angelo——'

'Shut up.' He came down on top of her in one lithe movement, pinning her flat with his superior weight. She was in the act of struggling to raise a punitive knee when he brought his mouth down hard on hers.

Still in a fury, she dug her hands like claws into his luxuriant hair and then the passion flooded her in a roaring tidal wave. It came out of nowhere, attacked and took her prisoner. A passion so instantaneous it wiped out everything that had gone before it. Electrified by the raw, devouring heat of his mouth, she was possessed by an excitement so intense that she felt dizzy and disorientated.

Her blood was drumming in her veins, her heart hammering like crazy. She was hot and cold all over and unable to keep still. He delved between her lips with his tongue and her thighs trembled. He kissed her until she was breathless and burning, not a single part of her body untouched by the sheer intensity of her arousal.

He hauled her sweatshirt off with more impatience than finesse, burying his mouth with a muttered imprecation in the sweet valley between her heaving breasts. He struggled out of his shirt. She heard fabric tear and reached instinctively up to bring him back to her again, lacing her arms round his neck, her fingers lacing into his hair in an ecstasy of excitement.

He muttered something in Italian. He sounded shaken, unlike himself. He came back to her again, the black curling hair on his chest abrasive against her taut nipples, thrusting his hands beneath her back to force her into even more intimate contact with his hard, muscular length. A choked sigh of satisfaction escaped her as he crushed her against him. She couldn't get close enough to him and evidently he couldn't get close enough to her.

He pressed his mouth to an achingly sensitive pulse at the base of her throat and sensation stormed through her. His hands found the proud swell of her breasts with surprisingly gentle hands and shaped and stroked, deliberately not touching the hardened peaks until her muscles clenched with frustration and she arched her back and helplessly invited him to that deeper intimacy.

And then, with a soft laugh, he captured a taut nipple and laved it with his tongue, teasing with his sharp white teeth before taking the unbearably tender bud into the moist cave of his mouth. It was a sweet torment that drove claws of raw need into her quivering body, and when he employed the same technique on her other breast she began to moan and tremble, utterly possessed by the power of sensation.

He ran the tip of his tongue down over her taut stomach and a rush of heat made her hips jerk. She wanted to drag his mouth back to hers. She wanted him everywhere at once because her whole body was beginning to scream with the hunger he had incited. He skimmed off the remainder of her clothing in one bold movement, rolling on to his side to devour her mouth in a series of rough, deep, drugging kisses while he dispensed with his own.

He came back to her naked. He was hot and damp and very male and she gasped at the power of her own pleasure in the feel of his body against hers. It was so different, so alien and yet, strangely, so gloriously right. Her fingers spread over the satin-smooth skin of his back and he jerked as if she had pulled a string. Moving without warning, he took her swollen mouth in a sudden explosion of renewed passion, holding her down, letting his hand travel over her silky, quivering stomach to the tangle of red curls at the apex of her thighs.

Nothing she had so far experienced prepared her for the wild excitement that overwhelmed her when he explored the moist petals of her femininity. His touch was so exquisitely pleasurable that she cried out. She was on a high of unbearable sensation, twisting, turning, entirely at the mercy of her own needs, but on another level she was highly attuned to the same build-up of excitement in Angelo.

His breathing was fractured, his heartbeat thumping a tattoo beneath her spread fingers. He moved with lithe determination, gripping her thighs and pulling her to him.

'I have waited so long for this, *cara*...' he muttered almost savagely.

A faint feathering of instinctive fear of the unknown momentarily gripped her as she felt the swollen hardness of his manhood against her. But it was shattered by the hunger he had unleashed inside her. That hunger, too long denied, sought only satisfaction at whatever the cost. Yet she was naïvely unprepared for the driving force with which he invaded her body with his own and the sharp pang of pain which momentarily clenched her muscles and made her bite into the soft underside of her lower lip.

Angelo stilled and stared down at her. In the dawn light she could focus on him with clarity. His lustrous golden eyes betrayed a brief glimmer of rare uncertainty and narrowed, suddenly raking her hectically flushed face. 'I'm hurting you,' he whispered, not quite steadily.

The pain had gone as quickly as it had come but her untried body had yet to adjust to that most intimate invasion. 'No.' The denial was jerky, swift.

'You're so small,' he breathed, sinking his hands beneath her slender hips, lithely shifting between her thighs with a stifled groan of pleasure and splintering control.

She felt possessed then, utterly and completely. He moved on her, slowly, deliberately until all she could focus on was the extraordinary response of her own body. All control was gone. The savage rhythm took a hold of her and she burned up in a heatwave of sensation, crying out at the moment of climax and subsiding into an aftermath of pleasure so intense she almost passed out. Angelo curved both arms round her so tightly she could scarcely breathe, and with a sleepy smile she fell blissfully asleep.

When she woke up, Angelo was making love to her again. The curtains were closed. She didn't know whether it was day or night. It didn't matter. She didn't want to think, only feel. Angelo allowed no time for thought, even less for conversation. It was as though there was nothing but the moment to be lived for. He was ruthless in his single-minded pursuit of pleasure.

'What time it it?' she whispered when she opened her eyes again, grudgingly reluctant to obey the rousing hand on her shoulder.

'After midnight.' Angelo was dressed and that struck her as extraordinary.

'Midnight when?' she muttered gruffly, removing her dazed eyes from him to conceal her consternation.

'Yesterday you were arrested,' he filled in obligingly, and settled a laden tray down on the wildly tossed bed.

They had slept and made love through an entire day. It didn't seem real. She couldn't believe it had happened. Her . . . and Angelo. A fight and an explosion of passion that had overruled every intelligent thought.

'Are you not hungry?'

He looked so cool. That inflamed her. She had to bite at her tongue to silence it before she impulsively spoke her mind. And what could she say? He was lounging on the end of her bed as though he belonged there. His strong jawline was no longer blue-shadowed. His hair was still damp from a shower. He was immaculately clad in an Armani sweater and black designer jeans. He took her breath away. Drop-dead gorgeous and deadly.

Self-preservation uppermost, she reached for the tray. Steak and a Caesar salad.

'It's the one meal I can make,' Angelo drawled with mocking self-deprecation.

'The only one you can be bothered to make, you mean,' she translated without hesitation, but inwardly astonished that he should have gone to that amount of effort for anyone other than himself.

'Why should I cook when I can afford to pay other people to do it?'

Why the blazes were they talking about the contents of her plate? It was impossible that Angelo could be feeling as awkward as she did. Angelo was no stranger to the intimacy of the bedroom. The morning after could hold no discomfiture for a male of his experience. But she refused to show her own desperately seesawing emotions. She chewed every piece of steak at least forty-seven times. As long as she was eating, he couldn't expect conversation, and all the while she was engaged in coping with the stark reality of the past twenty-four hours.

Why? Why Angelo? How could Angelo make her lose control to this extent when other men, even men she had liked and respected, left her cold? At eighteen, he had awakened her sensuality and she had buried that discovery deep. And whether she liked it or not there were ties between them that until now she had refused to recognise. From thirteen to seventeen, until that final year he'd spent abroad, Angelo had been the dominant male in her life. She knew Angelo on levels that she took for granted.

She had forgotten nothing in six years. She knew that he could not abide disorder or unpunctuality, she knew that he loved fast cars...and, discreetly, even faster women. She knew that he positively thrived on the pressure of wheeling and dealing on the international money-market. And she knew so many little things too.

His shirts were specially made for him in Hong Kong. She knew what size socks he wore because she had given him socks Christmas after Christmas in lurid colours she was well aware that he would never wear. She knew he had to shave twice a day. She knew he still kept the horse he had loved as a teenager in the ritziest stable in the block. She knew that he had perfect white teeth, had never had a filling but went a whiter shade of pale at the prospect of his six-monthly dental check-up...

And that knowledge made Angelo seem dangerously familiar. But they were only superficial things, she reminded herself painfully. Furthermore, her previous acquaintance with Angelo had been formed when she was a child and he had been an adult, who stood over her in a position of trust. Was it that awareness which had made it so difficult for her to believe that Angelo *would* actually hurt her? For, if that was true, if that was to be her excuse, she had never been more wrong about anything in her life.

Angelo skated a brown forefinger over the back of her hand. 'Are you usually this quiet?'

'Without eight full hours of rest and three regular meals... yes,' she dismissed and resisted the urge to jerk her hand out of reach.

Pride demanded that she protect herself. Angelo despised her and yet she had gone to bed with him. Not just once either. She had fallen off the bandwagon into an orgy which not the most self-deceiving argument could excuse. Her sexual infatuation had made a victim out of her but it didn't have to be that way... no, it didn't, she told herself fierily. She was no man's victim.

It had happened. Wishing it hadn't would change nothing. Angelo had not realised that he was her first lover and she was ferociously grateful for the fact. She could not have borne the humiliation of Angelo knowing that he had proved to be the one male the Iceberg found irresistible. Better that Angelo should think that he was no more special than any other man her name had been linked with . . . as it was, Angelo looked so *bloody* triumphant that her teeth ground together.

'I need a shower,' she said abruptly, and viewed him expectantly.

'With company,' Angelo attached smoothly, viewing her with brilliant dark eyes that devoured.

She lowered her lashes in shock. Every bone and muscle in her body ached. He was an insatiable lover but she had naturally assumed that he was currently at bay. He had actually woken her up and fed her to sustain her through another session of torrid sex. Her stomach quivered with nausea. 'Forget it,' she said tartly.

'I can't,' Angelo confided in a husky murmur. 'I let you sleep as long as I could but I can't forget that in a few hours we'll be on separate flights back to London.'

She had forgotten that. The reminder was timely and she embraced it with enormous relief. It was over. She could live with that. It was over and she could return home and, if not forget it had ever happened, at least forgive herself. Her sexual infatuation had been exorcised, she told herself. She had surrendered once to her basic instincts and now, she was effectively cured and free . . .

'And there we must necessarily practise greater discretion,' Angelo pointed out silkily but she could hear the cool menace of steel in the assurance. 'Your mother would be needlessly distressed by our affair.'

'We're not having an affair,' Kelda told him in a stifled undertone of distaste as she reached for her robe, thrust her arms into it and sprang off the bed.

Angelo closed a lean hand on her wrist before she could brush past him. 'Perhaps you'd like to tell me what we are having?'

'In the future . . . nothing,' she spelt out, emerald eyes colliding furiously with impassive gold. 'What we had? A one-night stand. A little tacky, a little foolish, but that's all.'

Beautifully shaped brown fingers moved caressingly on the tender skin above her wrist. 'I have never had a one-night stand in my life.'

'I find that very hard to credit!'

'I expect you would, *cara*,' Angelo held her fast when she attempted to coolly pull free, 'since tacky little foolish experiences undoubtedly litter your past,' he incised with succinct derision, watching the blossoming of pink highlight her exquisite face. 'But *I* do not intend to feature on such a list.'

Kelda was trembling with rage. She yanked her arm free. 'Sorry, *caro*... you're already on it,' she spelt out like a spitting cat.

'Are you scared?' Angelo drawled lethally. 'Are you scared of the response you give me?'

She could still feel his fingerprints on her skin. Her mouth felt swollen, her breasts tender, her body almost frighteningly alien to her. And she looked at him and her chest went tight. Angelo emanated power in a force-field of energy. He was one hundred per cent in control. Nothing she had yet said had even angered him.

'Why should I be?' She blessed the mask of indifference she had learnt to assume on demand for the camera, for deep down inside she was sick and squirming at the necessity of the hard-bitten act he was forcing her to assume. 'Did you think you were somehow different from the others, Angelo? Do you think I gave you something more than I gave them? That's your ego talking,' she asserted with a scornful little smile on her wide, generous mouth. 'You're good... but you're not so good that I want to repeat the experience.'

He had gone white beneath his naturally dark complexion. Hooded eyes of black ice surveyed her and every nerve-cell in her quivering body tensed. Raw threat had tasted the atmosphere. Every scrap of playfulness had been wiped from his clenched, hard features. She could feel the violence in him. Inches below the civilised veneer dwelt the naked predator as wild as any animal, and she had always known that, known that Angelo's savage self-discipline and seething intelligence alone controlled that side of his temperament.

She had called up the devil in him, but he had given her no choice. Better to deal with Angelo as the hostile enemy she knew best than as the passionate lover he had proved to be. *That* Angelo she did not feel equipped to deal with. She stood her ground, hanging on to her faintly amused smile with rigorous determination. It was over now. He would leave her alone. Angelo, chased by her sex practically from the edge of the cradle, would not continue his pursuit in receipt of such a scathing rejection.

'Have you anything else to add?' His wine-dark voice trickled like the gypsy's curse down her taut spinal cord.

'Angelo,' she sighed, shrugging a shoulder, 'you *know* what I'm like. I like variety——'

'You're a whore,' he breathed in a raking undertone of suppressed and seething rage. 'You disgust me.'

Disturbingly, the brutal admission stabbed like a knife into her. A sudden haze of moisture interrupted her vision of him, brightening her green eyes to luminescence. But she stared him down, only dimly registering that she was shaking all over, her legs like cotton wool supports.

'And to think that you excited me so much that I took no precautions,' Angelo drawled between gritted teeth, shooting her a look of such savage loathing that she was pinned there like a butterfly to a specimen board. 'I hope I do not live to regret the omission.'

As the door slammed on his exit, Kelda stared at the space where he had been with stunned eyes and parted lips. He had said... he had said he had not used contraception and he was afraid that *he* might live to regret it! Kelda was ingloriously sick in the bathroom, her body's response to the horrendous scene she had forced. Only then did the tears come, slow and painful as thorns being plucked from her flesh, and what was worst was that she really didn't know why she was crying.

CHAPTER SIX

'WE'RE dining with Tomaso and Daisy this evening . . .'

Kelda threw her head up from the English newspaper she had been doggedly studying. Her fiery mane of curls flew in all directions. 'I beg your pardon?'

Angelo dealt her a look of black-ice warning. 'I said that I would bring you with me——'

'An ambitious guy, aren't you?' Kelda snaked back at him, her eyes awash with disbelief behind the screen of her dark glasses. She had had to force herself to come down and join him for breakfast. He would have read a request for a tray in her room as weakness. Since she had been unforgivably weak in other departments, she could not fall short of her own expectations yet again. For that reason, she was seated here in the courtyard, struggling to swallow food that threatened to choke her and make no pointless comment concerning the passport and wallet which she had discovered by her plate.

'I have no intention of permitting the conflict between us to damage their relationship——'

'And when was this cosy little arrangement made?' Kelda breathed shakily.

'Before you left London. Your mother said that you wouldn't come——'

'She was right!'

'I said that you would . . . and you will,' Angelo swore with an emphasis that was disturbingly chilling. 'We will arrive together and we will leave together. We will be polite and pleasant to each other in their company——'

'*Bloody hell*!' Kelda gasped inelegantly, too disconcerted by this unlikely vision to conceal her reaction.

'Polite and pleasant,' Angelo repeated drily. 'Your mother's fears will then be put to rest. Your feelings will cease to be a matter of concern to her——'

'I'm not playing happy families for your benefit!' Kelda bit out.

Dear lord, she was thinking sickly, he had planned the evening even before she'd arrived in Italy. He had promised her mother what must have seemed the impossible and he had never doubted that he could deliver. Her blood ran cold.

'Your life will be a living hell if you don't, I promise you that.'

The husky deepening of his rich vowel sounds made the hair prickle at the nape of her neck. Accidentally she clashed with hard dark eyes, bottomless as a well shaft to the unwary. Her sensitive stomach turned over. She bent her head. She would have gone, no matter what he did or said. But Angelo would never believe that. He seemed to think that she had a malicious need to damage their parents' relationship.

Yet without even realising it, she had come to terms with that renewed bond. Once again, Daisy had unfairly dropped the news on her without any prior warning of what was to come. It had been rather like a ghastly re-run of the bridal couple's visit to her school all those years ago. And Kelda was uncomfortably aware that she had reacted with no more maturity this time than she had then.

But once the shock of Daisy's announcement had worn off, Kelda had accepted that her response had been entirely selfish. She had upset her mother. She had focused, not on her mother's potential happiness, but on her own determination not to be forced into contact with Angelo again. That admitted, however, Angelo had merely exacerbated the situation by launching straight into attack that night at her apartment. After all, she reflected bitterly, Angelo had had three months, not twenty-four hours to adjust to their parents' reconciliation.

'Is that understood?' Angelo probed.

She bit her tongue and tasted blood. It tasted of defeat. 'Yes!' she slung the word at him. 'But your interference was unnecessary.'

'The car will be here to pick us up in half an hour.'

Her throat closing over, she took the dismissal with head held high, but she seethed with such a turmoil of emotion that she marvelled she didn't just explode. Messily, loudly, stupidly. Perhaps, at last, she was learning. Impulse and temper, her two biggest failings, invariably got her into trouble around Angelo. Angelo rejoiced in being neither impulsive nor uncontrolled, and that, she registered painfully, was why Angelo was in the ascendant.

When would she start feeling better? *When*? Because right now... right now, she felt worse than she had last night and that was saying something! She had not slept. She had paced the floor. She had cried. Coming to philosophical terms with the fact that she had gone to bed with Angelo was proving far more difficult than she had hoped. His powerful sexuality had been her downfall. She wasn't the only woman to make such a mistake in the heat of passion... and she wouldn't be the last. But for how long was she to feel guilty, ashamed, miserable? And why should she feel soiled by the promiscuous pretence she had put on for his benefit?

Hadn't she only given him what he expected? Angelo despised her. But that hadn't prevented him from using her in the most vicious way of all. Her own wanton sensuality had been his weapon of destruction. She would not allow him to wield that weapon ever again. It was finished, over. One day of insanity. It had taught her a hard lesson. Surely there would be no further complications?

It wasn't that easy to get pregnant... was it? She was not some silly teenager... but she had acted as recklessly as one. Angelo had clearly assumed that she was on the contraceptive pill. Angelo, she thought hysterically, had been more concerned at the threat of having caught some dread disease. From a virgin. And he hadn't noticed. She had once read that men often couldn't tell the difference.

She never spoke a word the whole way to the airport in the limousine. Like a stretcher case, she was in limbo. But she could literally *feel* Angelo's presence. The atmosphere vibrated round Angelo. Always. Utterly different from his father, he had volcanic energy and equally volcanic moods. But here in Italy she had seen a side of Angelo that she had never known existed.

Angelo, flirtatious, teasing, infuriating. Angelo, passionate, irresistible, even sympathetic. As a teenager, she had not understood that, below the surface ice, Angelo absolutely seethed and burned with emotion. Then he had seemed merely grim, forbidding and sarcastic. Now, she was painfully conscious of the scorching atmospheric undertones.

'I'll pick you up at seven tonight,' he drawled.

Climbing out, she simply ignored him.

'Kelda . . . ?'

As she waited for the chauffeur to extract her case, a hand like an iron vice suddenly hooked on to her shoulder. Before she could react, she was flattened up against the side of the limousine with Angelo's hard, muscular body plastered to hes. He took her mouth in an unrestrained demonstration of sexual aggression. But she still caught fire and burned. Aware of every lithe line of his powerful body, she could feel the force of his own arousal, and that made her knees buckle.

She felt his fingers brush the back of her neck and she didn't realise what he was doing until he stepped back with the necklace in his hand. She blinked in bemusement. She had actually forgotten that she was still wearing it. He dropped the glittering emeralds into her palm and closed her unsteady fingers round them.

'Seven,' he said again. 'Or would you like me to come earlier?'

She scraped herself almost clumsily off the car, all the while helplessly hypnotised by the scorching hunger, blatantly burnishing his golden eyes. That hunger pulled hot strings inside her. Oxygen snarled up in her convulsed throat. It was the excitement that frightened her the most. The most incredible, explosive excitement that thrummed and throbbed between them in waves of heat.

'*Dio*,' Angelo sighed in a tigerish growl of dissatisfaction. 'I have a meeting at four.'

'I disgust you,' Kelda reminded him shakily.

'When I'm out of bed. In it, you drive me crazy,' Angelo dropped in a sizzling purr and swinging on his heel, he walked away.

Unnoticed by either of them, a photographer, standing on the far side of the car park, lowered his camera with a satisfied smile.

On her commercial flight, she thought of his far more comfortable journey in his private jet. Like a married man with a mistress, he was covering their tracks. But she had no intention of becoming Angelo's mistress and it was a shock to appreciate that her little performance the night before had not killed that ambition of his stone-dead. That utterly ridiculous ambition. If he hadn't taken her so much by surprise in that car park, she would have pushed him away, she told herself.

There was a promising call on her answering machine from the estate agent when she got back. A cash offer for her apartment and more than she had expected to receive. When she went straight back out again to see the agent, she was even more pleased to hear that the buyer was interested in purchasing most of her furniture as well. She would be moving to a rented apartment and she didn't want the cost of storage.

'There shouldn't be any problem,' the agent extolled cheerfully. 'He's a Swiss executive, buying on behalf of his company, and fortunately for you he particularly liked the location of your apartment. They want possession by the end of the month. Get round to your solicitor and sign on the dotted line as soon as possible... before the guy realises that he could have got a better deal elsewhere.'

She went straight away and it cost her a pang or two of regret. Owning her own apartment had symbolised success. Selling it underlined how much Danny Philips' lies had cost her. But she was sensible enough to acknowledge that she had aimed rather too high when she had bought, and that if ever she was in the same position again she would be much more modest in her requirements.

The bell went about six when she was in the shower. It was Russ Seadon, the photographer whose talents had first catapulted her to fame. He was engaged to Gina Delfont, another model, who was also Kelda's closest friend. She often stayed with them when she was working in New York and was happy to return their hospitality whenever she could.

Russ dropped his bag in her guest-room and spent half an hour catching up on all the news before settling down with a pizza in front of the television. Kelda paced her bedroom floor, dreading the evening ahead. Angelo wasn't going to leave her alone. He wasn't going to make things that easy for her.

And she was out of her depth with Angelo. When he touched her, intelligence went out of the window, and if anything more happened between them she would never forgive herself. He wanted to use her for sexual release alone. Her skin crawled at the awareness of how vulnerable she had become. Somehow Angelo had to be *made* to walk back out of her life again... but how? What would most anger Angelo?

Absently she winced at the clatter Russ was making in her kitchen and then her furrowed brow cleared. The belief that she had another man in her life would most anger Angelo...and here she was with another man staying under her very roof...

'You want me to what?' Russ echoed dazedly ten minutes later.

Kelda's cheeks were hot with growing embarrassment. 'Forget it!' she urged hurriedly. 'It was a stupid idea——'

Suddenly, Russ laughed. 'This guy won't take no for an answer...is that it?'

Kelda nodded. 'All I want you to do is look at home here, as if you're waiting up for me,' she spelt out awkwardly.

'He's not likely to get violent, is he?' Russ checked.

She shook her head and prayed that she was right.

Russ grinned on his way out of the door with her spare key. 'Don't worry, I'll be back in time. I think I'm going to enjoy this!'

Kelda got dressed, selecting a clinging trouser-suit in shocking pink. It had strategic and daring cut-outs and she wore it like a suit of armour, calculated to repel. Angelo's dainty little blonde women were invariably given to conservative wardrobes.

'You look like a trapeze artist. It suits you.' Infuriatingly, Angelo let his lustrous dark eyes travel over her with offensive and blazingly confident familiarity.

Kelda tossed the emerald necklace carelessly into the glove compartment of his Ferrari.

'Is that some sort of a statement?' Angelo drawled, lazily unconcerned by the gesture.

'I don't want it.'

'It belongs to you now. I gave it to you.'

Her breath quickened, her pulse-rate accelerating as her tension increased. 'But I don't want anything from you,' she stressed, striving to keep her voice level and cool.

'Perhaps this is not a good time to tell you that I am in the process of buying your apartment.'

Her head whipped round in shock. 'Too late. You've missed the boat!' she returned sharply. 'I agreed the sale today.'

'With whom?'

'A Swiss company.'

'I own the company.'

The soft assertion dragged a soft sound of incredulity from her throat. Wide-eyed, she stared at him. '*You* own it?'

'Who else would pay over the odds to secure your ownership?' Angelo queried drily. 'I'll sign it back to you as soon as the sale is complete——'

'Why would you want to buy my apartment for me?' Kelda demanded, anger and a kind of threatened horror coalescing out of her shock.

'I told you in Italy that I would pick up all the bills,' Angelo reminded her smoothly. 'And naturally that includes securing your home for your occupancy. I'll sort out all your financial problems. I will clear your credit cards, settle any outstanding debts and make arrangements for an allowance to be paid into your account.'

In a daze, she listened while he listed his intentions. A dark mist of humiliation enveloped her. Her fair skin reddened in a painful flush. And then anger stirred out of her disbelief. 'I'm not a fixture you can buy along with my apartment!' she asserted rawly. 'I am not for sale!'

'I didn't say that you were,' Angelo murmured with calm emphasis. 'But we made an agreement in Italy——'

'There was no agreement!' Kelda blitzed back at him.

'Shall we say that when you allowed me access to that exquisite body I rather took agreement for granted.'

The flush drained away, leaving her pale. She wanted very badly to claw at him for his ruthless determination to portray her as greedy, immoral and sexually available. She had never hated him as much as she did in that moment, could not comprehend how that hatred had failed to kill all desire for him . . . yet, it had failed quite spectacularly. All of a sudden, she was very grateful that if Angelo came back to her apartment tonight he would be greeted by Russ. Even Angelo would not be able to disregard so blatant a rejection!

Even so, she found that she was still trembling with the sheer force of her emotions. 'I told you that it was over in Italy. . . I made that crystal-clear,' she told him tightly, staring rigidly out of the windscreen. 'It was a mistake I don't intend to repeat and I never at any stage had any intention of becoming your mistress. So you've just bought yourself an empty apartment, Angelo. I will be moving out within the month.'

'I don't think so,' Angelo murmured silkily and parked the car.

She walked ahead of him into the restaurant, quickly espying her mother's blonde head in a corner. Daisy was openly relieved at their arrival, Tomaso rising with alacrity to at first advance his hand and then smilingly give her a light kiss on the cheek. He was thinner and older-looking than she remembered and her eyes pricked with unexpected tears as she registered the extent of the happiness glowing in her mother's face.

'A bit of a coincidence, you both being in Italy at the same time,' Tomaso observed heartily, ordering up a round of aperitifs.

'Were you——?' Kelda turned to Angelo with manufactured surprise.

'You wouldn't have run into each other,' Tomaso assured her. 'Angelo was in the south, inspecting a factory...isn't that right?' he added, addressing his son.

'How terribly boring,' Kelda sighed with mock sympathy, encountering a chilling black glance of warning from beneath Angelo's long, luxuriant lashes. A slight darkening over his hard cheekbones told her that he was not wholly at ease lying to his trusting *papa*. She was bitterly amused by the discovery.

In other circumstances, it might have been a pleasant evening. Tomaso was on tremendously good form. He kept on patting her mother's arm possessively, stealing little glances at her and smiling. It was clear that he too was very happy. The wedding was discussed. A date was already in the offing which suggested that Angelo's belief that she had the power to prevent their remarriage by influencing her mother had been grossly exaggerated.

'You really don't mind?' Daisy prompted in the cloakroom.

Kelda embraced her much smaller mother and murmured, 'If Tomaso makes you happy, I'm happy.'

'Good...so what's going on between you and Angelo?' Daisy enquired anxiously.

Kelda froze. 'Going on?'

'Don't treat me as if I'm stupid or blind,' Daisy breathed ruefully. 'I'm neither. A week ago, you were furious at the idea of Tomaso's and my getting back together again——'

'I was being childish and selfish——'

'When Angelo told me that he would bring you here tonight to dine with us, I told him he was aiming at the moon,' her mother shared. 'But here you are just like he promised and he keeps on watching you and you keep on touching him——'

'Touching him?' Kelda echoed blankly.

'A couple of times, you've put your hand on his arm when you've been speaking——'

'Really?' Kelda said weakly because she couldn't remember doing it.

'And I know you,' her mother persisted. 'You're not the sort of a person who touches others unless you're very familiar with them, and Angelo of all people——'

'Mum, don't you think you're——?'

'And why is he looking at you all the time?' Daisy demanded worriedly. 'And you never looked at him once——'

'Maybe I'm just not that comfortable with Angelo,' Kelda suggested unsteadily, shaken by her mother's unexpected perception.

'He is very, very good-looking,' Daisy remarked uneasily. 'And very clever. He has a lot of charm when he wants to use it——'

'You sound as if you don't like him very much——'

'I don't want you to be hurt again,' her mother whispered. 'Angelo isn't the settling down type and there's something different about you, Kelda...'

Dear heaven, the mother with X-ray vision! Concealing her panic at Daisy's persistence, Kelda forced a smile. 'Being pleasant to Angelo takes a lot out of me.'

After the interrogation about a couple of gestures she hadn't even been aware of making, it was a relief when the evening came to an end. Angelo slid silently into the Ferrari.

'Thank goodness that's over,' Kelda muttered, massaging her temples which were starting to ache with the onset of a tension headache.

'What did you tell Daisy?' Angelo shot at her without warning.

'Nothing! And you can stop treating me like your partner in crime,' Kelda told him flatly, bitterly. 'I am not in the habit of lying to my mother and I didn't enjoy doing it.'

'You told her something,' Angelo repeated darkly.

'One more word and I'm calling a cab!' Kelda swore. 'If I'd told her anything, she would have been so shattered, the entire restaurant would have known about it before we got out!'

'It won't matter once they're married. They'll spend most of their time abroad. It will seem natural that I should visit my stepsister——'

'Angelo...I want nothing to do with you!' she practically screamed at him in frustration. 'Why do you find that so impossible to accept?'

He insisted on seeing her right to the door of her apartment. He was walking right into the trap without the smallest encouragement from her. Her headache had turned into a killer by the time he took her key from her and unlocked the door. Russ would be waiting...she hoped. Then it would all be at an end.

'You're not feeling well.' Angelo pressed her over the threshold and followed her in. 'Can I get you anything?'

That he had noticed surprised her. 'I'll be fine.' Her exasperated gaze was probing the lounge for Russ. He wasn't there.

'Will you be all right?' Abruptly Angelo swore and stilled, the hand at her spine dropping away.

Kelda's strained green eyes widened to their fullest extent as Russ strolled out of her bedroom, only a small towel wrapped round his hips. 'I thought you were never coming home, darling,' he sighed reproachfully, and smiled at Angelo. 'Thanks for bringing her back safely.'

Outraged incredulity had clenched Angelo's hard dark features. He swung round. 'You bitch,' he grated in a shaken undertone, seemingly unable to take his eyes off Russ.

Kelda was trembling. The look in Angelo's eyes was flat and cold and dead. And somehow that terrified her. She had to resist an extraordinary and utterly ridiculous urge to start explaining that Russ was a close friend of the platonic variety, pretending to be something else at her request.

'I couldn't believe...' Angelo fell silent, shot her a glance of such smouldering violence that she stumbled back against the wall, afraid of physical attack. The front door thudded shut in his wake. Kelda sagged like a rag doll.

Russ sighed. 'How did I do?'

'You were incredible.' Her own voice sounded as if it was coming from miles away. Her head felt as if it was about to split wide open.

'You weren't having second thoughts about me doing this, were you?' Russ studied her shuttered white face anxiously.

'Of course not.'

It was done. It was over. Angelo was gone... but why did that knowledge hurt so much?

Russ expelled his breath. 'I thought it would be funny, but it wasn't,' he acknowledged. 'Rossetti was shattered.'

'His ego was dented... that's all,' Kelda mumbled, suddenly deathly tired and drained.

Kelda's week in New York modelling designer knitwear stretched to five weeks in the end. Russ had tugged some useful strings, put her on the cover of two glossy magazines and all of a sudden she had found that her career was taking off again. For a month she was heavily in demand. Ella was constantly on the phone to her and slowly but surely she got word of possible assignments back home as well. The world had a short memory. Danny Philips was old news.

She was flicking through her diary on the flight back to London when she noticed. She raked through the pages again, certain she had made a mistake. But she had not made an oversight. There was no familiar little cross marking the start of her last period. She was three weeks overdue.

She sat there in a blank haze of shock, suddenly cold and shivery. Her heart had plunged to her stomach and her stomach felt as if she had swallowed an indigestible lump of concrete. It had felt like that several times before over the past ten days. She had lost weight through her lack of appetite but that hadn't worried her. A model could never be too thin for the camera.

She had blocked out those days in Italy very efficiently since leaving London. Work had been her panacea, her saviour. She had been too busy and too tired to torment herself with vain regrets for what couldn't be altered. It was over. She had made a mistake.

She could learn to live with that... that was what she had told herself when her mind strayed.

And now this. It couldn't happen to her, she had thought in Italy, brushing that spur of fear away with confidence. She had never thought about being pregnant, couldn't even imagine being pregnant, and now she was faced with the possibility that she might well be. In defiance, she listed all the other things that might have made her late, but the cloud of dark foreboding refused to lift.

She bought a pregnancy test at the airport. Even that embarrassed the hell out of her. Her name came over the public address system while it was being wrapped and she froze.

Tomaso and Daisy had come to meet her off the plane but traffic had held them up. She was touched, but her recent purchase weighed like lead in her holdall.

'We've got a surprise for you,' Daisy asserted.

Kelda gave her mother a rather weak smile and climbed into the back of Tomaso's stately Rolls. 'What sort of a surprise?'

'The cottage is yours,' her mother pointed out. 'And after next week I won't be needing it any more——'

Next week—the wedding that Kelda was dreading.

'Tomaso wanted to buy your apartment but it went very quickly, didn't it?' Daisy sighed. 'I assumed it would be on the market for ages and I was wrong——'

Kelda bent her head, not knowing where to look. She had found a rented flat in Highgate before she went to New York and her mother had promised to supervise the removal of her personal possessions when Kelda had discovered that she wouldn't be back in London in time to make the move herself.

'I want you to have the cottage back. After all, you bought it for me,' Daisy stressed.

'A very generous gesture on your income.' Tomaso dealt her a warm approving smile. 'I will always be grateful that you looked after your mother when she wouldn't allow me to look after her.'

'I don't need anybody looking after me,' Daisy muttered a shade tartly, but she beamed at Tomaso all the same.

The cottage. Kelda hadn't even thought about it. But she was driven back there. Her own cushions adorned her mother's chairs. And Daisy's display of ruby glass in the lounge had been displaced by the ornamental frogs Kelda had been collecting since childhood. Her mother squeezed her elbow. Kelda blinked back tears.

The cottage had two dormer bedrooms, both with en-suite facilities, a lounge and a cosy dining-room open on to the kitchen as well as a small but very private garden. All of a sudden she had a home of her own again. She sat down on the edge of the bed and then tore into her holdall for the test.

'What do you want for dinner?' Daisy called upstairs brightly.

'I'm not hungry!'

'Rubbish!'

Forty minutes later she knew, but she sat on the side of the bath simply staring at the kit, telling herself that maybe she had done the test wrong and re-reading the instructions. She felt terribly sick and even more terribly scared. She felt just like a teenager, not like an adult at all. Pregnant. It was a black joke. She couldn't believe she was, couldn't credit that one mistake could lead to such frightening consequences.

Three days later, her mother found her being sick in the bathroom for the second morning in succession. 'You've caught some bug,' Daisy muttered anxiously. 'This time, I'm not listening to you, I'm calling the doctor!'

'No!'

Ignoring her protests, her mother marched over to the phone.

Kelda was already under sufficient stress '*Don't*!'

'Don't be silly.' Daisy continued to dial.

'For goodness' sake, I'm not sick... I'm pregnant!' Kelda suddenly sobbed in frustration and then a silence, utterly unlike any other, fell as Daisy stared back at her in disbelief and Kelda realised what she had said. She had not intended to tell her mother until she returned from her honeymoon.

It took an hour to calm Daisy down.

Her own eyes as swollen as her parent's, Kelda whispered, 'I didn't want you to know yet.'

'How am I going to tell Tomaso?'

'Don't you dare tell Tomaso!' Kelda gasped.

'He's going to have to know some time! Kelda... how could you go to bed with some man you hardly know at a party?' Her mother broke down in tears again.

That seemed the worst aspect of it all in her parent's eyes. Kelda turned her head away, wishing that she could have told the truth but in the circumstances that was impossible. She didn't sleep a wink that night. Tomorrow, Daisy and Tomaso were getting married. And she had ruined her mother's wedding for her with the sort of news few parents wished to hear. Her conscience was in agony. And as if that wasn't enough, she knew that tomorrow she would have to face Angelo again.

Would she tell him? How *could* she tell him? The right words for such an announcement evaded her. After he had seen Russ strolling out of her bedroom half naked, why should he even believe that her baby was *his*? Too exhausted to even think any more, Kelda lay there in the darkness, wrapped in turmoil.

When she came down for breakfast, Daisy was astonishingly all smiles and buoyance. 'You could get a nanny and we could keep the baby when you had to be away overnight. Tomaso loves children. He'll probably be delighted when he gets over the... the surprise,' Daisy selected tactfully. 'After all, society has changed. Single parenthood is much more acceptable these days. Would you like one rasher or two?'

'Mum, I——' Kelda hesitated and then abruptly found herself wrapped in her mother's arms. 'The smell of that bacon makes me sick,' she confided with a tiny catch in her voice.

The wedding was at a register office. The first person Kelda saw was Angelo, and the effect of Angelo sheathed in a superb light grey suit was powerful. She stumbled in the doorway, briefly unable to take her eyes off him. Dear lord, the ground beneath her feet seemed to tilt and her skin was damp and her heart was racing. Eyes of gold deep enough to drown in, ebony hair that felt like silk against her fingertips. A welter of erotic imagery she had locked tight within her memory banks suddenly overwhelmed her.

'That's Fiona,' her mother hissed. 'I forgot to mention that she'd be coming. Gorgeous, isn't she? Tomaso thinks she's been the most promising yet. She's a banker and she has two degrees——'

'Two degrees,' Kelda muttered jerkily, her stomach a rolling turmoil of nausea as she belatedly focused on the six-foot-plus-tall Amazon standing beside Angelo. From her waterfall-straight black hair and bright sapphire-blue eyes to the soles of her elegantly shod feet, Fiona was stunning.

'I was so silly that night we all dined together,' Daisy whispered in haste as Tomaso bore down on them. 'I had this stupid idea that Angelo and you were——'

Tomaso's arrival mercifully silenced her mother.

He has another woman. Well, what did you expect...why are you so shocked? Kelda couldn't answer that question. She knew only that the sight of Angelo with another woman had devastated her. The brief ceremony over, she swiftly spun on her heel and approached Tomaso's brother and his wife. 'Would you mind giving me a lift back to the——?'

'You can come with us, Kelda.' Angelo's husky voice was like a knife between her ribs.

Slowly she turned round. Angelo smoothly introduced Fiona. Fiona gave her a muted smile, her bright eyes sharply assessing. 'I've heard so much about you that I feel I know you already.'

'Bad news does tend to travel fast.'

'Kelda,' Angelo breathed with icy emphasis.

Treating him to the first look she had dared, she clashed with impassive dark eyes and felt the ice there like a chilly hand squeezing her heart.

'She's what?' she heard Tomaso roar very loudly several feet away.

'I didn't mean to offend you,' Fiona was saying drily. 'But I'm sorry if I did.'

'No, I'm sorry.' Kelda breathed in deeply, struggling to maintain her mask of composure. 'I'm a bit touchy today.'

'Do you want a lift?' Angelo enquired uninvitingly.

A hand came down on her shoulder. 'Kelda will drive back to the house with us,' Tomaso announced grim-mouthed. 'We have something very personal to discuss, Angelo.'

CHAPTER SEVEN

WHITE and strained, Kelda couldn't resist throwing a reproachful glance at her mother. 'You didn't waste any time, did you?'

'Naturally your mother confided in me,' Tomaso responded thinly. 'I am her husband and your stepfather. Is it true? Are you expecting a child?'

'Mum, how could you do this to me?' Kelda muttered in deep embarrassment.

'We're going off on our honeymoon and I don't like leaving you alone,' Daisy told her ruefully. 'I needed Tomaso's advice.'

'You always were... volatile,' Tomaso muttered half under his breath.

'It's none of your business!' Kelda burst out helplessly. She wasn't a child.

'But is it Angelo's business?' Tomaso's sharp dark eyes rested astutely on her startled face.

'What's this got to do with Angelo?' Daisy demanded blankly.

Tomaso had removed his wallet from an inside pocket. Opening it, he extracted a piece of folded newspaper. 'Don't you think Angelo would be preferable to some stranger at a party?' he said drily, and handed the cutting to his new bride.

'What's that?' Kelda demanded in a high, thin voice that was shredding fast into near hysteria.

'Where and when was this photo taken?' Daisy had paled in shock. She looked at her daughter with appalled eyes. 'Why didn't you tell me? I'm your mother.'

'It was taken at Pisa almost six weeks ago. That's the airport in the background. It was published in a minor gossip mag in Italy and someone sent it to me. I've had it for weeks,' her stepfather admitted with a small tight smile. 'I didn't want to upset you, *cara*.'

Kelda snatched at the cutting and turned a deep guilty-as-charged pink. It was a photo of them kissing at the airport and Angelo was very recognisable even if only a tutored eye might have guessed *her* identity.

'They were in Italy together,' Tomaso breathed harshly.

'You mean that they both pretended . . . they *lied*?' her mother gathered in horror. 'But why?'

'Since your daughter appears to have lost her voice, I'm depending on my son to fill in the blanks——'

'No, please!' Kelda broke in. 'It isn't Angelo's . . . I mean, definitely not . . . I just can't imagine Angelo and I together *that* way——' Literally stupefied by the horror of Tomaso's discovery that she had been in Italy with Angelo, Kelda was having a very hard time finding convincing words of denial.

Her stepfather dealt her an intuitive look. 'Can't you?' he fielded even more drily. 'You were alone with Angelo for what . . . three days? I wouldn't trust the two of you to be alone together for an hour——'

'Tomaso!' Daisy gasped in reproof.

'My son has wanted your daughter practically from the first moment he laid eyes on her, and judging by a certain episode six years ago Kelda was not——'

'It is not Angelo's child!' Kelda suddenly sobbed, covering her face.

'Then you have nothing to worry about when I tell him,' Tomaso told her speciously.

Kelda reeled out of the limousine outside the mansion she had spent five years of her life in. She surged through the wide open front door, deaf and blind to the housekeeper's greeting and dived into the downstairs cloakroom at the back of the huge hall. She lost her breakfast there.

When she made a strained reappearance, everyone was being seated in the ballroom which had been set out with tables for the reception. It was milling with guests and caterers and she had never been so grateful to see crowds. She was less grateful when she found herself at the top table, only several seats down from Angelo and Fiona.

The meal and the speeches were ever afterwards a blur. Tomaso had shattered her. Never before had she been made so aware of the likeness between father and son. Her stepfather had not previously shown that side of his temperament to her. There was dancing after the meal. She wanted to go home, but knew that she had to sit it out. Several men asked her to dance and grimly, for the sake of appearances, she obliged. She averted her eyes every time she caught a glimpse of Angelo and Fiona on the floor, didn't even question why she had to protect herself that way.

When Angelo smoothly cut in on her partner as the music changed, she was quite unprepared for the confrontation. Instinctively, she stilled and the lean hand at her spine pulled her closer. 'Smile,' he suggested silkily, raking dark eyes absorbing the sudden tense pallor freezing her beautiful face. 'Or I might suspect that you're pining for me.'

Her nostrils flared on the disturbingly familiar scent of him. Her fluid body was poker straight in the circle of his arms. 'I don't smile for you, Angelo,' she said.

'Except in my bed,' he murmured with black velvet satire.

Involuntarily, Kelda flinched and missed a step.

'Yes...you are rather sensitive today,' he mused softly into the veiling torrent of her hair and her skin tightened painfully over her bones as his breath warmed her throat. 'And you lack your usual glow——'

'Still stuck with my apartment?' Kelda interjected tautly. 'I hope you make a loss on it.'

'Sold at profit to an impatient Arab,' Angelo drawled. 'Though a loss wouldn't have bothered me. I had what I wanted, after all...and should I ever want it again,

I'm convinced I wouldn't be disappointed. You don't play hard to get by any stretch of the imagination——'

White as death, Kelda pulled free just as the music stopped. 'You bastard,' she whispered tightly and headed back to her seat, savaged by his cruelty.

Her mother dropped down into the empty chair beside her and said, 'Tomaso has calmed down.'

'Good...I'm sorry,' Kelda sighed. 'I've wrecked your day.'

'That's nonsense. I've never been so happy,' Daisy carolled a little tipsily. 'And if it's Angelo's baby, that makes it OK, doesn't it? Tomaso says, he'll have to marry you and so he should, seducing my little girl——'

'I am not a little girl, Mother!' Kelda hissed, aghast.

'You are measured up against Angelo. Tomaso says it serves him right...'

'It isn't Angelo's ba——'

Daisy frowned at her. 'Don't lie to me any more, Kelda. I deserve better than that.'

'I'm sorry.'

'I forgive you. It's your hormones. They make you moody.' With a dizzy smile, her mother drifted off again.

Suddenly suffocated by the crush, Kelda went for a walk. She would be able to leave soon. Tomaso and Daisy weren't going away until tomorrow. She wandered into the drawing-room past several elderly ladies tucking into champagne and talking Italian in staccato bursts of energy. She headed for the conservatory, certain of finding privacy there.

But the conservatory was already very much occupied. Angelo and Fiona were entwined in a passionate embrace beneath the palm trees. Kelda stood on the threshold for several taut, stricken seconds, watching Fiona pushing her fingers through his hair, her lithe body arched into his with the sensual intimacy of lovers who thought they were alone. It was X-certificate stuff and clumsily, slowly, Kelda backed away, her heartbeat pounding unnaturally loudly in her eardrums.

Utterly devastated. That was how she felt. For an insane moment she had wanted to tear their straining bodies apart and impose herself between them. Now wouldn't that have been a novel end to the day? She staggered dizzily into a chair in an alcove off the hall and sat down, hugging herself as though to ward off the intense pain.

Tomaso strode past, paused. 'Have you seen Angelo?'

She jerked a hand wordlessly in the direction of the conservatory, would have liked to say something smart like. 'I think you'll find he's busy,' but could not summon up the poise. She was hurting so much, she didn't think she could bear it without coming apart. She twisted her hands together, battling for control but the pain simply kept on biting at her from new directions.

Inside her head, she saw them together in a far more intimate setting. She squeezed her eyes tight shut in anguish but the image wouldn't leave her alone. She saw them intertwined in passion in tumbled sheets, lying together in the blissful aftermath that once she had known and about there she just wanted to press a button and die.

Someone pulled apart her shaking hands and gripped them tightly in his.

'I'm sorry,' Tomaso said heavily. 'I am very sorry you had to see that.'

The sympathy almost sent her over the edge. She didn't trust herself to speak.

'Kelda...what do you want me to do?'

Her lashes lifted. Her stepfather was hunkered down in front of her, fiercely holding her hands. 'Nothing,' she gasped pleadingly.

'Angelo has the right to know——'

'No, not now!' she forced out painfully. 'I couldn't stand it!'

'You love him.' Tomaso released his breath in a long pent-up hiss, kindly removing his perceptive gaze from her distraught face.

'No...' But even to her own ears it sounded false, empty, a foolish denial of the anguish she was enduring.

Tomaso sighed. 'He would marry you——'

She was appalled by the idea and it showed.

'I would get a car to take you home but you should stay here tonight. I don't like the idea of you being on your own,' her stepfather said quietly.

'I'll be fine.' From somewhere, she got the strength to give him a watery smile. 'I think I need to be on my own.'

Afterwards she couldn't recall a single moment of the drive. She found herself back inside the cottage without quite knowing how she had got there. And then she collapsed, but not into tears. Her eyes burned and ached but not with moisture. She couldn't cry. Tomaso's understanding kindness had almost been her undoing, but now that she was alone all she could do was stare emptily into space.

She *did* love Angelo. Why had she only found that out now, when it was too late to make any difference? But what difference could it ever have made? she asked herself. Six years of bitter misunderstanding lay between her and Angelo, and her own behaviour had only confirmed his opinion of her. Why, oh, why had she set up that scene at her apartment with Russ?

Of course, she hadn't even suspected then that she might be pregnant. But by staging that scene she had finally and most thoroughly confirmed Angelo's low opinion of her morals. There was no way now that she would ever tell Angelo that the baby she carried was his. He despised her but he had found her sexually attractive. That was all it had ever been on his side. Sex. The very last thing on Angelo's mind had been fathering a child.

How could you love and hate someone at the same time? Today she had hated him, but she had loved, wanted and needed him as well with a mindless craving that had shaken her to the very roots of her being.

Jealousy had not touched her until now, but Angelo had plunged her into instant agony. She could not have borne Tomaso's interference in the situation. That, at least, she reminded herself, was no longer likely.

It was after two when she heard a car raking into her driveway. She sat up in bed, listened to the slam of a door, crunching steps on the gravel. The bell went in three sharp, successive bursts.

'Who is it?' she called from the stairs.

'Who the hell do you think?'

Angelo. Weakly she sank down on the second last step. 'Go away!'

'If I have to break in, I'll do it!'

Her breath shortened in her throat. Tying the sash of her robe, she unbolted the door. 'Do you realise what time it is?' she demanded.

'Are you alone?' Angelo sent a slashing glance of suspicion up the stairs.

'What do you want?' Tension held her fast, a nasty flicker of foreboding skimming down her spine. Playing for time to compose herself, she walked into the lounge and switched on a lamp before taking up a stance by the fireplace.

Angelo looked uncharacteristically tousled. His hard jawline was blue-shadowed, his ebony hair ruffled. Although he was still wearing his grey suit, he had discarded his tie and his silk shirt was half unbuttoned. His brilliant dark eyes glittered with a cold menace, accentuated by the rigid tension etched into his striking bone-structure.

'I hear you're pregnant,' he delivered with a soft hiss.

Involuntarily, Kelda recoiled but she made a swift recovery. 'And where did you hear that piece of nonsense?' she managed to toss back boldly.

'Your brother——'

She lost colour. 'T-Tim?'

'He was rather drunk. I gave him a lift back to town,' Angelo divulged with slow, measured emphasis as though he was exercising immense self-control. 'After I'd dropped Fiona off, he began to laugh and crack some rather odd jokes. Your mother asked him to keep an eye on you while she was away and he told me why——'

Not a muscle moved on Kelda's face. 'That doesn't explain what you're doing here at two in the morning——'

'Are you pregnant?' Angelo demanded with ferocious anger.

'I owe you no explanations,' Kelda flung back. 'I don't have to defend myself against Tim's drunken ramblings.'

'In Italy, you said that somehow, some day you would get your own back on me for bringing you there.' The reminder lanced into the smouldering silence. 'If this is it, I'll fight you and I'll break you!' he swore with brutal clarity. 'You've told your mother that you're pregnant. I want to know if you're lying...and if you're not, I want to know now whose child it is!'

Hysteria was fluttering like a wild bird captured in her throat. Her stomach was churning. 'Relax, Angelo...it isn't yours,' she asserted through bloodless lips, holding herself proudly erect only by rigorous discipline.

The silence throbbed. He didn't relax in receipt of her assurance. He went rigid.

'Then why does your brother think it is?' he lashed back at her finally with splintering savagery, every powerful line of his lean body emanating his bitter anger.

'They know about Italy, and before you blame me for that, let me disclaim all responsibility. We were photographed at the airport. Someone sent your father a cutting,' she shared with a tiny tremor in the voice she was fighting to keep level.

Angelo said something raw in Italian and strode over to the window, his back squarely turned to her, scorching tension in the angle of his broad shoulders.

'I assured them that you weren't the culprit,' she muttered tightly, and that at least was true.

'Then who is?'

She made no response. Her wide green eyes were dark with exhaustion and stress.

'Russ Seadon...*si*,' Angelo decided, flicking her a glance of incandescent golden rage and bitterness. 'I did recognise him,' he ground out.

'Good for you,' she mumbled shakily because she didn't have the strength to fight Angelo after the traumas of the past thirty-six hours.

'*Is it his child*?' he demanded, coming back to her in one long, threatening stride. 'I demand to know!'

'You have no right to ask me that,' Kelda snapped, taking a step back from him.

'I want the truth!' Angelo grabbed her wrists with two strong hands and yanked her up against him. 'If it isn't mine, whose is it?'

'Go to hell!' she gasped, struggling to release herself from his fierce grip.

'*Tell me*!' he blazed down at her insistently, his striking bone-structure clenched with dark fury.

From somewhere deep inside her where outrage could pull on final reserves of energy, she found the courage to hurl, 'You see, I didn't pine for you, Angelo! Not for a day or even an hour...'

'You make me understand why men kill.' As Angelo stared down into her flushed and exquisitely delicate face, white hot rage flamed in his piercing gaze. 'I would rather see you buried than swollen with another man's seed,' he admitted through clenched teeth.

Losing every scrap of colour, Kelda momentarily sagged in his fierce grip. She looked at him in horror. 'Are you c-crazy?'

'Obsessed. Does that please you?' Angelo drawled with razor-edged softness. 'I doubt if it does. You want me to stay away, because you're obsessed, too——'

'No!'

'You don't like seeing me with another woman. That hurt,' Angelo savoured with primitive relish. 'You couldn't hide that from me. Like a knife twisting inside you. It made you sick. It terrified you——'

Perspiration beaded her brow. 'Don't...I hate you!'

Angelo hauled her even closer, wound a lean hand possessively into the tangled fall of her hair to hold her prisoner. 'A couple of centuries ago you'd have been burnt at the stake for witchcraft, but you can burn in my bed instead——'

'Let g-go of me!' In disbelief, she could feel her breasts lifting and swelling in hard collision with his muscular chest. He brought his other hand down to her hips and crushed her suggestively into the hard cradle of his thighs. The thrust of his erection sent excitement spiralling through her in waves and she squeezed her eyes tightly shut in wild rejection. 'No...no!'

She would not surrender to that excitement, she told herself furiously but he lowered his dark head and, instead of the aggressive assault she had expected, he let his mouth nip teasingly along the fullness of her lower lip, locking the oxygen in her throat.

'Angelo, please...' Her own voice sounded miles away, oddly strangled.

'Please what?' He let his tongue delve inch by inch between her parted lips and the world stood still and her knees turned to sawdust. Her entire body was pitched to that single caress.

'Stop,' she moaned.

'But you want this as much as I do.' His tongue flicked into the sensitive interior of her mouth and she clutched at him, every muscle jerking tight. He was pushing her backwards, lifting her off the carpet and then pressing her back against the wall.

He buried his lips hotly in a hollow of her collarbone and she trembled violently, her nipples peaking into painful sensitivity. His hands skimmed down the taut length of her thighs and she felt him shudder against her, his heart thundering against her spread fingers, as madly accelerated as her own.

He cupped the ripe curve of her bottom in his hands and she bit at his shoulder in frustration, what remained of her control evaporating fast.

'Tell me that you're lying,' he urged unsteadily.

'What?' she mumbled, slurring the word, lost in a world of intense sensation that utterly seduced.

'Tell me that you're not pregnant,' Angelo demanded in a roughened, almost pleading undertone.

'But... I am,' she responded on the peak of a sob of unbearable excitement.

'Bitch,' he groaned savagely, and suddenly tore himself back from her.

Kelda opened glazed eyes. Angelo was several feet away, his breathing pattern ruptured and audible. He made no attempt to conceal his blatant physical excitement. He looked back at her while she braced herself with shaking hands against the wall to stay upright. Luminescent gold engulfed her in the implacable force of his will.

'And the baby is not mine... it's definitely not mine?' Angelo persisted roughly, rawly launching the demand at her in raking challenge. 'How can you be so sure it's not?'

In her mind's eye, she saw him with Fiona and the pain and bitterness hit her afresh. To admit the truth would be the ultimate humiliation. 'Definitely not yours,' she spelt out.

He raked something at her in his own language and then spread his hands in a soundless arc of violent anger. 'I am not prepared to live with the reminder that you went to bed with another man after me! If you choose to behave like a whore, *you* take the responsibility for the consequences... I will not! I don't want you with another man's bastard!'

In increasing distress, Kelda put her hands over her ears, lowering her head as a wave of dizziness folded in on her.

Spots swam in front of her eyes. Angelo blurred out of view. She thought she was going to suffocate in the darkness before she passed out and slid down the wall in a faint.

She felt so sick coming to that she was afraid to move a muscle.

'She's coming round,' an unfamiliar voice said witheringly. 'As I said she would. Perhaps if you fed your wife a little more and let her go to bed at a more reasonable hour, she would be somewhat healthier. Pregnant women need extra rest and a sensible diet——'

'Pregnant,' Angelo echoed, not quite steadily, with the same revulsion that might have distinguished a reference to an unmentionable disease.

'If that is your attitude, I can quite see why she's starving herself into a skeleton...what has she had to eat today?'

'The icing off a slice of wedding cake. Nothing else.'

Kelda's eyes opened wide at this instantaneous and correct response. How had Angelo known that? He must have been watching her.

Angelo had called out a doctor. The gentleman in question was balding, beetle-browed and near retirement. He was also treating Angelo to a look of scathing contempt. 'And that didn't bother you?' he demanded.

'I'm fine...sorry you had to be bothered,' Kelda broke in hurriedly and tried to sit up.

The doctor's hand restrained her. 'Stay where you are. I want to see you in my ante-natal clinic Thursday afternoon at two and don't bother bringing your husband. We'll do very well without him.' With that blistering assurance, he took his leave. 'Don't trouble yourself, Mr Rossetti. I can see myself out.'

Long after the cottage door had slammed, the silence stretched. Angelo was poised rigid-backed by the window. He was staring out into the darkness beyond the glass. 'I don't know what I'm doing here,' he admitted with gritted abruptness.

Kelda glanced down at herself and discovered she was attired in one of her mother's frilly cotton nightdresses. Her cheeks flushed. She hadn't been wearing anything under the robe. 'You put this on me——'

'The least of my sins,' Angelo said half under his breath.

'I didn't need a doctor——'

'What was I supposed to do when you collapsed? Step over you and drive off?'

'Yes,' she said sickly, recalling all that had passed before. 'It would have been more in keeping.'

'I was very shocked and confused when I came here tonight. I did not fully consider what I was doing,' Angelo proffered in a murderously controlled tone. 'I should have waited until I had cooled down. Naturally you are pregnant. Why should you lie about such a thing?'

'It doesn't matter.' Kelda was drained, depressed, empty of all reaction.

'What was between us is finished——'

She closed her eyes in sudden pain, registered that she was not after all as empty of emotion as she had imagined. She could not cope with Angelo and she could not cope without him. She didn't know which was worst.

'It *has* to be,' Angelo stressed. 'I could never forget that you went to bed with Seadon after you were with me in Italy——'

Dumbly she shook her head on the pillow.

'I could never accept another man's child in these circumstances. How could you let him touch you after me?' he bit out in sudden slashing challenge.

'I don't want to talk about it.' She turned her head away.

'Are you finally ashamed of yourself when it is too late to make any difference?' he derided half under his breath.

'You could never trust me...all these years, never once have you trusted me or given me the benefit of the doubt,' she condemned helplessly, talking to herself, no longer listening to him. 'I can't handle that, I never could.'

'You won't be expected to handle it from now on.'

'And now for the good news,' she whispered unsteadily.

Dark, dark eyes without a shade of gold rested on her. 'I wanted you so badly, for so long that it was like a sickness in my blood. I was determined to have you at any cost. I thought I could exorcise you with sex but all that achieved was an even greater obsession. I don't like what you do to me,' Angelo confessed, his beautiful mouth thinning into a forbidding line. 'I don't like the way I behave with you. I like to be in control...a hangover from my childhood...I am not in control with you.'

Neither was she, and sometimes, like now, when he was tearing her in two, it was terrifying. She hated him for hurting her, for not loving her, for insulting her, but when it came to the image of him walking out of the door she wanted to trail him back to hurt and insult all over again. The destruction was more bearable than the emptiness.

'Go away!' she suddenly demanded.

Angelo expelled his breath in an audible hiss of rampant frustration. 'You look so fragile and yet you're strong enough to defy me. Even as a child you defied me!'

She had thrust her face into the pillow. 'I needed someone to put their arms round me and make me feel I *belonged*!'

'I couldn't trust myself that close,' Angelo muttered in a stifled tone of self-disgust.

'I wish you'd go.'

'No, you don't...sometimes I know what you feel before you even think it. Who is the father?' he asked again without warning, but this time his wine-dark voice was icily controlled. 'Is it Seadon?'

'Does it matter?'

'I would really prefer not to know for sure,' he admitted harshly.

'Damn you, Angelo!'

'You need to eat something,' he murmured prosaically. 'What do you want?'

'You're insane,' she accused weakly.

'Guilty as hell. You're sick, you're pregnant and your wrists have a full set of my fingerprints on them,' Angelo enumerated curtly. 'How do you expect me to feel?'

He left the room. Shakily, she lifted her wrists into the light and saw the purplish bruising he had inflicted earlier. She hadn't felt any pain at the time. Her fair skin marked easily but feeling a total heel had to be a new sensation for Angelo, and not one that would do him any noticeable harm. He would leave her now and go back to Fiona. Lying had been the right thing to do, she told herself wretchedly. The torturous cycle of destruction inside her would be stopped and she would heal. Angelo would leave her alone.

It took him a long time but eventually he reappeared with a bowl of soup.

They were in a state of temporarily suspended hostilities, she acknowledged. Dawn was breaking outside. She remembered another dawn and her cheeks burned, making her duck her head down and tuck into the soup. The soup was as burnt as her skin. She persevered beneath his taut scrutiny, ridiculously conscious all of a sudden of a desire not to reject even so small an olive branch. In the harsher light, the strain in his darkly handsome visage was pronounced. He looked as savaged as she felt.

The words he had employed came back to haunt her. Sickness . . . obsession . . . exorcism. And *sex*. Unhealthy, destructive, debilitating. Not flattering. And what was that hangover from his childhood? He liked to be in control. Scarcely a revelation to anyone in Angelo's radius! Angelo could turn an impromptu picnic into an organised field expedition.

'Why do you have to be in control?'

His eyes veiled. 'I grew up with a woman like you. A free spirit. Any man, any time, any place——'

Like you... She swallowed hard on her angry frustration. 'What woman?'

'My mother. And she wasn't ashamed of it either. My father adored her but he couldn't live with her affairs. That's why he divorced her, but she still got custody of me. I hated the life I had with her. She was suffocatingly possessive and very volatile——'

'So are you.'

Angelo dealt her a chilling half-smile. 'Only with you, and that I can overcome,' he stated with cool conviction. 'I don't want to live on the wild side with any woman. I want a quiet, well-behaved, conservative wife who would die of shock if I made love to her the way I make love to you. At times, she'll bore me...after a few years, I'll be walking out the door and forgetting she exists, and not long after that I will most probably set up a mistress.'

'And I hope like hell your wife throws orgies while you're at the office!' Kelda breathed in a blitz of stormy revulsion and pain.

'You might; she won't. She'll accept the package deal. Many women do. Status, money, children and a husband whose infidelities are discreet.'

'You burnt the soup.' Kelda rolled over, presenting him with her narrow back. Her fingers clawed like talons into the pillow beside her head. She could not deal with such honesty. He was not trying to hurt her. He was telling her what he believed would make him happy...or as happy as he believed he could afford to be and still be one hundred percent in control.

'You should keep that appointment with the doctor. If you need anything——' He hesitated. 'Try not to involve me unless it's an emergency.'

She listened to the car drive off, strained to hear the last distant sounds and then flopped. *He burnt the soup and I ate it*. And she started to laugh like a madwoman until the dragging sobs surfaced and finally she cried, cried for herself alone. Angelo, the Angel of Darkness, who made the City quail, was an emotional coward. A wimp like that wasn't worth her tears, and he wasn't fit to be the father of her child either!

CHAPTER EIGHT

'I'VE been laughing into my cornflakes every morning this week following Carol Philips' story of life with dear, misunderstood Danny,' Gina said mockingly to the table at large. She looped a straying strand of cornsilk hair from her brow with a beringed hand and giggled. 'He *actually* brought one of his women home to lunch and let her think that his wife was his sister!'

'Carol Philips was a doormat. She got what she asked for,' one of the other women remarked drily. 'I'd have thrown him and his floozy out... I wouldn't let any man treat me like that!'

'She had two young children and he kept her very short of money,' Kelda put in quietly. 'She was only eighteen when he married her. She had never had a job. I can understand how trapped she must have felt——'

'Oh, you!' Her friend Gina wrinkled her classic nose. 'How can you feel sorry for Danny's wife after what *he* did to you?'

'I must have hurt her as well,' Kelda pointed out ruefully.

'Even she admitted that you were the only one who dumped him immediately you found out that he was married——'

'And it's cleared your name of all that rubbish that was printed,' Russ commented. 'You came out squeaky clean, compared with all the others the wronged wife chose to name. There's been quite a few red faces on the catwalks this past week!'

Her companions continued to trawl over Carol's revelations, a tabloid exposé which had been running all week and causing more hilarity than anything else. Danny's wife had sold her story because Danny had left her practically destitute when he'd swanned off to New York, taking the children's curvaceous teenage nanny with him.

Kelda pushed back her chair and got up.

'Are you feeling all right?' Gina asked anxiously, searching her pale face.

'I'm off to the cloakroom again... don't draw everybody's attention to it,' Kelda begged with a wry grin.

She was feeling sick, although she was trying to hide the fact. In addition she had a nagging pain in her lower abdomen. It was not the first time that she had experienced such symptoms in recent days. The pain came and went, sometimes only irritating, but on at least one other occasion actually quite painful.

She had meant to make time to go to the doctor but she was quite convinced that she knew what was wrong with her. The thick pregnancy manual she had bought described what was called 'round ligament pain', something to do with the stretching of the ligaments that supported the uterus and nothing to worry about. She would make an appointment at the clinic for the day after tomorrow, she promised herself. Just to be on the safe side.

In the cloakroom she looked at her reflection and made a face. Her cunningly cut, flowing dress concealed the firm swell of her stomach from all but the most intent observers, but she still felt like a beached whale. Seven months pregnant and feeling it, she thought ruefully.

She had kept so busy over the past five months that the time had flown but sometimes, like now, in the middle of a convivial crowd of friends, something that was more than tiredness would swamp her. It was a combination of loneliness, self-pity and emptiness, and she thoroughly despised herself for the weakness. After all, she had been been very lucky and she was not alone, except in the sense that she did not have a supportive male in her life.

Every other day, Tomaso and Daisy were either on the phone or the doorstep, having failed to fulfil Angelo's prophecy that they would spend most of their time abroad. Tim appeared regularly, invariably clutching yet another fluffy toy to add to a steadily growing collection. And, best of all, Russ and Gina had returned to London to set up a modelling agency of their own and tomorrow they were getting married. That was one reason why Kelda had no intention of being a wet blanket.

Her friends had been marvellous. When the first unmistakable signs of her burgeoning stomach had forced her to stop modelling, Russ and Gina had stepped in to offer her a job. Gina was in so much demand as a model that it was impossible for her to devote much time to helping Russ with their agency. Russ, in turn, was either out on a shoot or in the studio. Kelda had been installed to handle the bookings and run the small agency on a day-to-day basis.

She was not rich but she was no longer in debt. She had managed to work long enough to clear all outstanding bills. Then she had cut up her credit cards and returned them, accepting that she had to learn to exist on a much reduced budget until such time as the baby was born. Her hand slid down to her stomach in an unconsciously protective movement. The years ahead would be a struggle and she had faced that reality head-on, but her commitment to her unborn child remained unchanged.

Gina was talking almost fiercely to Russ when Kelda rejoined them. One of those sudden awkward silences fell. 'Do you want me to go away and come back again?' Kelda said only half-jokingly.

'You look tired,' Russ told her abruptly. 'Do you want to go home?'

'Dear Russ...such fabulous tact,' Gina breathed, throwing her fiancé a dirty look. 'Why should Kelda scuttle off home because *he's* here?'

More even-tempered than Gina, Russ sighed. 'I only thought——'

Gina grabbed Kelda's arm. 'Look, there he is over there!'

Kelda didn't want to look. Suddenly she turned cold. Angelo was here. There was only one male capable of rousing Gina to such fury. It had to be Angelo. Sometimes, Kelda wished she hadn't told her friends the truth, but she had known they would be discreet, and a lie which promised to stretch ahead of her year after year had not seemed practical.

'*Lousy, womanising swine*!' Gina hissed in her ear. 'That's Isabel Dunning with him. She's really top-drawer.'

Isabel, Kelda rhymed inwardly, to follow on from Adele, Caroline, Felicity and Fiona. In five months, Angelo had worked through the English upper classes with a fine-tooth comb, but not one of the lovely ladies had lasted. The gossip columnists were agog at such volatile romancing. Then they didn't know what Kelda knew... Angelo was scouring society for a suitable wife. A conservative wife from a good background with no scandals in her past.

'She'll run to fat in a few years,' Gina said nastily.

Kelda was looking, although she had tried so hard not to. But there was this terrible, wicked craving inside her. She had not seen Angelo in the flesh since that night at the cottage. His partner was slender, blonde, impeccably dressed and distinctly beautiful. And Angelo? The air locked in her throat. A shudder ran through her. Angelo was Angelo. Striking, vital, magnificent. She could not dredge her hungry gaze from him.

'Care to dance?' Russ demanded.

'Yes, go ahead.' Gina gave her a determined push. 'Don't be a wallflower with him around!'

Kelda found herself out on the floor without knowing how she had arrived there. As Russ whirled her around with more enthusiasm than rhythm, she caught flickering glimpses of Angelo. His hard-edged profile... the uncompromising set of his jawline... the sheen of his ebony hair beneath the lights. Had he lost weight or was that only her imagination? Maybe it was the shadows which carved those dark features into leaner, older lines.

Suddenly, she was filled with self-loathing. She was not some lovesick teenager, still longing for some arrogant young male, who had treated her badly! Where was her pride? While she struggled to survive, Angelo had been breaking all known records with a constant stream of other women. And a sixth sense warned her that he might well be announcing his marital plans soon. Angelo, married, introducing her to his wife...she broke out in nervous perspiration.

The imagery summoned up made her feel sick and dizzy. Would Tomaso retain his silence when Angelo brought home a wife-to-be? She was painfully aware that her stepfather was finding that silence harder and harder to maintain. Five months ago he had perhaps hoped that his son and his stepdaughter might reconcile without any interference from him and then all constraint would be at an end within the family circle. But after this length of time Tomaso could no longer sustain such a hope.

'Could we sit down?' she gasped breathlessly.

'Too energetic?' Russ grimaced. 'Sorry, I keep on forgetting...'

I don't, Kelda reflected miserably. Russ curved a supportive arm to her spine and by the worst possible misfortune chose the path back to their table that went closest to Angelo's. They came face to face in the aisle.

'Kelda...' Angelo stilled. Tension thickened the atmosphere but he stared at her with impassive dark eyes, cold as charity. 'What a pleasant surprise,' he drawled. 'Let me introduce you to Isabel...Isabel, this is my stepsister, Kelda——'

'I'm delighted to meet you.' Isabel extended a polite hand.

Stepsister... the term, the very word shattered Kelda. Angelo had never used it before. Like a robot, she forced her arm up to meet Isabel's fingers, briefly, loosely connecting and dropping away again.

'And Russ.' Russ's arm tightened round Kelda's rigid back.

'Perhaps Kelda and Russ would like to join us.' As Isabel turned to address Angelo, she rested her left hand on his sleeve and the elegant diamond solitaire on her engagement finger caught the light. 'The more the merrier when one's celebrating, don't you think?' she said with a teasing smile.

'Sorry, we're with a party of our own,' Russ retorted with a distinctly forced smile.

A moment later, Kelda dropped heavily down into her chair, white as a sheet.

'What's wrong?' Gina asked of Russ.

'The bastard just introduced her to his fiancée.'

'Men!' Gina snorted, unlocking the door of her docklands apartment where Kelda was to spend the night. Russ was staying the night with his best man. Gina stalked over to the drinks cabinet. 'You need a brandy. You look like a corpse!'

'No,' Kelda shook her head.

'Not even this once?' Gina wheedled.

'Sorry.'

'Well then, I insist you get straight into bed and I'll bring supper in.'

'Gina, it's only ten——'

'We should have had a hen-night and stayed home,' her friend muttered crossly. 'That club was Russ's idea.'

'I was bound to run into Angelo sooner or later.' With a very real effort, Kelda tilted her chin and managed to smile. 'Don't worry about it.'

'Do you think I came down with the last shower of rain?' Gina enquired very drily. 'You are absolutely devastated!'

Kelda contrived a jerky shrug. 'It was on the cards. So, he's getting married... so what?'

'You should have told him the truth months ago!'

'Gina!' Kelda was shaken.

Her friend sighed. 'You deliberately drove him away by letting him think that Russ and you were involved——'

'I didn't know I was pregnant——'

'And then you tell him it's not his baby!' Gina recounted.

'Do you really think that he wanted to hear that it was?'

Presented with that angle, Gina winced.

Kelda managed to produce a wry laugh. 'I did the right thing, Gina, and I'm over him. I'm really not martyr material. Plenty more fish in the sea.'

Gina frowned. 'Is that really how you feel?'

'Yes.' Kelda walked into the kitchen. 'Now where is this fancy no-cook supper you promised me, and all the gossip?'

'Have you found out yet who is sending you those luscious hampers every week?'

Kelda smiled. For months she had been receiving luxury hampers of fabulous food from Harrods. 'Tomaso, of course.'

'Your *stepfather*?' Gina exclaimed in comical disappointment. 'I thought you had a secret admirer!'

'Chance would be a fine thing, the shape I'm in.'

'Are you sure it's him?'

'Who else?' Kelda said wryly. 'I taxed him with it and of course he denied it, but he hates being thanked for anything. It has to be him. He was really quite put out with me when I told him I wouldn't accept any financial help from him and Mum.'

Later, as she lay sleepless in Russ and Gina's guest-room, the tears trickled silently down her cheeks into her hair, making her skin burn. As fast as they came, she scrubbed them away. Angelo was getting married.

That was not the end of her world. She could get by without Angelo...hadn't she been doing so for months? Angelo's marriage was merely the last act in a grotesque black comedy.

Why should it upset her? Even if she had told the truth and Angelo had accepted that he was the father of her child...even if he had asked her to marry him, she would have turned him down. She had no doubts about that reality. She might love Angelo in that insane, unreasoning way that women sometimes loved, but she did not *like* Angelo, and literally cringed from the idea of living with him as an unwilling and no doubt unfaithful husband. No, much as it might hurt, Kelda was convinced that her future was far safer solely in her own hands.

The pain in her abdomen came back midway through Russ and Gina's wedding breakfast the following morning. She had to leave the table to be ignominiously sick but she managed to conceal her pallor with judicious use of cosmetics before she returned.

'I think you should go home to bed,' Gina scolded none the less when she was changing out of her unconventional scarlet designer wedding-gown. 'All that standing around for the photos has exhausted you.'

By then, Kelda was feeling pretty awful and just a little scared. The pain was worse. She knew she needed to see a doctor but she was determined not to cloud her friends' wedding-day. Half an hour later, she waved them off and walked back into the hotel, intending to call a cab, but without warning a sliver of absolute agony pierced her. With a stifled cry, she pressed a hand to her stomach. A red mist rose in front of her eyes. She took a staggering step in the direction of a chair but she didn't make it. She collapsed in the foyer.

'If she dies, I'll never forgive you!' Daisy launched across the waiting-room, her pretty face swollen and distraught with tears. 'Have you any idea how dangerous acute appendicitis is at this stage of her pregnancy? They *have* to operate but she might lose the baby! And if she loses that baby, Angelo, I'll never forgive you for that either!'

'Daisy... Daisy,' Tomaso soothed, tugging his almost hysterical wife into his arms. 'Angelo didn't come here for this——'

'Why did he come?' Daisy sobbed into his shoulder. 'What's he doing here *now*?'

'Today Kelda's two closest friends got married,' Angelo informed her tightly. 'That's why I'm here.'

Daisy surveyed him with blank incredulity. 'What has that got to do with anything?'

Kelda came back to consciousness in a strange room. Her throat was unbearably dry and her head ached and she was dully aware that she could feel a different kind of pain now. Thankfully no longer severe, the pain had been reduced to throbbing discomfort instead. There was a nurse bending over her. She focused on her with difficulty. 'Where am I?'

'The recovery-room.'

'Am I recovered?' she mumbled ungrammatically.

'We hope so.'

'My baby?' Kelda whispered shakily, suddenly terrified.

'Hanging in there like a Trojan.' The nurse smiled and blurred again.

The next time Kelda surfaced, she felt a little less removed from the world. Her mother was holding her hand and a nurse was taking her blood-pressure. 'What happened to me?' she whispered.

In a voice thickened by tears, her mother explained. 'Why didn't you go to the doctor?' Daisy scolded finally.

'I meant to.'

'Tomaso wants you to see Angelo,' her mother volunteered reluctantly.

'A-Angelo?' Kelda echoed, attempting to sit up and being firmly pressed back down again by the clucking nurse. 'What's *he* doing here?'

'Do you want to see him?'

Kelda shut her eyes tightly, an expression of weary pain crossing her drawn features. 'No... please, no.'

Kelda turned her face to the wall when she was alone again. Angelo? The very last person she had any desire to see when she was weak and in pain and quite frankly at the end of her tether. What was he doing here? And how dared Tomaso ask her to see him! In the cause of family unity, she supposed and she could see the point of that, even agree with his motivation but *now* was not the time to expect her to rise gracefully above selfish human feelings.

Later, she promised herself, later when she was feeling better and she could congratulate Angelo on his engagement and hopefully *mean* it. Right now, she needed time, time to adjust to that new set of circumstances and detach herself from the milling turmoil of her own confused emotions. And there was no doubt that she was desperately confused. She had honestly believed that she had her emotions under control... she had believed that she had come to terms with the complete impossibility of any relationship with Angelo... she had believed in that acceptance right up until the moment she saw that diamond on Isabel Dunning's hand.

Then her self-deception had been smashed. She had not merely been shocked, she had been agonised by the extent of her own pain and an unexpectedly fierce sense of rejection. And she *had* to learn how to handle those feelings. Her pregnancy had divided the family circle in two. For the past five months Angelo had smoothly avoided her, and their parents had made that relatively easy for them. But that could not go on for much longer without imposing intolerable strain upon Tomaso and Daisy. Somehow, some way, Kelda knew she had to face up to the situation and finally settle it.

In the middle of the night, the staff allowed her to have a cup of tea and a small piece of toast. When the door on her private room widened, she barely glanced up because the nurses had been in and out constantly throughout the night, checking up on her. She focused on a pair of male trousered legs and slowly angled her head back against the pillow. Her heart jumped into her mouth.

'I persuaded them to let me in,' Angelo revealed in a taut, uncharacteristic rush as though he was determined to get in first vocally. 'I've been here all day.'

He was poised just inside the door and, if she stared, it was because she didn't know Angelo like this. Badly in need of a shave, crumpled, tousled and very pale. Harsh lines of strain were grooved between his nose and mouth. His lustrous dark eyes were curiously unguarded as they rested on her. He released his breath in an audible hiss and his dark gaze wandered slowly and almost carefully over her.

'I don't want you here,' she whispered, and closed her eyes, shutting him out.

'I needed to see you...' The admission was rough-edged.

'Why?' she sighed.

'How can you ask me that?' he demanded in an incredulous undertone, abruptly sounding more like himself. 'The child you carry is *mine*——'

Kelda's lashes lifted. She studied him in sudden sharp distress, her every muscle tensing as though she was under attack. 'Where did you get that idea?'

'Well, certainly not from you,' Angelo responded with fierce emphasis.

'I don't know what you're talking about,' she said weakly, playing for time, wondering in despair if in the heat of her collapse Tomaso and Daisy had betrayed their knowledge.

'How could you think you could get away with a lie like that?' Angelo demanded in a low-pitched growl.

'Sooner or later, I would have found out. Russ Seadon and Gina Delfont are your two closest friends. You have never been involved with Seadon. Your name has never been linked with his and yesterday you played a starring role in their wedding.'

'And where did you get all this information?' she prompted unsteadily.

'Her bloody dress featured on the lunchtime news!' Angelo launched at her with sardonic bite. 'I was already trying to get hold of you yesterday when my father called me to tell me that you were in hospital. Don't try to tell me that you were sleeping with Seadon five months ago behind your best friend's back...I wouldn't believe you!'

'I never said that Russ was the father of my child,' Kelda muttered shakily.

'But you repeatedly denied that *I* was,' he reminded her doggedly. 'And that night at your apartment when he came out of the bedroom, you made no attempt to explain the situation——'

Kelda turned her face to the wall, filled by sudden expected guilt for the scene she had sprung on him. Apparently he had as yet no suspicion that she had deliberately manufactured that scene. That knowledge would have told him just how vulnerable she had felt herself to be all those months ago. But how long would it take for him to recall Russ's exact behaviour that night? Russ had not acted like a platonic friend.

'Why *should* I have tried to explain the situation?' she enquired, still unable to meet his eyes.

'If you cannot answer that, I refuse to answer it for you,' Angelo responded with a dark, driven bitterness that burned. 'The night I came to the cottage——'

'You came through the door in a rage!' Kelda condemned with equal bitterness. 'And you wanted me to deny that I was pregnant——'

'I did not behave rationally that night,' Angelo breathed tautly.

'Actually I think you were very rational,' Kelda muttered flatly, unable to look at him although she could feel his enervating presence with every fibre of her body. 'The very idea of my being pregnant with your child was your worst nightmare come true. You accused me of deliberately trying to set you up——'

'In the heat of temper,' Angelo inserted with raw emphasis. 'Try to put yourself in my position!'

'No, thank you. I'm more concerned with my own,' she said honestly. 'It would have saved everyone a lot of trouble if I'd been able to stick to the stranger-at-a-party fiction. I'm afraid I just wasn't prepared to be faced with the fact that your father knew we had been in Italy together.'

'The idea of your being pregnant with my child would not have been my worst nightmare come true...' Angelo stated flatly, unemotionally, as if he had all his feelings under strict lock and key.

The silence stretched. Kelda made no comment. She didn't believe him. Now that he knew the truth, he felt that he had to defend himself from such a charge.

'I find it very hard to accept that all these months everyone *but* me has known the truth,' Angelo continued grimly. 'How did you prevail upon my own father to keep quiet?'

'He saw you in the conservatory with Fiona and, being slightly more sensitive than you are capable of being, understood why I had no wish for you to know.' As she spoke, she rolled her head on the pillow, fixing huge shadowed green eyes on him with unhidden scorn.

Dark colour had sprung up in a line over his striking cheekbones. He had the rail at the foot of the bed between his lean hands and so fierce was the grip that she could see the whiteness of his knuckles shining through his brown skin. 'How could I have known you were pregnant?' It was a rare plea for understanding.

'You didn't much care either way,' Kelda retorted, fighting against the tremendous tiredness sweeping over her.

'That isn't true,' he argued rawly.

'It really doesn't matter now.' Her weary voice slurred the syllables, her eyelids lowering without her volition. 'All water under the bridge, not worth tussling about——'

'Not *worth*——?' Angelo bit off whatever he had intended to say with visible difficulty. 'How can you say that? If you had been alone at the cottage today, you would have died and my child with you!' he said with restrained ferocity, incandescent golden eyes flaming over her pale but now intent face. 'It was the merest good fortune that you collapsed in a public place. So don't tell me that what I feel now doesn't matter!'

He had shaken her, but still her long feathery lashes drifted down. She shifted uncomfortably on the pillows, her hair trapped below her shoulders. Somebody gently slid a hand beneath her spine and tugged the recalcitrant strands of red-gold across her slight shoulders. 'Thanks,' she mumbled, and slept.

After breakfast the next morning, the flowers were delivered. Great drifts of headily scented blooms that filled half a dozen vases and brightened her smart but serviceable surroundings. Her first visitor was her mother.

Daisy was wreathed with smiles. 'I see Angelo's flowers have arrived.'

'Angelo? I assumed you——'

'Well, I was going to, but when I overheard Angelo ordering them on the phone I decided to leave it to another day.'

Kelda, propped up against her banked pillows, was rigid. 'Why would Angelo send me flowers?'

Daisy opened her eyes very wide. 'Can you think of anyone else with more reason?'

'Reason? What reason?' Kelda demanded shakily.

Her mother sat down. 'When Tomaso called Angelo yesterday and told him that you were having emergency surgery, I was angry. When Angelo arrived, I was very upset... well, I said some pretty unforgivable things,' Daisy confided. 'All these months, you've been alone and he's been running round like Casanova——'

Kelda bit the soft underside of her lower lip and tasted blood.

'But here in this hospital yesterday, Angelo was distraught,' Daisy asserted quietly. 'Really, genuinely frantic with worry about you and the baby. I've never seen Angelo like that before. I never realised how emotional Angelo really is underneath the cool front. Tomaso always said he was but I have to admit that I thought that was the fond father talking. Well, as you can imagine, while we were waiting to hear how your surgery had gone, it was a very tense time——'

'Yes?' As her mother's delivery slowed up, Kelda prodded her on, prickles of foreboding tightening her muscles.

'We didn't interfere.' Daisy had stood up again, clearly becoming uncomfortable under the onslaught of her daughter's strained gaze. 'But when it emerged that you had actually told Angelo that your baby *wasn't* his, well, naturally Tomaso and I were very shocked——'

'Naturally,' Kelda repeated in a flattened whisper.

'How could you lie to him like that?' Her mother asked without comprehension. 'We tried to accept that you were both adults and that you knew what you were doing but of course we assumed that, when your pregnancy started to show, Angelo would hear about it and go to see you and things would be sorted out. Thank goodness, Angelo had enough intelligence to realise that you had been lying——'

'Clever Angelo,' Kelda muttered tightly, thinking that she would be hearing about Saint Angelo next. She was now the baddie in this scenario. Angelo now stood absolved of all insensitivity towards her plight in recent times. Then their parents were so innocent. They did not have a clue that Angelo's sole ambition seven months ago had been to buy her into bed and establish her as his mistress.

'I want what's best for you and the baby,' Daisy emphasised.

'I already have what's best,' Kelda said woodenly.

'Angelo had breakfast with us and then he went to bed for a couple of hours. He'll be in later. He says that you're getting married——'

'Does he indeed?' Kelda's pale complexion was consumed by hot colour. Angelo says...her mother had reeled that off with the same naïve faith as she so frequently resorted to 'Tomaso says...' When the males in Daisy's life spoke, she endowed them with oracle-like brilliance.

'I can't tell you how happy we are——'

'He hasn't asked me yet.' Kelda pushed out the admission through clenched teeth.

Her mother's gentle eyes rested rather unfortunately on the swell of Kelda's stomach and then flicked up to her daughter's burning face. 'You're hardly going to say no, are you?' she said, not with satire but with gentle conviction that no woman in Kelda's position could possibly say no to a respectable proposal.

'Mother, Angelo has just got engaged to Isabel Dunning——'

'Don't be silly. Isabel is engaged to his personal assistant, Roger Bamford,' Daisy contradicted with amusement. 'Actually Roger isn't his PA now. Angelo promoted him and now the Dunnings are a bit happier about accepting Roger into the family.'

Wide green eyes blinked at her bewilderment. 'But——'

'All's well that ends well,' Daisy murmured cheerfully, determined to ignore her daughter's response to the good news.

Kelda gritted her teeth and said nothing. It didn't matter whether Angelo was engaged or not. It made no difference. She was outraged that Angelo could calmly inform their parents that they were getting married without even mentioning the idea to her first. It was a subtle form of blackmail and not one which would profit him. She had not the smallest intention of being married off for the sake of appearances.

It was late afternoon when Angelo strolled in. Superbly turned out in a navy suit complete with fitted waistcoat and chain, he looked dressed to kill. He also looked so gorgeous that the nurse, engaged in taking Kelda's blood-pressure, kept on pumping and nearly cut off the blood supply to her patient's arm. Frozen with frank admiration, she stared.

'How are you?' Angelo asked in his rich, slightly accented drawl.

Something wild quivered momentarily deep down inside Kelda as she collided with his clear golden eyes. Resolutely she suppressed it as the nurse took her reluctant leave. 'Fine.'

'We'll get married as soon as you are out of here,' Angelo imparted with studied casualness.

Silence...cue for applause, she wondered or was he expecting her to leap from her hospital bed and embrace his knees with gratitude.

Like someone engaged in a high-rolling poker game, Angelo's keen gaze probed her exquisite face. 'We'll stick it out for about six months after the baby's born,' he murmured silkily. 'Then we'll have one or two loud disagreements. You could possibly contrive to run home to Mummy once or twice. We separate...we divorce but on a civilised basis, pleading mutual incompatibility. The family will be disappointed but two priorities will have been met. The baby will have my name and everyone will be happy. What do you think?'

CHAPTER NINE

KELDA, trapped humiliatingly between rage and disbelief, had found herself hanging helplessly on his every word. Sizzling emerald eyes rested on his starkly handsome dark features. 'Do you really want to know what I think?'

'I do appreciate that this has come as something of a surprise,' Angelo fielded with teeth-clenching arrogance and the most extraordinary smile playing about his sensual mouth. 'So, I'll leave you to mull it over, shall I?'

With a blind, shaking hand, Kelda swiped the vase of flowers off the bedside cabinet and threw it at him with a strength born of uncontrollable rage. That he neatly sidestepped the deluge did nothing to calm her down. 'You take your flowers, your bloody priorities and your proposal and get out!' she shrieked at the top of her voice. 'I didn't want to be your mistress but I want to be your wife even less and that's saying something! If you got down on your knees and begged for the next twenty years, I wouldn't say yes... so go and ask Adele or Caroline or Felicity... and don't forget Fiona! She does for conservatories what Jayne Mansfield did for sweaters!'

'I'll come back this evening,' Angelo drawled, astonishingly unconcerned by the reception he had received.

'Get out of here,' Kelda raged at him, 'and don't you dare come back!'

Sobbing with a wild mixture of emotions, Kelda was crawling awkwardly about the floor, picking up flowers, when the nurse came in. It hurt, and that only made her angrier.

'Miss Wyatt!' the nurse gasped. 'What are you doing out of bed?'

'Don't let that man in here again!' Kelda hissed, letting herself be assisted back into bed. 'I can't stand him!'

'Was it something he said?'

'Yes...no...oh, I don't know!' Kelda subsided in a damp heap, exhausted by her own loss of control.

'He couldn't have meant it,' the little nurse said shyly. 'My friend told me that he spent half of last night in the chapel. He must have been praying for you.'

Angelo, praying? Kelda could not imagine Angelo praying. She sniffed, had a tissue thrust helpfully into her hand. She had been propositioned with a divorce and even though she would not have agreed to marrying him in any circumstances that had been particularly hurtful.

What did it matter if the baby had his name? Why should she have to consider other people's happiness when she was so wretchedly unhappy herself? And to suggest that putting their parents through the distress of watching their fake marriage disintegrate within months was kinder than never marrying at all was ridiculous! She wanted to be open and honest. No more deception. How dared he expect her to agree to such a proposal...how dared he?

Angelo strolled in after tea as though nothing had happened. Kelda couldn't believe her eyes. He had shed his formal suit. In an oatmeal sweater that highlighted his darkness and close-fitting black jeans that hugged his lean muscular thighs, he looked soul-destroyingly spectacular.

Excitement burned through her nerve-endings, speeding up her heartbeat and sending her pulse-rate racing. She drew in a sharp, deep breath, battling in alarm against the surging tide of dangerous physical awareness.

'This morning I believed that I was suggesting the only kind of marriage that you would even consider,' Angelo imparted with unalloyed cool. 'I know how you feel about me.'

Kelda pushed unsteady hands in a raking motion through her torrent of curls. 'Do you?'

'Why didn't you tell me that Russ Seadon was getting married to your best friend?' he asked without warning.

She tilted her chin. 'Would you have believed me?'

'I don't think that's why you didn't choose to enlighten me,' Angelo fielded. 'I think you felt cornered and he was a good excuse to employ when I jumped to the wrong conclusion.'

'I didn't need an excuse. It wasn't important enough for me to feel I should explain myself,' Kelda told him carelessly.

A muscle jerked beside his unsmiling mouth. 'You didn't care what I thought?'

'It wasn't anything different from what you've thought so often before.'

'But these days you don't mind actually encouraging me to misjudge you... in fact, you get something of a high out of it!'

The condemnation roused colour in her cheeks.

Angelo scrutinised her with impassive eyes. 'And when he strolled out on to centre stage in that towel it was just too convenient for words...'

Every muscle in her body tensed. Striving to look blank, she stared back at him.

'You asked him to play ham, didn't you? It was prearranged,' Angelo essayed

Kelda decided defiance was the better part of valour. 'So what if I did? I wanted you out of my life again!'

He was pale beneath his bronzed skin, his dark eyes hooded. 'Game-playing is dangerous in relationships, *cara*.'

'I wouldn't dignify what we shared with the label of "relationship",' Kelda responded tightly. 'Men like you don't have relationships with their mistresses.'

'*Dio*...I've never had a mistress!' Angelo slashed back at her with sudden frustration. 'Do you remember cutting me dead that first night? Do you remember challenging me later in your apartment? Do you remember letting me believe that you would continue to come between our parents? Or was all that my imagination?'

Kelda had stiffened under attack. 'No but——'

'You drove me over the edge that night and you meant to do it,' he condemned.

'I certainly didn't ask to be lured out to Italy——'

'Where you had a hell of a good time in spite of all your complaints——'

'I did not enjoy being arrested and locked up!'

'But you had no complaints about what followed,' Angelo murmured softly.

That was unarguable. He had hit her on her weakest flank. Involuntarily she reddened, her undisciplined mind suddenly awash with erotic recollections. She bent her head. 'I have no desire to talk about that——'

'*That* is unfortunate, considering that your present—condition,' he selected smoothly, 'relates to mutual passion and an outstanding lack of common sense.'

'Is the lack of common sense laid at my door or yours?' she sniped hotly.

'I should think entirely at mine,' Angelo sighed, languorous dark eyes uncomfortably intent on her. 'Considering that I was the idiot who grossly over-estimated the extent of your sexual experience——'

Kelda very nearly dropped the glass of water in her hand. Her head shot up, fiery hair springing back from her disconcerted face.

Angelo dealt her a searching glance and then strolled gracefully over to the window. 'In Italy, I was still hung up on six years of bitterness. Your near-death experience yesterday may not have done much for you but, believe me, it focused my intelligence as never before on all the inconsistencies between rumour and reality. And the reality is that you have not had that many lovers...'

Kelda was appalled by what he was saying. Her brittle front of sophistication and bitchiness was her sole defence against Angelo. And he was coolly ripping it to shreds. Yet her pride depended on that front. She could not bear the idea that Angelo should even come close to suspecting that she was less experienced with men than he had assumed.

'And even now, when we have so many more *important* matters to deal with,' Angelo essayed drily, 'you're wondering how to overturn my assumptions because I have come painfully close to blowing your mystique right out of the water! In my opinion, you hadn't had a recent lover and I assume that you were not taking any contraception either——'

'Contraception fails sometimes,' Kelda responded with rich sarcasm.

Angelo shot her a glittering glance of naked perception. 'You may be the most passionate woman I have ever shared a bed with, but a woman who slept around with the generosity you suggest would have demonstrated practised skills that you did not——'

Her humiliation plumbed new depths. Her eyes blazing, her generous mouth flattened into a strained line, she snapped, 'Shut up!'

Angelo ignored the invitation. 'And because I rejoice in being equally obstinate, I persisted in holding on to my original opinion of your character even in the face of overwhelming evidence to the contrary.'

'Have you finished?'

Angelo took a deep breath and then swore. 'I am trying to say sorry, but you don't make that easy.'

Sorry was even less welcome than the most base of insults from his corner. Kelda ground her teeth together. 'Sorry for what?'

'For all this.' Angelo spread lean brown hands wide with in-bred elegance of movement. 'It's all my fault. I started it——'

'Finished it——' Kelda heard herself remind him.

'It didn't finish for me,' Angelo surveyed her with unreadable hooded eyes, his attention sliding almost compulsively to the visible swell of her abdomen beneath the bedclothes. 'And it isn't finished for you either.'

Kelda dealt him an outraged stare. 'Stop looking at me like that!'

'I like looking at you now...now that I know the baby is mine,' Angelo proffered without a shade of embarrassment. 'Five months ago that baby seemed like an unbridgeable barrier between us. But now it is a link that nothing can break. I wish you could have told me the truth then. If you had, I would have been with you. I never thought of having a child before but, since yesterday, I haven't been able to think of anything else.'

The truth of that confession was blatant. Kelda, hectically flushed, raised her knees slightly and rearranged the bedding to conceal the evidence of her fertility as best she could. A link that nothing could break, he said. She had refused to appreciate that fact before.

'Don't you think that for the sake of the baby we could live together?' Angelo demanded with sudden unconcealed impatience.

'Certainly not. I couldn't stand it!' she slung back at him, hot moisture scalding her eyelids.

'I offered the divorce as what you might term a sweetener to the deal,' Angelo admitted.

'Some sweetener!' Kelda muttered, pleating the sheet with restive fingers.

'You wouldn't need to feel trapped. I would give you a divorce at any time if you asked for one——'

'Angelo, when I want a discreetly unfaithful rich husband in place of my peaceful independence and freedom, I'll advertise! The idea of marrying you,' Kelda framed, fighting the tremor in her thickened voice, 'well, it appeals to me about as much as twenty years of hard labour in a swamp with no time off for good behaviour.'

Angelo had moved forward. The atmosphere vibrated with tension. Refusing to be inhibited by his proximity, Kelda surveyed him with a provocatively curled lip.

'With you in my bed, I would not be unfaithful.'

Kelda sent him a winging glance of forced amusement although her spinal cord had tightened up another notch. 'But I'm not going to be in your bed ever again, Angelo.'

'You want to lay a bet on that?' Angelo sank down on the edge of her bed, shimmering golden eyes ruthlessly pinned her. 'I look at you and you burn. I touch you and you go up in flames. You carry my child inside you. If I branded you with my name, you couldn't be more mine!'

'You arrogant sw——' Kelda began to spit.

Angelo reached for her in one powerful movement. Deftly angling his body to one side so that he would not hurt her, he took her mouth in a devouring kiss that she felt right down to her toes and back up again. She reacted like a woman possessed. With one hand she hit out at him in blind rage, but the other hand inexplicably dived into the springy depths of his hair, holding him to her.

He kissed her breathless. Great rolling waves of excitement overwhelmed her. The hand that had balled into a fist uncurled and slid under his sweater instead and exulted in the satin-smooth skin of his back before sliding across his taut flat stomach to rake into the furrow of silky hair that disappeared beneath his belt.

Angelo jerked violently against her and grabbed her hand, pushing her fingers in an unrestrained expression of need down to the thrust of his hard thighs. He groaned, swore against her mouth, momentarily stiffened as though he was striving to will himself into a withdrawal, and then gathered her fully into his arms with a stifled sound of all male satisfaction.

A loud knock sounded on the door. Angelo sprang off the bed, drove an unsteady hand through his wildly tousled black hair and shot Kelda a glittering glance of mingled frustration and grudging amusement.

Kelda was stricken when Daisy and Tomaso strolled in.

Her stepfather dealt both of them a satiric smile. 'I assume that congratulations are in order.'

'I should think so too,' Daisy teased.

Kelda could feel a painful flush engulfing her skin. Evidently the knock that had been heard had not been the first interruption. She remembered her stepfather saying that he wouldn't trust either of them in the same room for an hour. She remembered the last time they had been surprised on a bed. She burned hotter than ever.

'Congratulations would be premature,' Angelo delivered lazily.

'Kelda!' Her mother exclaimed reproachfully.

'It's my decision.' Embarrassed as she was, Kelda was still strong enough not to be browbeaten by opinion into a corner.

'I want to talk to Kelda alone,' Daisy asserted sharply.

'I don't think that would be a good idea,' Angelo intervened on her behalf, startling her.

The visit was short and sweet. Daisy, whose quiet temperament was only rarely stirred to anger, waited until Angelo had walked out of the door with his father before darting back and positively hissing, 'In my day, you married a man you couldn't keep your hands off...at least if you were lucky enough to be free! You're cutting off your nose to spite your face. I'm sorry but I have to say it. If I don't, who else will?'

'Me?'

Kelda jerked and her mother spun in dismay. Angelo cast them both a slow, splintering smile that did something utterly unforgivable to Kelda's already shaken composure. Daisy reddened and went into retreat.

Angelo studied Kelda from the foot of the bed. 'I'll see you tomorrow.'

'There's no point. I don't want you visiting me.'

When the door closed behind him, she felt incredibly, childishly lonely. She lay back and the baby chose that moment to kick and squirm. She smoothed a possessive and tender hand over her stomach. It was so stupid to love Angelo! If it had been within her power, she would have torn that love out brutally by the roots. She had tried to do that in recent months, had thought she was on the road to recovery...had learnt her mistake all over again.

Angelo was ruthlessly set on building bridges to pave the bridal path, but she couldn't marry him. He didn't seem to realise that no woman with any pride wanted to be married *solely* because an unplanned baby was on the way. Times had changed since her mother's day. Women didn't have to be forced into marriage to save their reputations any more.

Tomaso had undoubtedly made Angelo feel that he *had* to marry her. That was so degrading. She didn't need that pressure. She resented Angelo for giving way to such old-fashioned attitudes but, dismayingly, she suddenly realised that she would resent him even more if he ever chose to marry anyone else. And that was far from a logical attitude considering that she was not prepared to marry him herself.

She found her thoughts returning several times over to something that her mother had said. One of those careless statements which people made in temper without realising how much they were revealing. Daisy had said that in her day you married a man you couldn't keep your hands off...at least if you were lucky enough to be free!

There had been a bitter edge to that assurance. Kelda was shaken when she realised what she had found so disturbing about those words. They were her mother's acknowledgement that once she had been attracted to someone while she was married. Or had they been an acknowledgement of something more than mere attraction? Kelda frowned, angry with herself for thinking in such a way of her own mother. Her mother had adored her father, absolutely adored him, she reminded herself.

Angelo arrived the next day with magazines, books and two boxed sets of nightwear. 'You have no right to buy me that sort of stuff,' she objected.

'Relax . . . Harrods maternity department inspired me with no improper thoughts.'

'Maternity department?'

'I hate to tell you this, but you wouldn't make it into anything that didn't come from that department.'

She saw the size on the uppermost box and almost choked on her chagrin. It would have fitted an elephant, never mind a pregnant size eight. Her bottom lip wobbled. Her throat tightened. She studied her stomach with loathing and burst into floods of tears. 'Go away and leave me alone!' she sobbed.

'What did I say?' Angelo endeavoured to put his arms round her but she pulled away.

'Nothing!'

He got a nurse. The nurse came in to soothe, couldn't resist trying to interest her in the contents of the boxes and lifted out the enormous négligé set. 'Is this for you?' she demanded in a choked voice and went off into gales of laughter. 'Didn't anyone tell him that you buy the same size in maternity wear as you wore before you expanded?'

Kelda sat up and blew her nose. 'It would fit an elephant.'

'It would fit two elephants!' She called in two of the other nurses. Kelda's bed was swiftly surrounded by giggling women, bonded by the joy of sheer male ignorance. Kelda began laughing so hard it hurt. She was picturing Angelo in the maternity department, Angelo, who was quite incapable of acknowledging ignorance in any form.

Daisy offered to change them that afternoon. Kelda thought Angelo might visit her again in the evening. He didn't. She thought he might phone. He didn't. Since she had taken the trouble to put on one of the night-dresses, a now correctly sized version courtesy of her mother, she was irritated. She had wanted to share the joke with him. That was all, she told herself, watching the television with flat, disappointed eyes.

She waited for him in the morning. He didn't show. When Tomaso and Daisy rolled up, she was tempted to ask where he was but she fought the temptation. She didn't want to risk rousing the suspicion that she cared whether he came to visit or not. She didn't care. It was just that lying flat on her back with very little exercise was boring and, whatever other faults Angelo had, being boring was not one of them.

She drifted off into a doze at about ten and then a slight sound awakened her. Angelo was poised at the foot of the bed in a dinner jacket and bow-tie. Oddly enough, the sight was like a red rag to a bull. Kelda sat up. 'Where the hell have you been?' she demanded fiercely.

'You missed me...you noticed I wasn't there?' Angelo launched a sizzlingly provocative smile at her, dark eyes glinting like polished jet over her angry face.

'I did not miss you!'

'Obviously you did.'

'I'm stuck in here while you're out there enjoying yourself,' Kelda slung mutinously. 'That makes me sick!'

'My visit upset you so much yesterday, I decided to give you some space,' Angelo revealed flatly.

'Where were you tonight?' She *had* to know. She couldn't get past that raging need to know where he had been and who he had been with.

'At a charity dinner, full of long overblown speeches and pompous old windbags.'

Unexpectedly, she laughed. She told him about the mistake he had made with the lingerie. It was almost the first time she had ever seen Angelo look embarrassed. Suddenly uneasy with the sense of intimacy she was experiencing, she fell silent.

'You're doing it again...shutting me out,' he breathed with a raw edge to his voice. 'I hate it when you do that.'

'I keep on waiting for you to turn on me again.' She had not meant to be that honest but somehow the admission slid out.

He tensed, paled, dark eyes veiling as he paced restively across the room. 'It's taken me a long time but believe me...I've changed. Unfortunately for you, my misconceptions about your temperament were set in concrete that night six years ago——'

Kelda froze in dismay. 'I don't want to talk about that.'

'You had to almost die before I could be forced into facing the truth,' Angelo vented harshly. 'I was afraid of finding myself in a relationship which I couldn't control. I know what that did to my father. I was determined that no woman would do to me what my mother did to him. It was easier to walk away from you than stay...'

Kelda tore her eyes from his clenched profile, knowing what that confession of vulnerability must have cost him.

'Six years ago, I lost control,' he admitted fiercely. 'I overreacted that night. I was hardly an unprejudiced bystander. Even had you been making love with that boy, you would only have been doing what teenagers do, given the opportunity. No, I was brutal with you because I wanted you for myself and the sight of you with that boy drove me crazy——'

'Angelo——'

He cut in on her. 'I was almost twenty-six and you were eighteen. It was almost a year since I had seen you. I had deliberately stayed away. And I came home with such high hopes——'

'What kind of hopes?' She was remembering the way he had looked at her before that ghastly party, his unfamiliar warmth...the compliment.

'I thought that finally I might have a chance with you. Until then, I had had to repress everything I felt around you. Telling myself that I would marry you didn't make me any less ashamed of feeling like that. If you hadn't been so naïve, you would have guessed why I never, ever touched you in any way. You would have questioned the extent of my interest in your education and the amount of freedom you were allowed.'

'I didn't,' she whispered dazedly.

'I have a jealous, possessive streak a mile wide,' Angelo admitted grimly. 'Every time you went out of the door, I went through hell. I knew you ought to have all the normal adolescent experiences but I didn't want you to have them. That's why I had to leave for that year but that night, seeing you with that boy...I went off at the deep end. And now I have to live with the knowledge that you were almost raped. I not only added to your distress by my accusations but also gave way to my own animal instincts in a way which I deeply regret.'

Jealousy had been the source of his incomprehension that night. She saw that now so clearly. Almost immediately her memories of those fevered minutes in his arms were curiously cleansed of all humiliation and embarrassment. If she had been out of control, Angelo had been as well.

'I went to your room to make you listen to the truth, but somehow...' Kelda hesitated awkwardly.

'I opened my eyes and you were there. I thought you had come to me. I didn't remember what had happened earlier until afterwards...and then I believed that you had guessed how I felt and were taunting me,' he breathed savagely. 'But I should never have touched you. I had no excuse.'

Kelda plucked at the sheet. 'I enjoyed it. That devastated me.'

'Do you still feel that I'm about to turn on you?'

She didn't. But she didn't say so. Angelo had changed and she could not understand or even quite accept that Angelo could so suddenly revise his opinion of her. He had given her a completely clean sheet. A mean, jealous streak a mile wide, yes, well, she pondered helplessly, he hadn't been exaggerating on that count. She discovered that she had forgiven him for that night six years ago and that shook her.

But there was something so incredibly appealing about his acknowledgement about how he had felt about her then. True, it had only been rampant sexual desire but he had not intended to take advantage of her innocence. And the more he reminded her of that physical obsession, the more secretively secure she felt. In one sense, Angelo belonged to her. For more than six years, Angelo had continued to desire her. And for more than six years, Angelo, being Angelo, must have fought that hunger to the last ditch... yet still it persisted.

'I won't misjudge you again. I can safely promise you that.' Strong resolve hardened his dark features. 'You say you won't marry me. But have you thought about the future? Whether you like it or not, we'll have a child we have to share within a few weeks...'

Kelda swallowed with difficulty. 'Share?'

'Naturally I will expect to spend time with our child. Even the law would grant me visitation rights, but I doubt if either one of us wants or sees the need for legal intervention,' Angelo stated softly. 'The very existence of that child means that I will be a part of your life for years to come.'

Kelda studied her tightly linked hands. That aspect of the future hadn't occurred to her. Angelo was not disclaiming responsibility. Angelo was telling her up-front that he intended to be there in their lives. Shakenly, she attempted to envisage a purely platonic and civilised relationship with Angelo, the eventual introduction of his lovers into their child's life. Thousands of women had to endure similar situations for the sake of their children's security. But she *loved* Angelo. And Angelo had given her a choice. He had asked her to marry him.

'Couldn't you try being married to me?' Angelo proffered smoothly. 'Couldn't we at least give marriage a chance?'

'I don't want to get married because our parents think we should!' Kelda said.

Incredulity blazed in his eyes. 'What the hell do they have to do with it?' he demanded.

Kelda flinched. 'They want——'

'I'm talking about what I want,' Angelo emphasised drily. 'And I am long past the age of being influenced by what my father wants. Six years ago, he wanted me to marry you and I refused——'

'That night...' she registered with sudden understanding.

'Yes. All would have been instantly forgiven had I been willing to do what he saw as the "decent thing",' Angelo told her. 'But nobody makes me do anything I don't want to do.'

The assurance hung there in the throbbing silence.

'It wouldn't work,' she said tautly.

'How can you say that without giving it a chance?'

'Well, I can't, but how could it?'

'That doesn't mean we can't try. What does trying cost you?'

More pain, more hurt, but would it be any worse than watching him with other women, being forced to share her child with him whenever he made that demand? Wasn't she simply running scared? Riven with raw tension and uncertainty, she cast him an involuntary glance and surprised the same tension in him. He wanted her *and* he wanted the baby. Marriages had survived on considerably less.

'I am not going to beg,' Angelo slung at her.

'I'll marry you.' The instant she surrendered, doubts rushed in and her brow furrowed with anxious lines. 'After the baby's born——'

Angelo threw her a scorching look of anger. 'No!'

'Why not?'

'I'm not prepared to wait. You might change your mind.'

Her teeth ground together but she was very tired. Angelo, she registered, had a lot in common with water dripping on stone. He was incredibly persistent. She rested her head back. 'OK,' she muttered finally.

It was three weeks before Kelda was discharged from hospital. Her blood-pressure had for a time given cause for concern. Forty-eight hours after Tomaso and Daisy took her home with them, Angelo and Kelda were married in the small local church with only family present.

She found the ceremony curiously unreal. Once she had agreed to marry him, Angelo had visited her every day. He had done all the things expected of him. He had brought her gifts, filled her room with flowers and entertained her when her spirits were low. But in spite of that she felt as though he had distanced himself from her. There were no intimacies, no kisses, no hot looks. Angelo held himself aloof and Kelda, ever sensitive to the threat of rejection, was incapable of attempting to bridge the gulf opening up between them.

On their wedding day, she realised that she couldn't see her feet any more, but she told herself bracingly that that scarcely mattered. Angelo was clearly not attracted to very pregnant women. She could accept that, she could live with that, she assured herself. But the awareness that her sole attraction for Angelo was physical and that that sole attraction had vanished along with her feet and her once tiny waist made her feel more insecure than ever.

She wanted to shrink behind Angelo when they emerged from the church and discovered a barrage of cameras awaiting them. The media had finally found out about them and there was no greater joy for a tabloid than to publish pictures of a groom with an eight-month-pregnant bride, especially when the groom had been very publically romancing other women for most of that same pregnancy.

Kelda was trembling when they drove off in a chauffeur-driven limo. For the first time in her life she had felt threatened by a camera lens. Angelo covered her tightly gripped hands soothingly. 'A five-day wonder... they'll forget about us soon enough.'

But Kelda was too proud to forget how their marriage must look to outsiders. A shotgun wedding. She was annoyed that she had let Angelo pressure her into marrying him before the baby was born. Instinct told her that she would not have felt so threatened by the cameras had she regained her once lithe shape instead of resembling a barrage balloon in a horribly cutesy little maternity suit.

'Do you think so?' she breathed sharply. 'You've married down, not up. Working class girl makes good. The Press like that.'

'I rather think that I'm the one who has...made good,' Angelo countered.

Her teeth clenched. What did you do with a male who set your teeth on edge with exquisite courtesy and then refused to fight? Literally she gnashed her teeth.

'I hope you like Hedley Court.'

Angelo owned an Elizabethan manor. She had never seen it. All that had struck her about her future home was that it lay almost a hundred miles from London where Angelo necessarily spent the greater part of his time. He had an apartment in town. It would be very convenient for him, wouldn't it? A wife and a child a safe hundred miles away? Well if Angelo fondly imagined that he was going to turn her into a country weekend wife, who never saw him between Monday and Friday, he was in for a surprise.

She scrutinised the fine platinum band encircling her ring finger. Put there by Angelo, sealed by a cold kiss on her brow, the sort of a salute you gave to a child. You've been behaving like one all day, a little voice said drily. Insecurity made her nervous and abrasive.

Hedley Court looked spectacular in the crisp winter sunlight. Although it was late afternoon, the temperature had stayed below freezing all day and a white frost still iced the lawns and gilded the clipped yews. As Angelo assisted her out of the car, a cold wind made her shiver. He whipped off his jacket like a cavalier and draped it round her slight shoulders.

'Don't be silly,' she hissed. 'A puff of wind isn't likely to blow me away.'

'I wish we could have gone somewhere warmer for a few weeks.' Angelo pressed her across the gravel towards the front door.

Kelda stared blindly at the beautiful frontage of the Court with its mullioned windows. A trip abroad had been quite out of the question so late in her pregnancy. Her emerald eyes were overbright. She was mentally enumerating all the frills that had been shorn from her wedding day. A gown would have looked ridiculous and she was supposed to be taking things very easy, so a lot of guests and a reception had been ruled out on that count as well. Frankly, she suspected that Angelo had been grateful for an excuse to avoid a standard society wedding adorned by an enormously pregnant bride.

Without warning, Angelo bent and swept her off her feet.

'Put me down!' she shrieked in mortification, aware that she was no lightweight, waiting to hear him grunt with surprised effort.

'This is one tradition we can fulfil,' Angelo told her, carrying her across the threshold into a giant reception hall walled with linenfold panelling.

'It's beautiful!' Kelda craned her head back for a better view of the minstrels' gallery. 'When did you buy it?'

'My great-great-grandmother married into the original Hedley family——'

Kelda reddened. She was reminded that, unlike her, Angelo had a blue-blooded family tree. Angelo didn't have to *buy* his historic house in the country. He had probably inherited it.

'I remember coming here as a child.' He set her down gently at the top of the stone stairs. 'The Court eventually came to my mother. A great-uncle of mine lived here until his death a couple of years ago.' He showed her into a beautifully furnished bedroom. 'You should lie down for a while before dinner. You can meet the staff then. They appear to have beat a tactful retreat for our arrival.'

And then he was gone. It was a very feminine bedroom. Through a door she discovered a dressing-room that led into a marvellously sybaritic bathroom. She was checking through the empty wardrobes when her cases arrived and, with them, the housekeeper, Mrs Moss, who had clearly had no intention of waiting until dinner to meet Angelo's new bride.

When Kelda eventually lay down it was almost six. She was desperately tired but all she could think about was the absence of any male clothing in the wardrobes. This was not a room which Angelo intended to share with her.

Angelo made polite pleasant conversation over dinner until she wanted to scream. It was as if a glass wall divided him from her. She needed to smash it. Fingering her glass of mineral water, she cast him a glance from beneath her long feathery lashes.

'Which one were you going to settle on?' she asked softly.

Angelo elevated an ebony brow. 'Which what?'

'Adele or Felicity or Caroline or Fiona,' Kelda specified. 'Which one made the highest score?'

Lashes as long and thicker than her own dropped low over gleaming dark eyes. 'I find that rather a loaded question.'

'But a natural one to ask. After all,' Kelda breathed sweetly, 'you've spent the past six months auditioning potential brides, and I was never on the list even to begin with. Naturally I'm curious.'

Angelo leant back in his chair, his strikingly handsome features dispassionate and infuriatingly uninformative.

The silence gathered strength and Kelda refused to be intimidated by it.

'Adele had the best pedigree——'

'Only animals have pedigree.'

Kelda smiled with scorn. 'You were clearly shopping for a pedigree, Angelo. Every one of them was upper class and rich. None of them had had previous marriages. One worked in a museum. One worked in an art gallery. And one helped Mummy with her favourite children's charity——'

'Kelda——' he murmured warningly.

'Fiona was the only one with third-level education and a *real* career. Presumably she would have been too bright and too independent for the role. On the other hand, she was the most stunning-looking,' Kelda continued in the same chatty tone, ignoring the hardening line of his expressive mouth. 'Did you make love to all of them or none of them? And how does it feel to have decided exactly what you want in a wife and then have to come down to real basics and settle on one from a council estate?'

'Without your assistance tonight, I don't think I ever would have realised how desperately insecure you are,' Angelo drawled.

She froze as though he had slapped her.

'Does sniping at me make you feel any better?' he asked drily.

He hadn't answered her questions. She threw up her head in open challenge. 'As a matter of fact, it does!'

'I think you should go to bed.' Angelo rose gracefully from his chair. 'This conversation ends here.'

She sprang upright, her cheeks flaming. 'You haven't answered me!'

'And I'm not likely to. . . in the mood that you are in now.'

He walked out of the dining-room. She followed him to the door. 'We've only been married for eight hours and I'm bored stiff!' she flung.

He swung back, cast her a glittering, hard smile. 'I would hate to be the only one suffering.'

That hurt. That hurt much more than she could have believed. She cried herself to sleep. What had she wanted? What had she expected? Reassurance, tenderness, affection. Only a man in love would give her those responses. And Angelo didn't love her. It was their wedding-night, and because sex was out of the question he didn't bother coming near her at all. Eight hours and already she was wondering if she had made the greatest mistake of her life.

He apologised over breakfast. Very smoothly. In fact, he had a positive spring in his step and he smiled several times over nothing in particular. He told her that he would be back for dinner, reminded her yet again that he could be reached at all times by his mobile phone, and strode out to the helicopter that had arrived to pick him up.

He was less stiff over dinner that evening. For some reason, he was in an utterly charming mood. He suggested outrageous names for the baby, informed her that he was taking time off to accompany her to all her check-ups and dragged her upstairs to view the room he had decided would best suit as a nursery. They argued amicably about that. She went to bed that night, frantically wondering what had brought about his altered mood and hoping that it would last.

It did. Over the next three weeks, Angelo took part in every aspect of preparing for a new baby. He looked at the wallpaper books, wandered through nursery furniture displays and was quite touchingly astounded at the tiny size of newborn clothing.

Four days after that, Kelda went into labour. She did not initially appreciate that the increasing ache in her back was anything to worry about. By the time that she did, it was too late to give Angelo sufficient warning to get back from Glasgow, where he was involved with an international conference.

She gave birth at the local cottage hospital and not the fancy clinic Angelo had expected her to use. Her labour only lasted two hours and she was delighted, only slightly miffed when she heard the middle-aged midwife say something about 'good childbearing hips'! Angelo arrived long after the excitement was over.

'Don't you think you could have given me more warning?' he drawled from the threshold of her room.

'I didn't get much warning either.' She sat up, flushed and tired but consumed with pride. 'Look at her,' she demanded.

Angelo was very pale. He tiptoed over to the side of the cot and peered in. Their daughter chose that moment to squall. 'Terrific lungs,' he murmured, searching the tiny infuriated face. 'My hair, your nose...'

Her heart sunk. Was he searching for Rossetti genes? Was there still a shadow of doubt? Almost defensively, Kelda reached for her baby. 'She's got your eyes.'

'I suppose you didn't call me in time because you didn't really want me here,' Angelo asserted without a flicker of expression.

'There wasn't time!'

But she could see that he didn't believe her. And, if she was honest, she wouldn't have wanted him in the delivery-room. In the current state of their relationship, she would have shrunk from sharing something that intimate.

Was he disappointed that she wasn't a boy? He sank down on the edge of the bed and reached for a tiny hand, awkwardly traced a little froglike leg. He studied their child intently and wiped quite unselfconsciously at his dampened eyes. 'May I hold her?'

When he replaced her in the cot, he stared back at Kelda, fierce emotion unhidden in his golden gaze. 'No matter what happens between us in the future... thank you for her.'

Kelda had to bow her head to hide her tears. She had somehow expected him to put his arms around her, maybe even kiss her, but he didn't touch her at all. The only female in the room that Angelo couldn't keep his hands off weighed less than seven pounds, and if *she* cried she got instant attention. Kelda had never experienced a more savage sense of rejection.

CHAPTER TEN

'ALICE, my darling, you have it made!' Gina exclaimed, taking in the full glory of the nursery suite with astonished eyes. 'Is there anything you haven't bought this child yet, Kelda? A solid gold toothbrush in waiting for the first tooth?'

'Ask Angelo,' Kelda suggested rather tightly, returning her daughter to her four-poster cot. 'The world's biggest shopper at Hamley's.'

'And you're complaining? Some men don't want anything to do with their kids——'

'Nobody will ever angle that accusation at Angelo.'

'Do I sense a sour note in paradise?'

Kelda straightened with a fixed smile. 'No. Maybe I'm just a little tired.'

Gina giggled. 'Burning the candle at *both* ends?' she teased. 'New baby and a new marriage hardly out of the honeymoon phase. No wonder you've got shadows!'

Kelda forced a laugh. She wasn't tempted to weep on a friendly shoulder. The truth was so hideously humiliating. Alice was seven weeks old and their marriage hadn't even been consummated. Angelo had his bedroom; she had hers. No floorboards creaked in the middle of the night. Angelo clearly had his sights set on an annulment, rather than a divorce.

'If I didn't have Russ, I'd be green with envy!' Gina sighed helplessly. 'He's gorgeous, super-rich and crazy about Alice.'

Alice was all they shared. Alice was all they talked about in any depth. If Kelda hadn't adored her daughter with equal intensity, she would have been enduring agonies of jealousy. As it was, she felt disturbingly *used*. Angelo had wanted his child to carry his name. Angelo had wanted to ensure that he had maximum rights over that same child and those rights were only granted by the institution of marriage.

Angelo had persuaded her into marriage for very good reasons. But they all related to Alice. Kelda might have found it possible to forgive him for that to some extent had he not pretended that he wanted *her* equally. She felt sick inside when she recalled how much that belief had encouraged her to hope that they could have a real marriage. She had been so mortifyingly certain that Angelo found her ragingly desirable...until she married him. Now, she knew different.

And it was time she did something about it, she acknowledged unhappily. Time she took charge of her own future again. She had tried marriage to Angelo and she didn't like it. That was all she had ever promised to do. She did not need Angelo to survive. Ella Donaldson had called last month and had intimated that Kelda could virtually dictate terms for a new contract should she wish to enter the modelling world again.

Angelo was very entertaining over dinner. Russ and Gina were most impressed. Kelda's temper rose steadily throughout the meal. When she dined with Angelo alone, he was polite and distant. As soon as her friends had departed, Angelo strode off to the library which he used as an office. Five minutes later, Kelda decided to invade his privacy.

Angelo was not deep in work as she had expected. He was standing by the fireplace with a large whiskey in his hand, his darkly handsome features shadowed and taut.

'We need to talk,' Kelda said tightly, suppressing the sizzling leap of awareness which always consumed her near Angelo. In the past two months she had learnt to be ashamed of that sexual *frisson*.

He offered her a drink which she declined.

Kelda breathed in deeply. Pride demanded that she make the first move to the break. 'I think we should go for an annulment as soon as possible.'

'I beg your pardon?' Angelo said very quietly, narrowed dark eyes nailed to her with perceptible force.

Kelda wandered over to the window, her body tensing in response to the thickening atmosphere. 'Look, this isn't working for either of us,' she pointed out in a driven rush. 'I'll move out——'

'You take Alice from this house over my dead body,' Angelo spelt out dangerously softly.

'You can see as much of her as you like. I'll be going back to work anyway,' Kelda told him.

'Really?'

She flushed. 'Why the hell shouldn't I if I want to?'

'Country life too quiet for you?'

She was tempted to tell him that it was the nights. 'We don't have a real marriage,' she muttered jerkily.

'I can change that any time you care to ask.'

Kelda flinched from his sarcasm. 'I want an annulment and you can't stop me from getting one!' she stated, and walked hurriedly back out of the room and upstairs.

There it was done. He hadn't said much. Then Angelo liked to call his own shots. She had stolen his thunder. Doubtless he had planned for this farce to continue for a few more months. Dear lord, she conceded painfully, she had been so appallingly blind and trusting and stupid... and with Angelo of all people! Angelo was notorious for his calculating, brilliant moves on the international money market.

When he had first mentioned marriage, he had been honest. He had suggested a fake marriage to keep the family happy and give their child his name. A fake marriage and a convincing breakdown followed by separation and divorce. And how had she reacted? She had made it furiously clear that she would not even consider such a hypocritical deception. So Angelo had reinvented his case for marriage in terms calculated to win her acceptance.

She had fallen like a ton of bricks for that line because she loved him, and up until Alice's birth Angelo had played along. But from that same day, he had changed. Damp-eyed, Kelda slid into the cool embrace of her bed. Her thoughts were in frantic turmoil. Had Angelo actually believed that eventually she would get bored with motherhood and walk away, leaving Alice behind with him? Was that his ultimate goal?

He would acquire Alice, go for an annulment and then remarry someone more suitable. It was Machiavellian...it was Angelo. Since Alice's birth, he had been trying to freeze her out. All his emotional warmth was fully concentrated on their daughter. He had left Kelda out in the cold. As the door opened, she lifted her head and her emerald eyes opened to their fullest extent.

'Whatever we end up with, it won't be an annulment,' Angelo drawled silkily, glittering dark eyes raking her startled face.

He was wearing a black silk robe and nothing else. In one hand he had an uncorked bottle of champagne, two glasses in the other. Blinking bemusedly, Kelda simply stared as he deftly filled the glasses. He had settled one into her hand before she found her tongue again.

'What do you think you're doing in here?'

Angelo cast off the robe without a shade of inhibition. For a split-second her gaze was involuntarily welded to the lean, dark magnificence of his powerful physique. Hot colour drenched her complexion as he pushed back the sheet and slid gracefully into bed beside her.

'Angelo...'

He brushed his glass against hers. 'Say goodbye to months of sexual abstinence,' he murmured. 'If this is what you want, I am more than willing to oblige.'

'What *I* want?' She gave a sudden gasp of shock as he quite deliberately angled his glass over one pouting breast almost completely bared by the slipping sheet and let champagne drip over her heated flesh. 'A-Angelo!'

Her own glass dropped from her nerveless fingers and fell soundlessly on the floor.

'I would hate to think your boredom might extend to what I intend to do to you in bed,' Angelo breathed, hauling the sheet down with a determined hand and tipping her roughly back against the pillows.

'Stop it! I don't want this!' she cried, so shocked she had trouble framing the words.

'You've been gasping for it for weeks. You think I don't know that? Do you fondly imagine that I can't tell when a woman wants me?'

'You swine!' she launched, beside herself with rage and disbelief.

He bent his dark head and found the lush dampness of her nipple and her whole body jerked in electrified excitement. Her hands squeezed into fists as she fought the raw overload on her senses. It had been so long and she wanted him so badly. She could feel herself quaking on the edge of that wildness he had roused in her before. It was terrifyingly intense.

He followed the sweet trail of the champagne down over her quivering stomach and she made a sudden grab at his hair. 'No!'

But his hands were on her thighs and he had already discovered just how weak she really was. She was tender and damp.

'Evidently I wasn't the only one seething with silent lust over dinner,' Angelo murmured huskily, letting the tip of his tongue track the clenched muscles on her inner thigh until she trembled and shook and completely forgot that she was supposed to be fighting him off.

She shut her eyes, her heartbeat like a hammer pounding in her eardrums, and nothing existed but Angelo and what he was doing to her. She had never imagined...had never dreamt that she would let *anyone*...but she couldn't have stopped him, couldn't possibly have regained control of her shudderingly responsive body. He had devastated her with a depth of intimacy far beyond her limited experience and she was utterly overpowered by the incredible waves of pleasure.

She heard her own voice rising, heard herself moan his name over and over again and then her back arched and her teeth clenched and her wild cry of release was literally torn from her as he sent her plunging into a climax that blocked the whole world out for timeless minutes.

'Maybe you'll deign to smile at me over dinner tomorrow night,' Angelo said roughly, sliding up over her and taking her mouth with explosive passion.

He ground his hips into her pelvis, letting her know just how aroused he was while his tongue possessed her mouth in a raw imitation of a far more basic sexual union. Hard hands tugged her thighs apart and he lifted his head, golden eyes stabbing into glazed green as he thrust slowly into the quivering depths of her body.

He thrust deeper; she melted. He moved; she moaned.

'Bored?' Angelo demanded thickly.

The sole response he received was a panted attempt to breathe at the peak of the most unimaginable pleasure.

'Tell me you want me.' He rolled over, carrying her with him, and let his mouth enclose the engorged tip of one sensitive breast.

'All the time...oh, God, don't stop...!' she almost sobbed as he mercilessly stilled.

'No divorce.' A lean hand wound with painful thoroughness into the cascading tangle of her red hair.

'Angelo...' she pleaded.

'No divorce.'

'No divorce.' She would have done anything, said anything, sold herself into white slavery for the next half-century just for him to continue. Tuscany all those months ago could not have prepared her for the savage seduction of what he was now making her feel.

He made love to her with smouldering sensuality and wild passion. He drove her over the edge of ecstasy more than once, and when he finally took his own pleasure she buried her tear-stained face into the sweat-slicked muscularity of one powerful shoulder and clung, still shivering with tiny after-shocks.

'I hate to tell you this, but your mother was right,' Angelo murmured in a black velvet purr as she abstractedly pressed tiny kisses against whatever part of him was within reach as he shifted languorously against her. 'You can't keep your hands off me. Think of how humiliated you would feel as an ex-wife, still falling into my bed at every opportunity...'

Kelda froze, dragged from her sensual languor by sheer shock.

She collided with incandescent golden eyes as fierce as knives. 'And don't think I wouldn't take advantage,' Angelo drawled softly, savagely. 'I *would*. I'd be the wolf at your door, and every time I got you flat on your back I'd make you pay a hundred times over for the divorce. Does that prospect appeal to you?'

Shattered, she stared up at him, her blood chilling in her veins, pallor driving away her natural colour.

'I think we understand each other perfectly, *cara*.' Angelo scored a mocking forefinger along the reddened fullness of her lower lip. 'And since regular sex appears to be the key to that locked-tight, unforgiving little heart of yours, I don't think you'll have any complaints in the future.'

'Get out of here!' she launched, relocating her ready tongue.

Angelo reached out, switched off the lamp and reached for her with arms that brooked no argument. 'Any bed you occupy will also be occupied by me from now on.'

'I won't stand——'

'You'd be surprised what I can make you stand,' he whispered mockingly.

She was feeding Alice at six in the morning when he strolled into the nursery.

She felt ridiculously shy of him. He crouched down in front of her and ran a caressing thumb along the downy line of Alice's cheek. Her lustrous dark eyes swivelled and she gave an angry squawk round the bottle. Their daughter did not like to be disturbed when she was feeding.

Kelda was in turmoil. Yesterday she had been convinced that a separation was the only answer. Yesterday, she had believed that Angelo no longer wanted her. And then last night... well, last night had completely wiped out her every assumption. Angelo had destroyed any prospect of either of them seeking an annulment and had then gone on to ruthlessly delineate what would happen if she sought a divorce.

He had talked as though all she needed from him was sex. She reddened, wondered dismally if he found her abandonment and eagerness abnormal. He touched her and, frankly, everything else went out of the window. She felt enslaved by what he could make her feel both physically and emotionally. When he made love to her, it made her feel so *close* to him. She needed that closeness to survive.

'I'm going to Geneva. I'll be away until tomorrow evening,' he divulged. 'Start looking for a good nanny. If Alice has you all day, I expect to have you all night.'

She jerked as he sent a possessive hand skimming over a slender thigh, exposed by her carelessly parted robe.

'And at dawn,' Angelo added huskily.

'I thought you didn't think a nanny was——'

'I've changed my mind.'

It was the following morning that the sound of constantly ringing phones woke Kelda up from a sound sleep. She always went back to bed for a couple of hours after feeding Alice. After a quick shower, she went down for breakfast, dressed in a figure-hugging apple-green dress that made her feel like a million dollars. Green was also Angelo's favourite colour... dear lord, was she turning into a doormat?

The newspaper she normally read over breakfast was missing from the pile. As Mrs Moss came in with her coffee, she asked for it, and the instant she saw the older woman's strained face she knew that something was badly wrong.

'You want that one, Mrs Rossetti?' the older woman prompted unnecessarily.

'Yes.' Kelda frowned. 'Is something up, Mrs Moss?'

The housekeeper cleared her throat. 'Your mother phoned to say she was coming over straight away.'

A cold hand clutched at Kelda's heart. 'Why were the phones ringing?'

'Newspaper reporters, Mrs Rossetti... would you like me to disconnect them?'

'No...' Slowly Kelda stood up, her face as white as a sheet. Why was her mother coming over? Why hadn't her mother asked to speak directly to her? Her stomach churned with sick horror. Her mind rushed to burning visions of plane crashes and explosions and car accidents and Angelo starred in every disaster. 'Angelo...' she whispered. 'Has something happened to Angelo?'

'Good heavens, no!' Mrs Moss hurried to reassure her. 'It's just that dreadful newspaper, that's all!'

'Newspaper...what newspaper?' The one missing from the pile, she gasped, absolutely sick and weak-kneed with relief that whatever was wrong did not involve injury of any kind to Angelo. 'Could I see it, please?'

Something upsetting—hardly a new experience, she thought, watching the housekeeper's reluctant reappearance with the item. 'Thanks,' she said.

Mrs Moss looked even more tense. 'Your mother didn't want you to see it until she arrived...'

The front page was practically all headline. 'The Banker and the Bank-robber's daughter.' What a mouthful, she thought, until she focused incredulously on the photo beneath. It was a picture of Angelo and her on their wedding-day.

She began reading, her heart hammering sickly behind her breastbone. It hurt to breathe. She had to read every melodramatic sentence at least twice over to understand it. Shock was starting to take over. But it was complete and utter rubbish and she would sue, she told herself. Even Angelo would back her on that! How dared these vultures print such monstrous lies about her father! Her father had never been in prison in his life! Clearly they had got him mixed up with somebody else. Outrage began to take over from shock.

'K-Kelda?' She lifted her head from her taut stance by the table.

Her mother stood several feet away, her face a mask of distress. 'You've seen it?' She hesitated, her hands tightly clasped together. 'I am so sorry.'

'*Sorry?*' Kelda echoed in disbelief. 'What have you got to be sorry about? We'll sue! They're the ones who'll be sorry!'

'But it's true,' Daisy practically whispered. 'Every word of it is true.'

Kelda stared back at her mother, willing her to take that unbelievable statement back. 'Dad worked abroad on an oil-field,' she said drily.

Daisy flinched and tearfully shook her head. 'Tomaso was right. I should have told you the truth years ago. I should never have lied. Steve was in and out of prison practically from when you were born. He stole cars. He burgled houses. Of c-course,' she stammered painfully, 'he wasn't very good at it. He always got caught.'

Kelda couldn't stay upright any longer. It was like a nightmare. Her whole childhood was suddenly caving in beneath her feet. She collapsed down in a chair, trembling like a leaf and sick to her stomach.

'When you were a baby, I used to take you to visit him,' her mother told her. 'That was when I still thought he would go straight and I tried to be loyal and supportive. I was crazy about him at the beginning. He was so much fun, so handsome, so exciting. But every time he let us down again, a little bit of the love died——'

'Oh, God, no...' Kelda mumbled, totally devastated.

'You see, he didn't really mind prison with his mates. The sentences were always short. I used to plead with him. He used to make all these promises...but he always broke them. We moved all around the country. One new start after another. I was so ashamed. And then, when you were seven, Steve took part in a bank robbery,' Daisy told her shakily. 'A security guard was hurt. That was serious crime. He was put away for years...'

'But the letters!' Kelda suddenly shouted at her mother in a tempest of anger and humiliation. She refused to believe that what she was hearing could possibly be true.

'I didn't want you to know. You loved him so much.' Her mother shot her a pleading look. 'He loved telling you those stories. He had a terrific imagination. Don't you understand, Kelda?' Daisy sobbed. 'Steve was only nineteen when you were born and he never really grew up. He wanted so badly to keep on being your hero and that was the only way he could...'

Kelda covered her contorted face with both hands.

'I might as well tell you all of it,' her mother muttered grudgingly. 'I met Tomaso three years before your father died!'

Kelda bent her head and looked away in an agony of pain and rejection.

'For both of us, it was love at first sight. Tomaso wanted me to divorce Steve but I couldn't do that, not when he was locked away with nothing but us on the outside to live for. So I kept on visiting, kept on pretending that everything was all right,' Daisy shared wretchedly. 'But I couldn't stop seeing Tomaso. I tried to several times——'

'*You* were his mistress,' Kelda framed sickly, thinking of the time she had been told about the blonde Tomaso had been taking away to discreet country pubs for years. That blonde had been Daisy.

'No! I never ever took a penny of financial help from Tomaso!' Daisy protested vehemently. 'I *loved* him, Kelda, the way I think you love Angelo. And he was prepared to wait for me to be free, no matter how long it took, and he would have waited. Your father's heart attack was a total shock. He was a very young man when he died——'

'Conveniently,' Kelda could not resist saying, and then covered her face again, suddenly ashamed. 'I'm sorry, I didn't mean that. You must have had so much unhappiness with Dad——'

'My marriage to Tomaso broke up the first time because of guilt,' Daisy whispered unsteadily. 'I couldn't live with my conscience. I couldn't allow myself to be happy because I had been disloyal to your father and in the end I simply couldn't cope. It was only when I was away from Tomaso that I was able to sort my feelings out. Your father made his choices, Kelda. I wasn't responsible for them. He put himself in prison. He didn't much care what that did to us as a family. He was too irresponsible to think of anybody but himself...'

Silence greeted that final speech. Kelda was rocking soundlessly back and forth on her chair, fathoms deep in shock as her mind skipped agilely over her childhood and saw all the inconsistencies she had innocently accepted. She was shattered.

'Tim has known for a couple of years.'

Kelda choked back angry words of desperate hurt. She should have been told the truth a long, long time ago.

'I wish Angelo had known!' Her mother suddenly burst into tears.

Kelda was dragged from her stupor with a vengeance.

'How do you think Angelo will react to this?' Daisy sobbed. 'Worse, finding out about it in a newspaper!'

Tomaso came in, looking grim and strained. He comforted her mother while Kelda simply stood there in the grip of a horror that put everything she had previously experienced into the nursery stakes. Yes, how *would* Angelo react to the humiliation of the discovery that he was married to the daughter of a criminal? A criminal who had robbed a bank, of all things!

'I don't blame you, Mum.' Abruptly unfreezing, Kelda rushed to put her arms round her sobbing parent. 'You did the best you could.'

'But if this damages your marriage, I'll never forgive myself!'

'Angelo is on his way back from Geneva,' Tomaso sighed. 'We'll stay, deal with this as a family should.'

'No...' Kelda was appalled by the suggestion. She didn't want an inhibiting audience when Angelo came home. That wouldn't be fair to him.

It took persuasion but finally Tomaso and Daisy left. It would be hours before Angelo got back. Kelda darted upstairs and dug out the worn and faded stationery box in which she kept her father's letters. Anguish had returned, only now it was strengthened by fear.

What chance did their marriage have now? Angelo *had* unwittingly married the bank-robber's daughter. A lot of people were going to find that hilariously funny. And what about the rumour that he was soon to be offered the position of chief executive in the Rossetti Industrial Bank? Wasn't there a possibility that that too could be affected by his unfortunate marriage?

With scorching tears in her eyes, Kelda went in search of her suitcases. An hour later, she had packed. She was totally choked up by then. Her swollen eyes fell on the box of her father's letters and with sudden explosive bitterness, she sped downstairs to ask Mrs Moss for matches. Crouching down in front of the fireplace in her bedroom, she shook out the first letter, tears streaming down her face. The paper was worn thin by repeated readings, the ink faded.

She struck the first match and a split-second later there was a sudden step behind her and a hand snatched the match from her before she could ignite the letters piled in the grate. Still on her knees, she spun. 'What the heck do you...Angelo!' she gasped. 'But...but you're not due back until——'

'I cancelled my meetings and flew back immediately.'

Wordlessly she stared up at him. He reached down and raised her up but she wouldn't meet his eyes. She was drowning in angry humiliation. He already knew. Someone had told him. Why else would he arrive back early?

'Why were you about to burn your father's letters?'

'That's a very s-stupid question,' Kelda stammered.

'Once they're gone, they're gone, and those letters are all that you have of him,' Angelo pointed out almost gently.

The confrontation was not going in any expected direction. Her brow furrowed. 'Those letters are full of nothing but lies!'

'Does that really matter so much?' Angelo smoothed a straying curl from her damp temples. 'Your father loved you. He must have spent hours writing them and they made you happy when you were a child. Those letters made you feel secure and loved——'

'But they were *lies*!' Unable to comprehend why he was behaving this way, Kelda almost screamed at him and attempted to pull free.

'And don't you think your mother had something to do with that? Whose idea do you think it was that he should pretend to be working abroad rather than admit the truth?'

Kelda's breath escaped shakily.

'It was probably your mother's, and her motives were very much based on protecting you. She wanted you to have a father you could admire, a father you could talk about freely with your friends . . . it was an utterly insane charade but it kept you happy. You were safe in Liverpool. But you would have found out the truth if he had lived,' Angelo murmured intently, holding her fast by her shoulders. 'Sooner or later, you might have discovered that there is *no* oil in Jordan . . .'

'No oil?' she echoed dazedly.

'No oil. He couldn't have been working on an oil-field there.'

She frowned up at him. 'In Italy,' she whispered. 'You *knew*! But you said nothing...'

Lustrous dark eyes arrowed over her distressed face. 'I was curious to find out exactly how much you did know. You see, *cara*...I've known for almost ten years——'

'But you couldn't have——' she broke in, her eyes clinging to his.

'When my father married Daisy, I already knew they had been having a very discreet affair. The sudden marriage shook me as much as you,' he confided wryly. 'I ran a security check on your mother and the report was very thorough. I'm afraid to say that I didn't interpret the facts with much generosity. A late husband, who had been a regular prison inmate, two children stashed conveniently in another city. Haven't you ever wondered why I misjudged your mother so badly then?'

Kelda was shaken. Angelo had always known. Angelo had known from the beginning.

'I was only twenty-two and rather arrogant. I couldn't understand why my father had married her...'

She was remembering Angelo's cold antagonism towards her mother and suddenly she could understand why he had been so prejudiced from the outset.

'I had to become a little more mature before I could accept that the sinner was not your mother,' Angelo imparted quietly. 'And that, when you love somebody, you accept *everything* about that person, not just the facets that you like.'

'You knew...' She was still fumbling with that discovery. 'And yet you never threw it at me...not even when I accused your father of having a mistress and you probably knew then that the other woman was in fact my own mother——'

'Yes,' he sighed.

Why was he being kind and understanding? Kelda trembled, her emotions still raw and bleeding from her traumatic morning. 'Well, why didn't you throw it in my face?'

'When you were a child, I wouldn't have hurt you, and when you were almost an adult I still wouldn't have hurt you.' Angelo brushed a caressing hand gently over her wobbling lower lip. 'And when you became an adult I found that I *couldn't* hurt you.'

'But why?' she whispered.

He expelled his breath and abruptly let his hands drop from her. 'Because when you were sixteen I fell in love with you... and somehow I never quite managed to fall out of love again,' he said harshly.

The confession froze her in her tracks. He was standing with his back to her by the window, the muscles in his broad shoulders clearly clenched with tension beneath the well-cut jacket.

'Evidently I'm a one-woman man.' Fierce satire edged the statement. 'Six years ago I wanted to marry you because I loved you. Of course, you were far too young and you were not in love with me——'

Distantly she recalled him telling her in Tuscany how bitterly he had resented being forced into playing a father figure when Tomaso opted out. And finally she understood why. She also understood why he had gone over the edge that night when he'd found her in the library with that boy.

'I spent the past six years haunted by you. I framed that *Vogue* cover. It hangs in the bedroom of my London apartment.'

'Angelo...' she muttered softly, shock receding, delight and the most humbling sense of gratitude taking her over.

'*Dio*... do you think I want your pity?' he slashed back at her, swinging round. 'All those years reading about your other men! At times, I hated you more than I loved you. I brought you to Tuscany because I believed that you were really only a fantasy. If I actually made love to you, I believed, the fantasy would die. Only it didn't. It simply got me in deeper!'

'I thought you were a sexual infatuation,' Kelda told him dry-mouthed.

'I can live with that,' Angelo shot at her grimly. 'I can live with that better than losing you.'

'You're not going to lose me.' She smiled almost shyly at him.

'Then perhaps you can tell me why you have packed?' he demanded not quite steadily, pallor visible beneath his dark skin.

'I was being really stupid...I thought you'd be so angry and humiliated about the story in the paper——'

'All I had time to worry about was what that story was doing to you. Why should I be angry? It was your feelings I was most concerned about.'

The truth of that had been so plain from the moment he'd stopped her impulsively burning her father's letters that her throat closed over with tears. All the tenderness and caring she had ever sought had been there for her instantly. 'If you love me, why have you been so aloof since Alice was born?' she asked helplessly.

'I wanted to be with you when she was born. It was so obvious that that would not have been your choice...I felt rejected,' he breathed tautly. 'I had tried so hard before that to make you relax with me and I thought I was getting somewhere...then I realised I wasn't. Treating you like a sort of sister had been such a strain——'

'A strain for me too. I thought you found my shape...revolting,' she confided in a rush. 'You never touched me.'

'I didn't think you would allow me to. I was trying to build a bond of trust between us. I had made such a mess of our relationship in Tuscany. I went overboard that night at Daisy's cottage,' he relived unsteadily, beautiful golden eyes clinging to her intent face. 'I couldn't trust myself near you. I was scared I would make an even bigger fool of myself.'

'You didn't make a fool of yourself that night. If only I hadn't lied, if only we had talked . . . *really* talked,' she said with bitter regret.

'I wanted so badly to hear that your baby was mine,' Angelo confessed roughly. 'Couldn't you see that?'

Kelda had paled. 'Even though you thought I had slept with Russ?'

'Yes,' he admitted ruefully.

'All I could think about was Fiona,' she admitted. 'My pride was hurt. I was bitter and hurt and jealous and I really did believe that the last thing you wanted to hear was that the baby was yours.'

'You were wrong. And when I realised that you had lied, I think that was the worst rejection of all. I thought you had to really hate me to have lied. You didn't even consider telling me the truth or approaching me for help all those months that you were pregnant,' he pointed out. 'That stood between us from the hour I married you...that even pregnant and alone you wanted nothing to do with me.'

The pain that conviction had given him was in his dark eyes.

Kelda shook her head. 'That never even occurred to me. All I could think about was Adele and all the other women——'

'I haven't slept with anyone but you since Italy.' Angelo absorbed her incredulity and a slanting smile tilted his handsome mouth. 'Not even come near it. I couldn't have used another woman just for sexual release when the only woman I really wanted was you.'

'Not even Fiona?'

Angelo laughed heartily. 'She dumped me the day after the wedding. She said she wouldn't be used to make another woman jealous but that if I ever got over you she might give me a second chance.' He hesitated. 'Did you use the food in the hampers?'

'Hampers?' Kelda repeated, her brow creasing. 'From Harrods? *You sent them*?'

'Didn't you even suspect?'

'I thought your father was behind them!' Kelda groaned. 'I never would have dreamt that they were from you... not after the way we parted at the cottage.'

'You were so thin.' One of his hands clenched and he shrugged jerkily. 'I wanted to be sure you ate properly...'

She was unbearably touched that he had been concerned about her even when he'd believed that her child was not his. Her whole face glowed. 'I love you, Angelo.' It was extraordinary how much courage it took to say it.

His brilliant eyes narrowed, his hard, dark features tightening, and then suddenly he reached for her, his lean hands bruising. 'You don't need to say that!'

'I fell in love in Tuscany. Maybe it was the emeralds that did it,' she teased, pressing her lips against his throat, breathing in the gloriously familiar scent of him with sensual pleasure. 'Or being flung in jail. Or maybe it had been brewing for six years and it was just waiting for an opportunity to blaze. But the fact is, Angelo, I am absolutely crazy about you too!'

'I thought the only thing you wanted was my body——'

'I hope it's included in the package.' She ran a flagrantly possessive hand over the breadth of his chest. 'And by the way,' she added, in a uniquely generous mood, letting her whole body rest against him, 'I haven't had any other lovers...'

He tensed, collided with her amused gaze and suddenly crushed her mouth hotly beneath his. It was a couple of hours before a sensible word was spoken again. Curved round Angelo's sprawling length, Kelda suddenly jerked and gasped, 'Alice! I forgot about her!'

'Inga will be with her.' Angelo trapped her with a powerful arm before she could move.

'Inga?'

'I brought her back from Geneva. I dined with friends last night. Inga had been with their children for several years. They don't need her any more and she was working out her last week, so after I'd heard a glowing testimonial and talked to her, I engaged her on the spot and brought her home with me.'

'Inga. Swedish?'

'Her English is excellent.'

'Danny Philips ran off with his children's nanny,' Kelda couldn't help remarking. 'I suppose she's blonde.'

'Jealous little cat,' Angelo breathed in her ear. 'She's fifty and built like a tank.'

'Oh.' Kelda relaxed.

'I'm sorry about your father,' he murmured. 'But he wasn't the hardened criminal the newspaper made out. He was never involved in any form of violence——'

'But the bank robbery——'

'He was the driver and he was unarmed. He put a stocking mask over his face, double parked in the wrong street just round the corner of a police station and blew the whole show for his partners in crime. A bit inept, your father.'

Kelda found that she was trying not to laugh. It still hurt, but reality was better than a fairy story. If Angelo could live with it, she could still hold her head high. 'I love you,' she told him fiercely, staring down at him.

'Enough to stay forever and ever?' Angelo enquired silkily, running a lean hand possessively over one slanted cheekbone.

'Are you likely to be a good investment?'

'Highly profitable,' he promised, sensually capturing her parted lips with his. 'As well as loyal, loving and constantly in a state of arousal round you,' he virtually completed on a groan.

'And the next time I have a baby you'll——'

'Be there, share everything.'

'You learn fast.' Kelda slid a provocative hand over his flat hard stomach and smiled at his instantaneous response.

'Move fast too.' With a husky laugh, he pinned her flat. 'How does the idea of six weeks in Tuscany appeal to you?'

'The peach and cherry orchard.' She sighed luxuriously.

'*Si* ...' And for a long time the rest of the world was forgotten as they lost themselves and yet found each other in loving.

Emma Goldrick was born and raised in Puerto Rico, where she met and married her husband Bob, a career military man. Thirty years and four children later they retired and took up nursing and teaching. In 1980 they turned to collaborative writing. After sixty years of living over half the world, and a full year of studying the Mills & Boon® style, their first submission was accepted. Between them they have written over forty books and have sold over twenty-two million copies worldwide. Goldrick hobbies include grandchildren, flower gardens, reading and travel. Sadly, in 1996, Bob Goldrick passed away. Emma continues to write in his memory.

BABY MAKES THREE

by

EMMA GOLDRICK

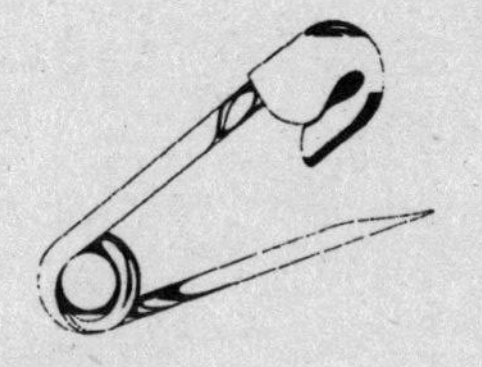

CHAPTER ONE

'LOOK, Charlie,' his forty-year-old lawyer and boyhood friend cautioned him as they idled along the pavement across from the pyramid-shaped building which housed the magazine. 'Things aren't the way they were in your uncle's day.'

Charlie Mathers looked across the street and chuckled. 'You didn't have to say that, Frank. Who's responsible for the Egyptian rococo monstrosity over there? The city was never like this, was it?'

Frank Losen winced, and looked around cautiously to make sure nobody was listening. '*She's* responsible,' he murmured. 'You wouldn't believe! Way out here in the boondocks, Rachel Hammond is publisher and editor of one of the nation's wildest scandal sheets. Of course, Libertyville is only a few miles from Topeka, which is the print capital of the Middle West.' Said with a sense of pride that Charlie acknowledged by a tip of his hat. 'Her father was a tough cookie, if you might remember. His daughter makes him look like a Franciscan friar!'

'I'd believe almost anything after spending a year in the Near East. It hardly matters, does it? Don't they make up all their news out of whole cloth? And didn't the old man have a son to inherit?'

'A boy,' Frank told him. 'Little Jimmy. Learned to drink the hard stuff at fifteen, and wrapped his motor-cycle around a lamppost when he was twenty-one. And that left——'

'Yes, I know.' Charlie chuckled again. 'Just *Her*.' He could almost hear the capital letters in *Her*. 'His daughter? Little Rachel? I can't believe that. She was just a kid when my uncle wrote about her. Sent a picture, too. Too bad Uncle Roger died before I could come and find out what he wanted. What is she—twenty—twenty-five?'

'You forget a lot of years,' Frank said. 'And don't call her Rachel. She prefers to be called Hammond. I would guess she might be all of twenty-nine or thirty by now.'

'I'd like to see this harridan. Why don't we walk over there and drop in on her?'

'Not me.' Frank stepped a pace or two away almost as if he were trying to put real distance between himself and Charlie Mathers. 'You must be crazy or something.'

'Or something,' Charlie agreed as he came to a halt and surveyed the yellow-brick monstrosity across the street. His lawyer stared at him as intently as he stared at the building. Charlie Mathers had spent five years after college in the stock market. Then he had put all his money in trusts, turned its management over to his lawyer, and dropped out of sight. Now here he was, back but two days from—wherever. Charlie Mathers. Just barely clearing five feet eleven, but built like some barbarian conqueror, his hair down to his neck in unruly disarray. The neck itself a short, thick steel pillar laced with muscles.

The hair had once been yellow-blond. Now it was bleached almost white by a tropical sun. In the warmth of the Kansas springtime he was wearing a loose, well-worn sports shirt, from which his arm muscles bulged, and a sloppy pair of trousers. From a distance he appeared to be an ordinary but solid man; not until one came closer did his actual size meet the eye. Everything not covered by hair or clothing was a deep sun-brown. Except for those commanding deep blue eyes.

'And you won't just walk across with me,' Charlie teased again. 'After all, the Hammonds and the Mathers were once great neighbours.'

'Sure. About a century ago,' Frank said. 'Yes, you did inherit from your uncle Roger, and included was forty per cent of the shares in the Hammond-Borgen Corporation, which includes the Bar Nine ranch, and that damn magazine. The *National Gossiper*, would you believe? And no, you don't get me into that—that bitch's lair!'

'She must be something,' Charlie laughed. 'Bitch? And you a staunch Methodist!'

'Listen to me, Charlie. You've got more money than I can count. Even the bank president tips his hat when you walk by. You don't *need* to know the Hammonds. Leave the sleeping dogs alone. You might get yourself cut off somewhere south of your hip pockets. And that's my last word on the subject!'

'Amen. Well, you go on back to your office, Frank. You've done a good job managing my money. I think I'll just leave it in your hands while I sniff around the town and edge my way back into civilisation.'

'That makes a lot of sense, old buddy. And I think I'll—run along.'

'Yeah, why don't you?' Charlie encouraged. 'I do believe somebody important is coming out over there.' He turned around to offer some other comment, but by that time his lawyer, laden with forty years of worry and a heavy briefcase, had already disappeared.

That's what I need, Charlie told himself. Something intriguing to do. Something with a lot of—gentle adventure. Something where I can have some fun without being shot at! I don't intend to set foot in an F-15 cockpit for the rest of my natural life.

Women, that's the proper subject for a middle-aged man these days. Isn't thirty-four middle-aged? Women. But then I suppose the lady's as ugly as they come. Isn't that what sours a woman? Ugliness? Or lack of love?

A grey stretch limousine pulled up at the opposite kerb. The double doors of the building swung open and two very large men came out cautiously on to the pavement. One looked like a misplaced basketball player; the other like King Kong in a business suit. The pair of them turned in a semicircle, searching opposite ends of the street. Unconsciously Charlie Mathers did the same. There was not another soul in sight—except for himself.

The men held a very short conversation, and then made a bee-line for Charlie. You've been a long time away, Charlie thought, as he watched the pair move in his direction. Things really *have* changed.

'Hey, you,' the Kong-type said. 'Doin' somethin' special here, are you?'

'Nope. Just hanging around.' Charlie Mathers had long been noted as a violent man, but this pair certainly wouldn't know his reputation. Sometimes his patience lasted for as long as ninety seconds. On his good days, of course.

'Something I can do for you?'

'Yeah. How about moving down the block a ways?' The beanpole spoke politely, but he kept pounding one big fist into the palm of the other with monotonous precision.

'Why is that?'

'Because Hammond's coming out, and she don't like gawkers. Move along.'

'Well, I'll be damned.' Charlie shook his head and smiled. 'Just what I need. I've been aching to see this Hammond. And she's coming out right now?'

'Achin' you'll get,' the gorilla said. 'Seein' you won't.'

'She's been shot at a time or two,' the taller man said. He sounded conciliatory, but his fist was still pounding into the palm of his hand, and making heavy popping noises as it did.

'Just move,' the other growled, and reached one big hand out for Charlie's shoulder. A genial smile flashed across Charlie's face.

'Why, you two aren't being friendly at all,' he crowed. In one friendly little swoop he lifted the hand off his shoulder and the gorilla off his feet and threw him about six feet, where he canonned into his partner and left both of them sprawling in the gutter.

Rachel Hammond, twenty-nine years old and counting, paced her office one more time. The idiot who had designed the pyramid had long since been fired. Having your office at the top of such a structure gave you four windows, four slanting walls, and not much room for pacing. Rachel was a woman who needed pacing room. The elderly man sitting on the stiff-backed chair followed her with his eyes.

'Look, Elmer. I said dig up a little scandal, but I didn't mean in Libertyville, for heaven's sake. Who in the world gives a damn that someone on the town council is selling favours? Kill the damn thing. I want something juicy!'

Elmer Chatmas had been with Rachel's father, and her father's father, and was not about to run for cover. 'There doesn't seem to be anything to meet the requirement,' he said quietly. 'We might do something with this thing over in Topeka in the city solicitor's office, but it's a little staid. Just an ordinary embezzlement.'

'So jazz it up,' she told him. 'Add a couple of babes. Get a couple of leg pictures. You know the routine—"CITY OFFICIAL STEALS TO SUPPORT SEX HABITS"—or something like that. Come on, Elmer, I've got an important appointment in fifteen minutes.'

'Just make up a blatant lie?'

'Not a lie, Elmer. That's what we call creative journalism. You know what to do. We print the real news on page two, and save page one to make money enough to keep this old scow afloat. Now come on. Put the issue to bed!'

'I don't know how you do it,' he said as he got up and gathered his papers together. 'Whatever happened to that sweet little girl I used to dandle on my knee?'

The *sweet little girl* smiled at him. 'Rachel Hammond?' she asked. 'She grew up, Elmer, and found out that the world isn't round, it's crooked.'

'What you need is a good man,' the editor told her as he walked out of the room.

'Sure I do,' she called after him. 'But God isn't making any more of that model.' The door swung shut, locking her in. A shiver ran up and down her spine. Of course it wasn't locked, only closed. Am I coming down with claustrophobia? Or chicken-pox? She changed her route, and opened the door of the tiny lavatory adjacent to her office. The mirror lied to her.

She felt fifty years old; the mirror said twenty-nine. Her hand brushed through her mop of curls; blonde beautiful curls, the mirror said. And blue eyes, with rose-red cheeks to go with her pearly complexion. Fine white teeth, a sharp little nose, a determined chin, medium height, and a figure that would have sent Michelangelo into shock!

And soon I'll be thirty, she told herself ruefully. The woman who had appeared on the late-night talk show two months ago had hit it just right. Rachel Hammond could hear her biological clock ticking!

It was the sort of problem a woman might possibly discuss with her friends—if she had any. Or with her pastor—if she didn't think he was such a wimp. And that was the trouble. She wasn't interested in finding a 'good man', someone who could dictate to her as her father had. What she wanted was a baby. Somebody you can dictate to? her conscience asked. 'No, not that,' Rachel muttered to the empty office. 'Someone I could love and cherish. Someone who might love me back!' Which immediately ruled out any adult she could think of.

She hadn't been a success at loving during her own childhood. Her mother gave up the cocktail circuit just long enough to bear her, and then had died. Her father, once he discovered she was not a boy, had treated her like a misdirected parcel, come in the mail with no return address.

But not all of Rachel's education had been wasted. No matter how she squirmed around it, to have a baby you had to have a man. And that was the idea around which she had built her campaign. She trusted her doctor. A woman, of course. They had put their minds together, and finally had come up with a newspaper advertisement.

> Wanted: strong, healthy male, willing to accept high-paying, short-term job.

'And that,' Rachel had said, 'will bring in a flood of

strong, healthy, lazy males, willing to take my money for almost anything.'

'So we'll say "willing to participate in hazardous short-term experiment at high pay."'

'That sounds more like it,' Rachel had agreed. 'And you'll screen them out?'

'Dr Greenlaugh first. She's a psychiatrist. When she finds the ten best she'll send them over to me for a physical.'

'A damn thorough physical,' Rachel had added. 'I don't want to get to the end of the search and find the guy can't—well, you know.'

'I know,' Dr Saunders had agreed with a chuckle. 'But give it more thought, Rachel. There's a lot to be said about home and hearth and husband and baby. And the child really ought to have a father when he's grown a little.'

'Great,' Rachel had returned. 'When the time comes, I'll buy him one.' Another shudder raced up her spine. I'm doing what you told me to, Dad, she whispered. Only her lips moved. I'm going to continue the Hammond line. Isn't that what you wanted? I'll select a man all carefully designed, and if the baby looks like a Hammond it'll be a surprise. This child will be perfect. Isn't that what you wanted from your worthless daughter?

'Crying?' her doctor had asked.

Hammonds didn't cry. But all the rest of them had been hard-driven men.

'Me? Crying? Hammonds don't cry.' Rachel had brushed at her eyelid. There *was* a tear there. 'All the rest of that talk is sheer garbage, Sue. Listen, when you get it down to one, send him over to me for an interview.

But make damn sure he hasn't a clue about what I really want!'

And that, Rachel told herself now as she splashed a little cold water on her nervous wrists, had all been accomplished, and today was the day the winner came!

She went back to her desk, sat, stood up again, paced the room, craned her neck trying to see something—anything—from the window, and then jumped when the buzzer rang. Oh, God, what am I doing? she almost screamed at herself. Am I doing what my father wanted so badly? He wanted a son. And since I obviously didn't qualify, it's up to me to make up the shortage. She covered her ears, trembling. She could still hear her father's hoarse voice plaguing her. 'I need a boy, Rachel. And quickly! A girl isn't good enough!' She moved over to the desk and sat down. Her father's chair, that. A comfortable, over-stuffed swivel chair mounted on a six-inch-high platform, so that all of her visitors would have to look up at her. Lesson sixteen in her father's lexicon. 'Catch them at the door and make them sweat!' To complete the scene she swivelled around so that her back was to the door.

The door opened with a squeak; there was the sound of movement behind her, and then a rush of feet. 'We got him, Ms Hammond,' somebody yelled. Rachel whirled her chair around. Things were very much out of control. A chunky, husky man with white-streaked hair was standing in the doorway, one of his big hands on the throat of each of her two remaining security men. 'We got him,' one of the two repeated weakly.

'Yes, I can see you've got him.' Sarcasm dripped all over the floor. 'Cut it *out*!'

All three of them quit the ruckus on cue. 'Now, what's going on?'

'I'm——' the very big stranger started to say, but she interrupted.

'I *know* who you are. What I don't know is what's going on.'

'This is the guy,' Leo Gurstner insisted. 'I seen him out the front door. Fritz and Habblemeyer walked over across the street to see what he was doin', and he dumped them both. Both at the same time, mind you! You want I should call the cops?'

'I want,' she said, sighing, 'that you both would go far away and let me talk to this—gentleman. He has an appointment with me.'

I have? Charlie Mathers shrugged his shoulders and rearranged his torn shirt. Well, perhaps I do. Uncle's letter was short on specifics but long on 'wants'.

> I want you to get your butt up here and help me straighten out this girl. Do anything necessary. I can see the vultures circling around her head already.

Only his uncle was more old-fashioned than that. Butt was the polite word, which the old man would never use.

The two guards hesitated for a moment, then ducked out of the office and closed the door gently behind them. The woman was looking at him as if he were a side of beef. 'And how did all *that* happen?'

Charlie shrugged his shoulders again. She had a nice voice. Deep for a woman, and marvellous control. 'I was standing across the street waiting to meet you when these two yahoos came running at me. And then they both tripped over each other. One of them grabbed my shirt to keep from falling. Never saw such a thing in my whole life. I knew they came out of this building, so I thought it might be neighbourly to come and tell you all about it.'

'Very appropriate,' Rachel said as she pursed her lips and went back to her executive chair. He was coming to see her. The game had started. Her control was instantly renewed. Perhaps her father *was* still haunting that chair. Damn. She shifted her position nervously. The big man sauntered across the room, moved the two straight-backed chairs off to one side, and pulled the couch from under the window over to take their place. Then, without a by-your-leave, he slumped into it, with one foot dangling over the end.

And now, Rachel told herself, I take control of the situation by—by how? Rack her brain as she might, she couldn't think of a sensible thing to say. So she stared. As he did.

'And what do I call you?' she finally blurted out.

'Charlie,' he said softly. 'Leastwise that's what my pa called me. Don't tell me that you're——'

'I'm Hammond. Now, what did the doctor tell you about me or this job?'

'Not a blessed thing,' Charlie told her in all honesty. 'Not a thing.'

'But you can't help wondering, I suppose?'

'You could say that.'

'Well, I'll tell you all about it,' she said. 'But first you and I have to get to know each other a great deal better than we do now. So for that purpose we'll go out to my ranch and spend a month just making ourselves acquainted. You are free to travel, I suppose?'

The big man waved a casual hand.

'And you have better clothing?'

He looked down at himself, and then up at her in chagrin. 'This stuff looked pretty good when I left the hotel this morning,' he said mildly. 'I never expected a bunch of goons to try to tear my clothes off.'

'Don't worry about that,' she told him as she got up briskly, reached for the briefcase she normally took home with her, and then rejected it. No extra work, she told herself as she pressed the button on her intercom.

'Beth. I'm going out to the ranch. I'll be gone for a minimum of four weeks, and I want no interruptions while I'm out there. Absolutely none!'

'Yes, ma'am,' the intercom burped. 'But there's this man in the outer office who keeps trying to tell me he has an appointment with you.'

'Well, call Security and have them bounce him,' Rachel snapped. 'I don't have any other appointments!' Rachel thumbed the switch off. For the first time in four years, Hammond Enterprises would function with nobody at the helm. 'Come on—er—Charlie.' She beckoned with her imperial little finger. It wasn't until moments later, locked into her private lift with him, that she recalled how gracefully he had come to his feet and followed. It was a good beginning, she told herself. A big, healthy man, smoothly functional—and mannerly, she added as he helped her into the limousine.

'It will take some time to drive out to the Bar Nine,' she told him.

'Don't mind me.' He was already at the window. 'I like to look at the scenery.'

'That's not exactly what I had in mind,' she countered. 'There are a million things I want to know about you. This dossier was compiled in a hurry, so naturally there are a few things missing. Now then—you were born in...?'

'Waco, Texas,' he replied. 'Thirty-four years ago. Is that the kind of thing you want to know?'

'Approximately. Any communicable diseases?'

'Not now.' He gave her another one of those quizzically gentle looks. 'Oh, you mean childhood diseases? I guess I had everything most kids have.'

'I see. And none of them—er—impaired any of your—physical functions?'

'Only one I know of is when the bull stepped on my foot,' he said, nodding sagely. 'On occasion when it rains the damn thing aches a little. But the Air Force doctors said there was nothin' wrong with the foot. Psycho something, they said.'

'Psychosomatic?'

'The very word,' he acknowledged. 'Besides, it doesn't rain all that much up here in Kansas, I hear. If you're worried about experience, I ran a good-sized spread by the time I was fourteen. Horses, cattle—even——' a little tinge of contempt slipped in '—sheep.'

'Yes, that relieves my mind,' Rachel said and, for the life of her, despite all the lists she had made beforehand, she couldn't think of a single other question to ask. For the rest of the ride she alternated, staring out of the window, and, when he did the same, shifting to stare at him.

What in the world am I doing? Rachel pondered. I could get all this information from behind a desk, on a personnel form. And that's not what I want to know. So how do you go about asking a man a question like the one I want to ask, when I can't even phrase it to myself?

Besides, he's not exactly what I expected. There's something free and easy behind all that—muscle. When he smiled he looked downright handsome. When he had something to say he seemed to think it over before wagging his tongue. But of course, as her father had warned her a time or two in her young life, 'There's more handsome men sittin' on death row over in

Leavenworth than you'll find singing in any church choir!' So she leaned back against the cushions, shut down her mind and, because she seldom got more than five hours sleep a night, promptly dropped off.

Charlie Mathers watched out of the corner of his eye as the girl swayed slightly, slumped, and snapped herself back up again. He was without a night or two of sleep himself, but long training had made it easier for him to adjust. He slid over carefully in her direction, and the next time she slumped her head landed on his shoulder and stayed there.

He shrugged himself into the most comfortable position he could find, and slipped one arm around her shoulders to keep her from bouncing away from him. Her mind might be tough, he told himself, but her shoulder is a tender morsel indeed. 'Harridan'. Who said that, me? It just goes to prove something or other. A lovely creature, no doubt about it, living on nerves and coffee, I suppose. I wonder what she'd be like totally relaxed? And I wonder what kind of a game I've fallen in to? Soft shoulders under his hand, soft, rounded hip pressed against his own, a narrow waist, and pert, proud breasts that bounced, unfettered, under that silk blouse. The car moved off the paved highway on to an unpaved ranch road. Charlie licked his lips appreciatively, and settled back to see what the future might bring. 'Do anything you can,' Uncle Roger had written, and suddenly doing just that had pleasant overtones. He licked his dry lips and settled back against the upholstery.

The famous Flat Plains of Kansas were not all that flat. Along the eastern border of the state, where the Missouri River chased itself in yellow flood, there were more than enough hills to make a decent-sized mountain. A few miles to the west, in the neighbourhood of

Manhattan, Topeka, Cottonwood Falls, the land looked like a child's landscape puzzle, piled up on itself. The limousine was taking them on a south-westerly line away from the town of Libertyville, up on to the rolling hills and prairie land known as the Flint Hills.

But the road went on—and on. Until finally the limousine broke out of the bottoms, across a line of sheltering trees into a little watered valley on the other side of the ridge, and rattled over a cattle-guard. The weathered sign said 'Bar Nine'. A few head of well-fed cattle lifted their eyes briefly as the car plugged on by them. Herefords, he judged, and, penned in the far corral, what looked to be a few head of Texas Longhorns. And then they were at the ranch house, a native stone building that seemed as old as the Oregon Trail, where they had started. The car came to a halt, the girl woke up in his arms, startled, and a pair of hound dogs came baying down the wind from around the corner of the barn.

'Excuse me,' she said hesitantly as she moved as far away from him as she could get.

'No excuse necessary.' He grinned. It was his first tactical mistake.

Her jaw hardened. 'Let's be sure there's no further need for such,' she snapped.

His deep blue eyes assessed her, and decided. 'Yes, ma'am,' he acknowledged.

'And don't call me ma'am,' she snapped. 'My name is Hammond.'

'I see,' he said gravely. 'It's just, where I come from, it isn't considered polite to call a woman by her last name without a name or title to go with it.'

The first sign of rebellion, Rachel told herself. If I were in my right mind I'd fire him here and now and let him walk back. But I want more than a day's work from this man; it would pay to be a little conciliatory, just this once.

'All right,' she conceded. 'You may call me Rachel. Now, what's your last name?'

He seemed about to answer. At least, his mouth began to form words, but by that time the chauffeur had opened the back door of the limousine, and the hounds were on them. One of them was a middle-aged bitch who sat quietly beside the door and wiggled and whined. The other was a dog, barely a year old, exuberant, anxious. 'Get down, Blue,' Rachel commanded as the dog squeezed into the car and began to slobber over her. But she said it with affection.

And that, Charlie told himself, is the first time I've heard her sounding pleased about something. He squeezed out of the car, not an easy feat for a man his size. The elderly bitch looked up and inspected him carefully, then offered a triple tail-wag.

'Henrietta approves of you,' Rachel said. 'That's in your favour. A good judge of people, is Henrietta.'

'I'm glad somebody likes me,' he replied as he stooped to pat the animal. Henrietta growled. 'I see,' he said, laughing. 'Wag, but not touch, Henrietta? Don't you think that's a half-hearted commitment?' The woman behind him was startled for a moment, then controlled her face.

'We'll go up to the house,' she said, indicating the broad wooden steps that led up to the porch.

'The place looks empty,' he commented as he walked up the stairs behind her.

'It is, Charlie——' she said, leaving a space for him to volunteer his last name. He ignored her offer. Rachel was caught off guard again, and a tiny blush swept over her cheeks. She brushed him aside, and led the way into the house.

The front door opened directly into the small living-room. She felt the need to defend herself and her possessions. 'It gets cold in Kansas in the wintertime. That's why we have small rooms and low ceilings. If you would sit down on the couch, Charles?' It wasn't exactly a request, but rather the polite expression of an order that she intended he should obey. He paused to look around the room. She stood there, fuming, as he did so.

An old fireplace was blocked up, and a Ben Franklin stove stood in its recess. The wallpaper was clean, but oh, so very dull. The furniture was in good shape, but old. Grand Rapids, turn of the century, his roving eye told him. And the carpet on the floor had seen too many boots stalk across it for its own good. It might have once been burnt amber. On the wall across from the stove hung a painting of a fierce old man. 'Your father, Rachel?'

'Grandfather,' she replied. 'My father thought that paintings were a waste of time and money. Please sit.' She indicated the couch. He chose the adjacent Morris chair and sank into it with a comfortable sigh.

'There's never been a more comfortable chair than a Morris,' he commented as his big hands patted the worn wooden arms. And all the while his eyes had been studying her. There was no doubt in his mind that tension was building within her, that she had kept something of extreme importance to herself that she wanted to tell him, and that she was not the type of woman to stand for delays. So he changed his tactics—for the moment. 'I take it you want to tell me something?'

The air came out of her lungs in an explosive gasp as she collapsed on to the couch and tucked her skirts in.

'Yes. This month in front of us is to be a sort of test run, an opportunity for you and me to get to know each other better. There are other people on the ranch, but they will stay out of our way. Mrs Colchester will come over every afternoon and fix us supper. There are a few head of cattle around the area, and perhaps enough outside work on the spread to keep us busy, but that's not terribly important to the test. Except for Mrs Colchester, we will have to make do for ourselves.'

'This is a test? Which one of us, do you suppose, is being tested?'

Her fleeting blush was back again, for longer than before. 'That remains to be seen, doesn't it?'

'And that's all I'm to be told about it?'

'Oh, no,' Rachel said coolly. 'There is one more item. If the test is successful, and you comply with all the terms, you will be paid a thousand dollars a week. I imagine that a month will be enough to complete the—er—tests.'

And that, Charlie Mathers told himself, is enough of all this stalling around. He pushed himself up out of the Morris chair and strolled over in front of her. 'I think I could save you two or three weeks of your valuable time, and maybe a couple of thousand dollars,' he offered as he pulled her up off the sofa.

'What——?'

'I have this theory,' he told her. 'When two people want to get close to each other, they really have to get *close*. No amount of talking will help. Close—like this.' Her hands were resting in his as she glared at him. He offered her another one of those vacuous smiles, then tugged her closer. Her breasts served as a capable bumper. She almost bounced off his chest, but his hands were on her shoulders before she could slip away from him. 'And then, like this,' he said softly.

Rachel whimpered as his head bent over her, blocking out the light from the windows. One of his hands moved to the small of her back, bringing her tightly into his web. His mouth moved gently down on hers, brushed against her lips, and then fled upward to the lobe of her ear. She managed a breath, and a phrase. 'Don't——' she started to say, and then his lips were back on hers, sealing off her mouth in a heady attack that registered shock, amazement, fear.

Charlie could feel her fear, read the shock. He lightened the pressure against her mouth. 'It's all right,' he murmured in her ear. 'It's all right; relax, you could get to like it.' And then he sealed her mouth again with his own. Rachel felt the first returning shock, but from then onwards she *experienced* the wild, roiling flashes of excitement that shot up and down her spine, blinded her to everything else, left her hanging in his arms because her own knees refused to function.

He moved her slightly away from his steel frame. She sobbed for breath. Only his arms supported her. 'See,' he murmured again. 'That's all there is to it.' Gently, as if she were a china doll, he deposited her back on the couch, where she slipped sideways, still struggling for breath.

'Now I'm sure we've saved at least a thousand dollars,' he observed gently. 'Care to make it two?'

'No,' she whispered, and then shouted, 'No! Damn you, no!'

'OK, OK.' He spread his placating hands out in front of her. 'Don't take it too hard, Rachel. It was only an experiment, nothing more. If you liked it we could try it again some day. If not, just say the word and I'll be off back to the city.'

'I—no,' she stammered.

'No what? No city? No more kisses?'

'Just no,' she said, and then staggered to her feet. Another one of her father's platitudes: To dominate people you have to be standing toe to toe with them!

But when she came that close she was trembling. She balled her fingers up into fists, but left them hanging at her side. It was only a kiss, she told herself fiercely. Plenty of women get kissed in all sorts of ways. All I have to do is settle down. Count to ten. Get the breathing settled, and then tell him off. Or do I want to do that? If this is the best man to be winnowed out of the field, I don't really want to lose him. After all, it certainly can't take long for me to get what I want from this—giant—and then I can write him off to expenses and forget about him! Two more breaths. She was so close that her breasts were rubbing gently across that steel chest of his. She blushed and put more space between them.

'I realise, Charlie, that you are—sort of—in the dark about what's going on. And I won't be surprised to learn that in Texas your sort of—enticement—might work very well.'

He had both hands in his pockets, his head slightly cocked to the left, and a wide grin on his face. But there's more than that, Rachel told herself. Look at those eyes. Deep, dark blue. Behind his face there was a calculation going on, as if his mind were a computer. How in the world did *this* man get by her screening process? She coughed a couple of times to hide her embarrassment.

'But up here in Kansas we don't go on like that,' she continued quickly.

'Well, you could have fooled me,' he said, chuckling. 'There seem to be plenty of kids all over this part of Kansas.'

'Stop that!' She tried to stamp her foot, but the rug was too thick to make a practical noise.

'I understand—Hammond.' He reached over and wiped away the tiny bit of tear-drop that was working at the corner of her left eye. 'I really understand. It isn't that sort of test, huh?'

And that left Rachel Hammond far up the creek without a paddle. Lying was not her usual cup of tea, but how could she answer truthfully? Because that was exactly the kind of test it was to be. 'Excuse me,' she said, all in a rush. 'I forgot the coffee. Please sit down, Mr—Charles.'

CHAPTER TWO

RACHEL HAMMOND staggered out on to the porch the next morning, rubbing her eyes. She did not normally require more than a few hours sleep, but her machinery wasn't working well this morning. She stretched, seeming to reach higher than she ever had before in all her life. There was an itch right in the small of her back. She tried vainly to scratch it away against the porch post, with no success.

'If you was to scratch it there any more you'd get splinters.' She whirled around. Charlie Mathers looked bigger and better and more—dangerous—than he had on the previous day. And he proved the point by reaching around behind her and scratching at almost the perfect place.

'A little lower,' Rachel murmured, and wiggled slightly to match the occasion. He complied. She groaned with a sort of ecstasy. Naturally, with the two of them facing each other, and his hand around behind her, pushing against her, they could not help but move close together. And, Rachel realised, I haven't dressed and this nightgown is too—— But it felt so damnably comfortable that she took one more tiny quarter-step in his direction.

Life was measured in millimetres, not centimetres. Nothing else would have happened except that she felt a sudden shuddering sensation run up and down her spine. Her breasts swelled, her nipples stiffened, and the millimetre that separated them was gone. 'Oh, God,' Rachel muttered.

He made some comment, but its meaning passed completely over her head. Her nerves tingled from scalp to toenail. He swayed slightly from side to side, adding massage to contact. 'Lightning,' she muttered, convinced that a storm had struck.

'What?' His hands landed on her shoulders, trying to move her another millimetre forward. But this time the contact was too much. *Or too soon*, she told herself as she backed away.

'No more itch?' She looked up at him. That silly grin was on his face as he looked down at her.

'I—no,' she said. 'No more itch. I—thank you for your help.'

'No trouble at all,' he said, chuckling. 'Anything you need, you just call on me. Anything. I thought I'd go look over the stables. Like to come along?'

Her heart said yes, but her mind knew better. 'No, I mean to get breakfast and get dressed. Why don't you go ahead? I might join you after a while. We could go for a ride—you *do* ride?'

'Anything with four feet,' he replied. 'Born and raised in a saddle, I was.'

'That must have been some feat,' she murmured sarcastically. 'Your mother must have had considerable discomfort. Excuse me, Mr—er—Charlie.'

He tipped a salute with two fingers and grinned again as she whirled away from him and disappeared behind the screen door. Yes, Charlie, he chided himself. *Do* excuse me. 'The lady doth protest too much'? He shrugged his shoulders and started towards the barn.

Inside, Rachel watched him through the interstices of the muslin curtains. Big, powerful, assured. His walk told it all. Ordinarily she wouldn't have a man of his type within five miles of her. Here at the centre of her dream, the ranch house was almost a cloister. Herself, Mrs Colchester, and the ranch-hands. And now this man? What was it about him that had caused Sue to nominate him? He hardly matched any two of the ten requirements she had laid down. And so? Declare him unusable and send him packing? Or give him a long trial—if that can be done without burning my fingers. She closed her eyes for just a moment, and memory crowded her. 'I vote to keep him,' she said, chuckling, as she sat down to a bigger breakfast than normal.

'You've got a couple of fine quarter-horses in this pair,' Charlie told her as he led the mare out of her stall and walked her in a circle. 'Good form, nice fetlocks—her left shoe's a mite worn on one side. Want me to saddle up for you?'

Rachel Hammond had had enough time to restore her perpetual grouch. She was wearing a pair of blue jeans, the legs tucked into her boots, and a loose red blouse, open at the neck, but contained by a blue and red bandana. And a white ten-gallon hat, covering all her magnificent curls. Besides, he was so damnably big. Lord knew what he might do if angered. 'Oh, so now you're a blacksmith too?'

He grinned at her, that amiable grin that irritated her even more than normal. 'Like to keep my hand in most anything,' he said, and then he had the colossal nerve to look her up and down as if she were a prime heifer. 'Saddle up?'

Rachel would have loved to reject his offer. Unfortunately, her working Western saddle was heavy. There was always a borderline between getting revenge and getting a hernia, she told herself. One of her dad's old sayings. God, how I worshipped that man, and for what?

'Saddle up,' she mumbled, and turned away so that he could not read her face.

He was a quick worker. He hummed as he worked. One good item, one bad. Having no ear for music herself, she hated to hear other people enjoying themselves with song. She tucked up her hair under her riding-cap, brushed by him, and mounted, all with an economy of motion that he could not help but admire. 'Well, don't just stand there, cowboy.'

He grinned up at her again, and swung into his own saddle as gracefully as anyone might. Another tip to the brim of his hat. 'Yes, ma'am.'

'I told you not to call me ma'am,' she snapped at him as she turned her mare out into the farmyard.

'Yes, ma'am,' he acknowledged. Fuming, Rachel admitted her defeat by refusing to repeat herself. Instead she clapped her heels against her mount's sides, and went cantering off up the hill south of the house.

The area around the house was hard-packed dirt, as with most ranch houses. But just a few yards away from that empty area, they were riding stirrup-deep in the yellow and green and red flowers that constituted true prairie grass. 'Never seen anything like this back in Texas,' he admitted. He pulled his high-stepping gelding to a halt and pushed his hat to the back of his head. 'Oooee. Ain't that something?'

She nodded in agreement. From horizon to horizon the land sparkled with colour, and she loved it. And if this simple soul feels the same, we have *something* in common, she decided.

'There aren't many places like this left in the country,' she told him. 'Flint Hills here is about the biggest stretch of prairie in the West. When the first settlers came to this land it was all prairie. Mile after mile in all directions. For a time it was all ranching. Nothing could tame that tough soil. My grandfather could still remember when the prairie grass was as tall as a horse's saddle. Somewhere around 1836, somebody brought in the steel plough. It broke through the crust and Kansas became farm land. Well, not everywhere. Nowadays you'll see wheat and corn and oil-wells and factory zones. And occasionally one little space of the prairie left. The name here will tell you why. Flint Hills. Even the steel plough couldn't break through this rocky land. But the prairie grasses can—and do.'

'And here I rode all this distance expecting to find the tall corn growing,' he said mournfully. 'And look, there's not a tree in sight.'

How it's possible for a big man to look so downtrodden I'll never know, Rachel told herself. He has such a mobile face. Sometimes I wonder if it's all a put-on?

'More likely wheat and manufacturing—and the Army,' she said. 'And tornadoes and prairie grass. Trees spell the death of a prairie. It destroys the ambience of the soil. Ride out west of here. You'll see trees phasing in, and the gradual ending of the prairie. It's a delicate balance.'

He reined his mount in and stepped down from the saddle. She watched as he kicked at the dirt. His horse pawed, and there was a little spark of fire where the iron-shod foot scraped over the hard flint.

'And that,' she told him, 'is why this little patch of ground was never ploughed under. About as scrawny and scratchy a piece of land as you ever did see. But the prairie grass grows here, mainly because the roots go straight down for a considerable distance. And as long as we don't over-graze the area, all this will survive. Come on, Mr Texan, let's see what you can do.'

She rode without spurs. As soon as her heels touched the mare, the beast was off like a shot of lightning. His own gelding pranced for a moment, adding another second or two of delay before he could tuck his boot into the stirrup and swing aboard. And then, to make things worse, his mount began to move out after the mare before Charlie could get himself fully settled.

'Maybe it isn't the woman I'd better watch out for,' he muttered as he fumbled for his other stirrup. But once in the saddle his much bigger animal proved its worth. Within five minutes they were neck and neck, close enough to touch, until an ancient pinnacle of flint separated them. He came around the far side of the pinnacle, racing for all he was worth. Just out of the corner of his eye he noticed that Rachel had reined in her mount, and her mare dug in her heels and wheeled to a stop.

He was still racing and whooping, feeling like a fool as her mare performed in the old tradition, 'Turn on a dime and give you five cents change.' By the time he could wrestle the gelding to a stop and turn him around, the woman had dismounted. When he came up to her, Rachel Hammond was thin-lipped as she tried to keep from laughing.

He drew up beside her, solemn-faced. She let a giggle escape. Still no reaction. 'Isn't there anything that'll make you mad?' she asked.

'Nothing recently,' he drawled as he swung down and ground-reined his mount. 'Of course, there's no telling. What's that old saying? "You fool me once, shame on you. You fool me twice, shame on me!"'

Although he was still smiling, Rachel could feel the cold radiating from him. Cold steel, she told herself.

Watch out, girl. This is not a man to be crossed! Still, she could not hold back.

'Now, I think we'll go down to the corral,' she announced, 'and you can show me how good you are at roping one of those steers.'

He walked over and confronted her, barely an inch away. 'You mean one of those longhorns?'

'Why, of course.' She slapped the dust off her jeans, using her hat as a fan. The mare snorted, and did a stutter-step, but the girl controlled her with ease, and swung aboard.

'You want me to rope one of them steers, single-handed? Inside that tiny corral?'

'Why, yes. And hogtie it. You aren't scared, are you?'

'I'm not a rodeo rider,' he told her softly. 'And you're darn well right I'm scared,' he told her as he swung back up on to his mount. 'Only a fool would take a chance like that. And my pappy never raised any fools—ma'am. Out in the open with a lot of running room, where the other cattle could spread, that would be a different thing. But penned up in there with all those longhorns? No, thankee, ma'am.'

He was off before Rachel could muster up another word. And when she *did* find the word, it was the sort that her mother would have paddled her for! So she said it again, and trailed back to the ranch.

They met for dinner that night. She was pacing the living-room. Take her miles away from Libertyville, he told himself, and she's beginning to change a bit. Her hair was up in a classic chignon, her body masked by the masculine double-breasted suit. But there was a softness about her. Her face was no longer masked by that impenetrable look of command. Even without make-up there was a subtle femininity. There were differences between her and the picture of her grandfather hanging on the wall. *But* she's no longer a unisex businessperson, Charlie thought as he wandered into the room. She was standing by the closed-off fireplace, a martini in one hand.

'You're ten minutes late.' She confirmed by looking down at her wristwatch, then took a sip of her drink.

'You said eight-thirty,' he replied as he tugged at a gold chain that led to his shirt pocket. She glared as he hoisted out a massive gold watch and flipped its cover open. 'Eight thirty-five,' he commented. 'By golly, I *am* late. Five minutes late!'

'Ten minutes,' she said, using her most frigid tone. Just at that minute, the big grandfather clock in the hall struck the half-hour.

'We're both wrong,' he said, chuckling. 'It's only eight-thirty. Which means I'm not late at all.' He rushed across the room and began to pat her on the back. She had been taking another sip of the cocktail when he came out with that ridiculous statement, *We're both wrong!* Somehow the liquid got down the wrong pipe, and Rachel was choking.

He whipped her around in front of him, her back hard against his massive chest. His hands joined in front of her, knuckles in, just at her solar plexus. With one massive heave he forced the alcohol back up, and cleared her breathing tube. Unfortunately, since alcohol was a liquid, it sprayed out through her half-opened mouth and soaked the love-seat in front of her.

Rachel gasped, but managed to refill her lungs—and her temper as well. 'Now look what you've done,' she raged.

'Better wet the furniture than let you choke to death, lady.'

'That's a very valuable piece of furniture.' She wanted to shout at him, but had not enough breath left.

'Is that so?' he drawled. 'Looks like Grand Rapids, 1900.'

Rachel forced herself to settle down. It took some doing. And, while she did her deep-breathing exercises, she thought. When he's right, he's right. He just saved my life by applying the Heimlich manoeuvre. And then I complained because he made me spit up over a relatively useless chair. I owe him an apology.

Apologies were a thing that Rachel Hammond had long since discarded. But she could not just stand there, blinking her eyes at him. 'Grand Rapids, 1897,' she said. 'Would you like a drink?'

He grinned at her. He knows, she told herself nervously. He understands what's going on. Dear lord, what have I done? Chosen a man who's too smart for me?

'I could use a shot of red-eye,' he suggested. 'Seems to me it's been mighty cold in these parts all night long.'

'Red-eye?'

'Rye whiskey.'

'What sort of mix?'

'Nothing,' he said, and that grin—that infernal grin—was back again. 'My pappy told me that the only way to avoid getting drunk was to stick to one choice and drink it straight.'

'Your pappy seemed to have a lot to say,' she returned, gesturing him to a chair. 'Now. Tell me something about yourself, Mr—Charlie. Something real, for a change. Your pappy?'

'Not like me,' he started out. 'My pappy died young. In the wars, you know. Now my grandpappy is a *big* man. Spent a part of his life as a sky-pilot, and then switched full-time to ranching.'

'Sky-pilot?' she said sarcastically. 'You're beginning to sound like a very poorly written Western novel. So your grandfather was a preacher?'

'The best, lady. Still is. Got him a deep, strong voice. When he says "hell-fire" you just know that if you look around you the flames is coming straight at you. Evangelical. Preaches the old-time religion. Hell-fire and damnation! In these parts, too.'

'You mean he had a parish in this neighbourhood?'

'Well, not exactly. Gramps was a chaplain in the Army. Served over here at Fort Riley, then up at Fort Leavenworth. When he retired from the Army he went off back to Texas, and the family spread down there. A hard, God-fearing man. Yes, ma'am.'

Mrs Colchester came into the room, her face flushed, her white head bobbing back and forth like a pigeon on the strut. 'Dinner,' she said. Charlie pulled himself to his feet and offered Rachel his arm. She shrugged it off.

'We don't bother with that sort of nonsense,' she said, and floated by him and out of the door. Notice that, he told himself. Floated. It almost seemed to be. A longer skirt—the 1890 model, where her legs were invisible—and she'd look like a Navy destroyer, steaming up to dock! On the other hand, any man who would do anything to hide those magnificent legs of her ought to have his head examined! He came into the dining-room with a wry grin on his face.

'Something's funny?' She might have done away with *some* of the old customs, but she was standing there beside the chair at the head of the table, waiting for him to pull it out and seat her. He moved around Mrs Colchester to do just that.

'Funny? No, something pleasant, ma'am.' He pulled her chair out and waited while she seated herself.

'And don't call me ma'am,' she said. She glowered up at him. Her lips were already formed to say the same thing.

'You'll have to excuse me. I'm trying, but it's a hard thing to forget. My apologies.'

All the food was already on the table. There'll be no fancy serving in this house, he thought as he lifted the platter of steaks and offered her a choice.

'I can reach everything on the table,' she snapped. She sounded like some ambitious lieutenant on his first night in the field mess, and for a moment former Colonel Charlie Mathers felt like chewing her up one side and down the other, but decided on a twinkle instead. He set the platter down near her plate.

'And now what are you grinning at?'

'Nothing, ma'am—I mean, nothing. This all reminded me of a play I once saw.'

'A play? You saw a play?'

'Well, I didn't spend *all* my time chasing the north end of a cow headed south,' he drawled. 'I believe the author was Shakespeare. Or something of that nature. I *did* go to school,' he mused. 'Right nice it was in those days.'

'Don't tell me. Texas Agricultural?'

'Now that's a nice school too,' he agreed. 'But I didn't go there. I went to Southern Methodist. One of those little religious schools. My Gramps being a preacher and all——'

'Yes, yes, I understand.' She was eating with both hands, industriously. Steak and potatoes and greens.

And there's another thing I could do, he told himself. Get her out of the stable and into the living-room. Eventually they arrived at the coffee.

'What do you think about children?' She threw it in his face to watch the reaction. There didn't seem to be much of a change.

'Children,' he mused. 'Well, I can take them or leave them. That is if we're talking about *other* people's kids. Now my own—well, that's a different matter.'

She jumped on the phrase. 'You have children?'

'Not that I know of. On one or two occasions I thought—but, well, it was a minor mistake. You know how that is.'

'No, I don't know. Tell me.'

'Somehow it seems to me that there's a conversation going on beneath a conversation. If you want to know something specific, why don't you just come out and ask it? Or maybe give me a chance to ask a question or two?'

'All right. If you want to know something, go ahead and ask.' And if it isn't too far off base, she thought, I might even answer it. What in the world is the matter with me? I'm going all soft inside. If Grampa could have seen this performance, he'd have got a big stick and beat me something terrible! 'But Mrs Colchester will want to clear the table right now. Why don't we go out on the veranda and talk?'

It was not an invitation, he noted. It was a command. He smiled, helped her with her chair, and followed her outside, to where a broad veranda circled three sides of the old stone house. A couple of lounge chairs were already grouped around a small table, and a steaming pot of coffee sat in the middle of the table.

'Now, then?'

'First of all, what the devil connection is there between all this——' he waved his hand outwards to the stomping of the cattle in their pen, the sound of night-birds closing in on them, the smell of the flowers in the prairie grass '—and that muck-raking magazine down town? Which, I am told, you run with considerable enjoyment?'

Her face flushed for a moment. She sipped a little coffee to help control her impulse to anger. 'Money,' she said. 'My grandfather left me this ranch to save or kill. My father left me the magazine. The magazine makes money. The ranch doesn't. I wish it were the other way around, but it isn't.'

'So you plough all your profits into the ranch?'

'Not exactly,' she retorted. 'I don't own all this outright. There are other stockholders. All of whom groan and complain every year when I tell them how much money the ranch is losing.' She looked at him over the rim of her coffee mug. Her eyes were sparking. 'And don't, for heaven's sake, ask me, "What's a nice girl like you doing in a place like this?"'

'Oh, I wouldn't ask a fool question like that. I already know the answer. You're just not a nice girl.'

Her mug trembled in her hand, and almost fell to the floor. Got you with that one, didn't I? he thought. The dear little girl wants to appear to be a shrew, but doesn't want to be called one! Step one; now let's move on.

'It seems to me, ma'am,' he said, 'that you're going at this the wrong way around. It's the ranch that's losing money, not the magazine. Why don't you hire some smart hombre to run the ranch, cut down on a few of the sore spots, and make the ranch run a profit? It *must* be possible. Aren't there four or five other big spreads in the area? Some of them must be making a profit.'

'Seven, to be exact,' she snapped. She set her mug down on the table with considerable emphasis. 'I suppose you think you could take things in hand yourself?'

'Well now, I may not be the best cowpoke ever came down the pike, but I can see one or two little things that might be worth while.'

Cold seemed to settle between them. Not an arctic cold wave from the North Pole, such as winter might bring, but an emotional cold. Rachel Hammond had disappeared; Hammond the executive had taken her place. 'Give me a sample or two,' she commanded.

'Easy enough,' he drawled. 'Oh, if you don't mind, ma'am, I don't smoke, and I don't like to be around people who do.'

Rachel, who had a cigarette halfway to her mouth, paused. Her ordinary reaction would be to light a fire under the man, which would send him running straight back to Texas. 'But just for the hell of it,' her little devils whispered to her, and she killed the flame and dropped the butt into the nearby ashtray.

'You think that's important, do you?' Another struggle was going on beneath the surface, he could see. Her fists were clenched.

'Yes. Have you ever tried kissing a girl who's been smoking? Tastes like you were licking an old, greasy rag. Now, I was about to say——'

'I can't say that I've made a habit of kissing girls who smoke,' she interrupted. 'And before you go any further, Charlie, I've read Shakespeare myself. *The Taming of the Shrew*, wasn't it?'

He watched her, curious to see what other responses might erupt. When none followed, he went back to his story. 'Take those longhorns,' he said. 'There's a big speciality market for lean meat these days. But you can't raise enough beef to satisfy the market by keeping them penned in. You need to let them run the range.'

'Sure I do,' she muttered. 'Only then I need to keep them from interbreeding with my Herefords, and I have to put more men riding fence lines and watching, otherwise those longhorns will raise the devil with everything else that walks.'

'Not if you take the time to de-horn them,' he said. 'Ain't no big problem. De-horn them, put your brand on them, and turn them loose. How many men have you got riding for the brand right now?'

'Two,' she said, sighing. 'It's all I can afford.'

'You have to spend money to make money,' he said. 'One or two cowpokes could do the work, providing you had a helicopter to do it with.'

'Helicopter! I'm barely keeping my head above water, and now you want me to trade an inexpensive cowpoke for an expensive helicopter pilot? You're mad, man. Mad!'

He stood, stretching, and looked down at her. The moon was up, a three-quarter silver dollar, and its soft rays had erased all of her worry lines, all of her sternness. Very suddenly, Rachel Hammond looked like a frightened little girl. And Uncle Roger wanted me to come up to Kansas, he reminded himself, because he feared something would happen, or was happening, to this last of the Hammond family. What?

'Chopper pilots.' He half turned away from her. 'The woods are full of chopper pilots. All those thousands we've trained for Vietnam, for the Persian Gulf. They're all around you, lady, looking for a chance to make a buck.'

'And how do you know that?'

'Because I'm one of them myself, ma'am. And I'll bet that I could scratch up half a dozen more. Good cattle-men, who also can fly a chopper. What say, Ms Hammond?'

She struggled to her feet, with his hand helping, biting her lower lip. 'Just who are you?' she asked softly. 'What the devil is going on around here? I didn't hire you to be a cowpoke—and yet you are one. I don't need a ranch foreman—and yet you talk like one. I didn't want a heli-copter pilot—what else are you?'

'Just an ordinary man looking for work,' he said. He spoke as softly as she, so she moved closer.

'I wish I could believe that.'

'Believe it,' he answered. 'What you see is what you get. And if you didn't hire me for any of those particu-lars, just what the devil *did* you hire me for? Or, come to think of it, did you hire me at all?'

Rachel felt something in the pit of her stomach. Not exactly a pain, but rather a disturbance. Brought on either by this man or the things he talked about. Was there really something she could do to make the ranch profitable? Would it be possible to make over the *Gossiper* into something more to her liking? And what effect would any of that have on her primary goal?

Without realising it, she found his arm around her shoulder. The night winds were chilling. His warmth was just what she needed at the moment. And it was just then that her practical mind shifted into gear. She shrugged out of his grasp, settled her blouse and skirt, and cleared her throat.

'Yes, I'm hiring you,' she said. Charlie could feel the change. Hammond was back with him; lord knew where Rachel had disappeared. 'And I don't mind your taking a little interest in the ranch. After all, the primary reason for all this is for us to become acquainted.'

'Why?' he asked. 'Why do we go through all this just because you want us two to become acquainted?'

She moved away from him. A safe distance, her mind told her. From this point on I've got to keep the barriers up. I've got to remember that it's a business proposition I'm working at. Strictly business. Gawd, Daddy, why did you lay this on me?

'What I want,' she told him, 'is for you to give me a baby.'

CHAPTER THREE

A MILLION raging thoughts went through Rachel's mind as she watched Charlie's broad back disappear into the evening darkness. If I had the strength, she assured herself, I would go after him and hit him over the head with—whatever I could find on the way! But I don't have it—the strength, that is. How dare he turn his back on me?

And not a word about her statement. It had taken her the whole day to decide exactly how she planned to say it to him. And when he heard the sentence he had stood quietly in front of her, his lips had pursed in and out a time or two, and then, without saying a word, neither yea or nay, he had solemnly tipped her a salute and stalked away. The nerve of the man!

Only then, as she leaned against the pillar that held up the porch roof, did she begin to doubt herself. Did I say it wrong? she asked herself. Too explicit. Not explicit enough? Or does he expect something more than a straightforward business proposition? She leaned against the post. Whatever he planned to do, it would be done out of sight. Suddenly all her memories crowded in on her, and they hurt.

Her father was a disciplinarian of the worst sort. He had driven his only son to drink and death, and then tried to convert shy little Rachel into a replacement. It had been a soul-piercing conversion, ending up with the stone-faced Hammond of *Gossiper* fame. Only on the most difficult occasions, and then only in private, had

Rachel come out from behind her Hammond disguise to cry.

This was one of those occasions. Mrs Colchester had left to go back to her own cottage. And Charlie whatever-his-name-was had stalked off into the night. Weary, feeling twice her real age, Rachel stumbled down the hall in the semi-darkness, fumbled with her door, and threw herself on her bed.

The tears finally ended. She gathered herself up. No mere man was going to control her. There had to be a way around this initial set-back. What was it?

She flipped on the overhead light. No mollycoddling lamps for Hammond. Only a bare bulb in a ceiling fixture, just the way her father had always prescribed. With the light on, she was facing herself in the full-length mirror behind the door. And another startling thought. One which she had never thought before. Not in all her life. Am I not—good-looking enough?

I thought that men were ready to—do that at the drop of a hat. In fact, from her readings she had come to believe that not even an invitation was needed! And besides, that wasn't the way she meant to have it accomplished!

Warily she scanned her reflection. No, not beauty. A mannish look would be desirable; instead she looked like a Dresden doll. Not at all satisfactory. The blonde curly hair looked almost artificial in the bright white light from the ceiling. Her face was round, with pearly skin. A little too perfect. And blue eyes, tear-swollen eyes. Slowly she slipped off the rest of her clothes and studied the reflection. Her breasts bothered her the most. Her father had required that any feminine appearance be suppressed. Over the years, as she developed normally, everything appeared abnormal. In the last year of her father's life she had taken to binding her breasts. And now, as she was standing nude and alone, their size and shape could not be accepted.

Her narrow waist was no help at all. It pinched her in, and then swelled out into hips that seemed... Disgusted, she turned away from the mirror, slipped into her simple cotton nightgown, and pushed the light switch.

The electricity went off on command, but the moon was something else again. It poured through her two bedroom windows, and refused to go away. Although she savoured the summer night's breeze, she forced herself to pull the drapes, and then felt her way across the darkened room and fell into her narrow bed.

Not to sleep. Sleep was something that came after days of overwork. Then one took two sleeping pills, hurried into bed, and was eventually slugged into unconsciousness. But she hadn't worn herself down physically on this day, and she hated the thought of the pills. So she struggled and tossed and turned throughout the night. Nightmares raged through her mind. Black and white dreams of all the worst things her mind could conceive. Not until the rooster over in the chicken coop began to sound off, an hour or more before dawn, was she able to fall asleep.

Charlie Mathers was not a man who had trouble with sleeping. He worked or played all the hours God sent, and then fell into an easy, well-earned sleep. It was a light sleep, though. All the nights of his adult life he had slept with a secret internal alarm watching over him. He took a long walk up the hill to the corral where the longhorns had bedded down early. Now, almost at midnight, the herd leader stirred, and all the others moved at the same time. It was a sort of simple ritual, such as humans might do, rolling over in their sleep to find a more comfortable position. Far in the distance, out on the range, a coyote shrilled.

What in the world is going on? his busy mind asked. Did she say what I thought she said? In those exact words? 'What I want is for you to give me a baby'? More than one woman of his acquaintance had sent him signals of that nature, but always in insinuation, never in specific words. Did she think I was going to jump on her? Slam, bang, thank you, ma'am?

This girl was one crazy, mixed-up creature. Was this what Uncle Roger had seen, the sight that caused him to write to me to hurry home? Of course, when you were serving in the Air Force, you could hardly hurry off at a moment's notice. Generals might; colonels certainly didn't. They waited until they had their retirement papers in hand before they came steaming across the oceans to home, where Uncle's letter had been waiting. Play it cool, he told himself, as he wandered back down the hill towards the house. There was a dark shape waiting for him on the front porch.

Guard dog? It hardly seemed likely, yet it was so. Old Henrietta battered the porch floor a time or two with her tail, and offered to lick his proffered hand. Lord, even the dog is waiting for me to do *something*, he told himself. And I'm the only dope on the spread who doesn't seem to know just what *something* needed to be done! Disgusted with himself, he wandered down the darkened hall, guiding himself with one hand on the wall, until eventually he found his own place, went in, and collapsed on to the bed. Where, despite all the niggling, he promptly fell asleep, and made not a move until the cock crowed at dawn, Kansas time.

* * *

Nobody appeared at the breakfast table at seven o'clock. Mrs Colchester shook her head. No good can come of it, she told herself as she loaded up the plates in the kitchen and brought them through. No good can come of a man and a woman sharing the same house, unmarried. Her Calvinist soul screamed for her to do something. But all she knew to do was to put the cooked breakfast on the table and go back to her cleaning. So she did.

When Charlie appeared at eight o'clock the eggs were cold, the oatmeal had congealed, and the coffee looked as if it had grown moss. But Charlie, knowing it was his own fault, did the best he could with the eggs, ignored the oatmeal, and really enjoyed the coffee. At least its heating pad had kept it warm, and everyone knew how rotten the coffee could get to be in the military.

When Rachel appeared at nine o'clock, she looked like the wrath of God had struck her. Her hair was all pushed to one side, her robe just barely covered her nightgown, and her eyes were filled with sleep.

'Good morning,' he essayed.

'Shut up,' she groaned. 'Nobody talks to me before my coffee.' She fumbled over to the table and dropped heavily into a chair. Charlie, who was feeling almost human, poured her a mug of coffee. She surrounded the mug with both hands, treasuring the warmth, and then took a sip.

'Great day in the morning!' she howled. 'You're trying to poison me! Who made this slop?'

'Not me. That's the way I found it. I thought it tasted pretty good.'

Rachel carefully grounded the mug on the table-top and pushed her hair back off her eyes. 'You?'

'Charlie,' he said. 'You remember? Charlie. You invited me out to spend a month on your ranch, and then——'

'Stop. Don't tell me any more. Have you eaten anything?'

'Yes. Cold eggs. Not bad, except they were fried in grease, not in butter, and they——'

'Dear lord protect me,' she muttered as she picked up a piece of burnt, cold toast. 'Look, Mr—Charles. We need to talk. But not now. Would you please go away and then join me in my office after lunch?'

'You're the boss.' He scraped back his chair and made a quick exit. In the hall he ran into Mrs Colchester. 'You enjoyed your breakfast?' the housekeeper asked. Charlie took a good look at her. She didn't sound sarcastic, but then one never knew.

'Yes,' he said. 'The coffee was fine, but I don't care for fried eggs. And I don't see how Hammond is going to eat that oatmeal.'

'Hah!' Mrs Colchester did her best to look him straight in the eye, which was difficult because she was so short. 'If you'd come at the right time, it would've been a good meal. God's punishment, that's what.'

Charlie Mathers, who had spent all his formative years within the family of a parson, perked up his ears. God's punishment for coming late for breakfast? Probably something out of the Old Testament? There was a time he could spot almost any quotation from the Bible, but not any more.

'And her father would never have let her leave the table if she came in late, without eating everything in sight. A firm, sound man, her father was.'

'Yes, I can see he must have been,' Charlie said. He looked back through the open door into the dining-room.

Rachel Hammond was hunched over, fighting to swallow the oatmeal, her face almost screwed up into tears.

'Spare the rod and spoil the child,' the housekeeper said as she swept out of the hall.

'Yes,' Charlie repeated. 'I'm sure he must have been some sort of man.' Mrs Colchester smiled at him. It was the first time he had seen the old lady smile. She evidently thought he was agreeing with her. Shaking his head, he stomped out of the house and headed over to the stables.

Much to his surprise, there were three men in the area. One of them came stalking over towards him. 'And just who the hell are you?'

Charlie looked him over. A tall, bony man, half-bald, with a face much wrinkled from an outdoor life. Not too old, on second look. He was the sort of man who had been pounded out on life's anvil and left without any finishing touches. And obviously he was—or at least he thought of himself as—a man. 'You must be the foreman,' he offered tentatively.

'Yeah, I'm the foreman. And you?'

'Oh, I came out with Hammond. I'll be here a month, I guess.'

'Hey, boys.' The foreman waved the other two men over. 'Look what we've got here. Ms Hammond's fancy boy!'

'Don't look like no lap-dog,' the first man commented. 'Looks more like a fire hydrant.'

'What I want to know,' Charlie said gently, 'is what happened to those twenty head of longhorn cattle that were in the corral last night?'

'Oh, is that all you want to know?' the foreman jeered at him. 'Curious fellow, are you?'

'Got my share of it,' Charlie said, and offered his most vacuous grin for their approval.

'Hot damn,' the foreman said through clenched teeth. 'A curious pilgrim. Where are you from, boy?'

'Texas. Now, about those longhorns.'

'Ain't been any longhorns around this spread in twenty years,' the forman told him. 'Now why don't you slip back into the house and get about pleasing Ms Rachel? I'm sure there's somethin' you could be doing in the kitchen. We've got man's work to do.'

'Yes, I'll bet you have.' Charlie stepped out of the way and watched the three of them saddle up and ride out. A few minutes later he located the gelding he had ridden the day before, and followed suit.

The horse seemed to remember him. It whickered as he mounted, did a round dozen prancing dance steps, and then headed out in the generally south direction. The horse wanted to run; Charlie slacked off on the reins and let him go.

The prairie seemed to go forever over rolling, climbing country. The prairie did, but the fence seemed to stop. Charlie reined in and took a better look. About fifty feet of barbed wire fence was gone. Not down, but gone completely. It was hard to track individual cattle tracks in the high prairie growth. On this side of the fence, that was. On the other side it was easy to see the tyre tracks of a huge truck. A truck that had come more than once to the same spot. And, in the distance now, Charlie could hear the subdued roar of auto traffic. Route 35—he knew the Kansas Turnpike lay over in that direction.

'Well, now, horse,' Charlie murmured. 'It would seem that there's more than one fish in the sea in these parts.' He checked with his wristwatch. It was almost noon. Almost time for his next appointment with Rachel. He turned his mount back towards the ranch house. The horse seemed disappointed at having its run curtailed, but after a moment he picked up speed. They both had worked up a sweat by the time they pulled up in the stable area. The lunch bell was ringing.

Charlie ducked his head in the water bucket sitting next to the horse trough, and ran for the house. He had many interesting questions he wanted to ask, and was afraid of what some of the answers might be.

Rachel Hammond had preceded him into the dining-room. 'About time,' she said gracelessly. 'You don't seem to understand. We prize promptness here. Another minute or two and you'd go hungry.'

Charlie dropped into the chair at her side, rather than the place set at the far end of the table. 'At least I don't have to eat cold oatmeal,' he said.

She flared up immediately. Flared up, grew tense, showed colour on her face, and on the parts of her neck that her dress revealed. But said not a word. She *had* dressed, Charlie noted, comparing her presence to what he had seen at breakfast. Her hair was neatly combed, the unruly curls tamed for the moment. Her utilitarian high-collar grey dress failed her purpose—to be unnoticeable. It clung lovingly to a figure that was more than adequate. Her blue eyes shot spears at him.

When she had regained her control, she said, 'You try hard to be obnoxious, don't you? I'm not sure that——'

'That I'm the man you want? Maybe I could suggest a few other things I might be able to do for you.'

Mrs Colchester came in at that moment, carrying a single tray and two plates. What you see is what you get, Charlie told himself as he looked down at the tiny sandwich and the decorative pickle on the plate that was put before him.

Rachel picked up her fork and began. 'You were saying?'

'I think I could suggest some ways for you to make your ranch pay,' he told her. 'That would give you a chance to relax from the magazine.'

'Why do you think I would want to relax?' Rachel sat up straight in her chair and pulled her shoulders back. What in the world would I do with time to relax? she asked herself. Sew a fine seam? Lord, I hate sewing. Does this—man—think he can run *my* life? Her chin tilted just the slightest bit higher.

'Can't eat if you can't see the plate, lady. About the relaxing?'

'All right. What about it?'

'You have a foreman here for the ranch?'

'Of course. Mr Hendrix. He's been here since before my father died.'

'And about how often did you manage to get out here? Before this present visit, I mean.'

'Are you trying to say I neglect the ranch?'

'No, nothin' like that. How often, please, ma'am?'

'I—oh, the devil with it. I make it a practice to come out here four times a year. Well, theoretically, that's my schedule. This last year we've been having trouble with the magazine. I didn't get out at the Christmas season, nor at the autumn round-up.'

'Pressing business at the magazine,' he commented. 'Of course, if you have faith in your foreman there'd be no problem.' He had to stop talking at this point. His insulted palate was trying to tell him something. Sandwich? Not beef, or ham, or make-do peanut butter. He picked up the quartered corner and did his best to inspect without actually doing so. Watercress and cucumber?

'A family tradition,' she told him. 'My father enjoyed it.'

'I'll bet he did,' Charlie murmured, and did his best to hide the look of repulsion on his face. 'But for a working cowboy——'

'Yes?'

'As I said yesterday, Ms Rachel, I've been running spreads bigger than this since I was fourteen years old, and if you would like to take advantage of my experience for as long as we're going to be here I would certainly enjoy it. A month is a long time for a man like me to have only one objective.'

He knew the moment the words were out of his mouth that he had said too many of them. *Only one objective?* But the girl beside him was considering, and to his surprise she picked up a different point from that he had expected.

'You ran this spread you speak of all by yourself?'

'Of course not. Pa was busy most of the time, and Ma was helping him. But I had plenty of help. I was the oldest kid in the family, but with four brothers and three sisters——'

'That many?' He had struck an interesting point. Her eyes lit up, and her head snapped out of is customary crouch.

'Yes, ma'am. That many. We managed to rub along real well. To tell the truth, if you didn't rub along in my family all the rest would gang up on you. That was before they all got married, that is.'

'*All* got married?'

'Well, all but me. After schooling, I decided to go adventuring. My brother Albert took over the home spread, and all the others found jobs in our corporation. And then they—well, my mother used to say it was an old Irish tradition. If you can't out-fight your enemy, out-populate them!'

Rachel's fork fell on to the plate with a dull clang. 'You—they all have families?'

'You'd better believe it,' he said, chuckling. 'Our family reunions are like the mustering of the clan back in the old country. I can't remember the exact count, but I have a birthday remembrance book with three or four entries for every month. Now, how about it? Would you like me to help you around the ranch?'

For the first time that day, Rachel Hammond seemed to light up all over. 'Well, Charlie,' she said eagerly, 'I think there are lots of things you could help me with. Now, have you finished your lunch? Is there something else you'd like?'

Charlie Mathers looked up over Rachel's head. Mrs Colchester was standing in the doorway, a large smirk on her face. 'Yes,' he said, 'there certainly is. I'd like a couple of hamburgers and a cup of real coffee.'

It was late that afternoon when the serene calm of the ranch was almost totally destroyed. Charlie had settled himself in the living-room next to the telephone, and had made half a dozen calls in private, when he heard a horse come galloping up to the house, and a few minutes later a pair of loud voices from the office. To snoop or not to snoop had never been a problem for Charlie. One gathered as much information as one could, in whatever manner, if one intended to be a success in anything, from love to labour.

When the voices rose higher, he got up and stalked down the hall. Outside Henrietta was whining on the porch, upset by the sound. The office door was half open. Without a 'by your leave', he walked in. Rachel was sitting behind a huge desk, almost bouncing up and down in the grip of some excitement. The range foreman, Hendrix, was leaning over the desk, pounding his fist on the mahogany finish.

'Look here,' Hendrix said. 'I'm the foreman. I run this ranch. Whatever happened to those longhorns is my business! I've been running this ranch according to all your father's rules for almost half your lifetime. Who put you up to this, Hammond? That imported wimp you brought home with you?'

Rachel was in such a state that she was almost weeping. She runs the magazine with whip in hand, Charlie told himself, but she doesn't seem to have any control at all over the ranch. Because she felt she had to run it the way her father did? Lord, what a lot that man has to account for! But this is where the changes need to begin. He came up behind the foreman and tapped him on the shoulder. Hendrix straightened up and turned around. He was a tall, well-formed man, this foreman, standing inches above Charlie's height, and perhaps twenty pounds more in weight. But he hadn't the muscles, the build that Charlie had. He tried to shrug off Charlie's hand from his shoulder to no avail.

'We mustn't forget,' the Texan said softly, 'that it's Ms Rachel who's in charge around here, must we?' He flexed his fingers. They bit into Hendrix's shoulder, and the foreman winced. 'Isn't that true?'

'I—yes, damn you! Turn me loose!'

'When I'm ready. Ms Rachel wanted to tell you that I'm going to be assisting you around the spread for a few weeks. Isn't that right, ma'am?'

'Yes,' Rachel agreed, as she sank back into her chair and sniffed at an incipient tear. 'Yes. He's going to help!' Spoken with much more conviction, that last part.

'After thirty years around this ranch, I don't need no help from him,' Hendrix roared. 'Your father would never do anything like that!'

'But her father isn't with us any more.' Again that soft but persistent voice from Charlie, compounded with another dig of his fingers into Hendrix's soft shoulder muscles.

'Well, I'm not going to——' Hendrix roared, and then broke off. Charlie Mathers had transferred his one hand from the shoulder muscles to the lapels of the bigger man's shirt, and had picked him up an inch or two off the floor.

'Before somebody says something that he might regret, why don't you and I walk out on the veranda for a private conversation?' The foreman hardly had the capacity to rebel. His feet paddled as he was towed out of the door. Charlie winked at Rachel as he stepped out of the room. The girl sank back again in her padded chair, and sighed.

'Why?' she asked herself aloud. But she knew the answer. Her father had always limited her. He pushed her into impossible situations at the magazine, and drove her into the mould he wanted, but had never given her control at the ranch. 'Magazines are for women,' he said more than once. 'Ranching is man's work!' And only now did Rachel Hammond see that that sort of statement was fuel for so many of her rages.

When Charlie came back about fifteen minutes later he was alone. 'I only asked him a question,' she said defensively. 'I can't make heads nor tails out of these ledger books, so I only asked him a question. You'd think that the owner was entitled to a simple explanation, wouldn't you?' She came up out of her chair and pushed it back so hard that it slammed into the wall and fell over.

'You would certainly think so.' Charlie came straight to her, around the desk, past the chair's spinning little casters, holding his arms out. Without thinking, Rachel took that one step forward and was enveloped in the warmth.

They stood that way for about five minutes, until Rachel began to reason beyond the comfort and the warmth. She pushed herself away from him. He let her go without a struggle, bending down to set her chair back on its wheels. She sank into its safety with a sigh. 'Why did you do that?'

'Do what? Hug you?' He tilted her chin upward, to where he could look into her eyes. 'You've never been hugged before?'

'Not much.'

'But you enjoyed it?'

'Yes.'

He sat down in the big chair in front of her desk. 'Hugging,' he lectured, 'is a primal need for human beings. You said we ought to get to know each other better. There's no better way for that to happen than hugging.'

'Not kissing?'

'No, not kissing. Kissing builds up—other—tensions. Hugging is the thing, Ms Rachel. Now then, about your Mr Hendrix.'

'He—he's not really *my* Mr Hendrix. He's my *father's* Mr Hendrix. What about him?'

'He claimed that you didn't know beans about running a ranch. That your father never let you put a hand to ranching, not once.'

'I—I'm afraid that's true. He wanted me to run the magazine, to make a lot of money that we could plough back into the ranch, and he—never——'

'That's all right,' he interrupted. 'It doesn't matter. Anyone can learn this business if she has a good teacher.'

A tiny spark of independence returned to her. 'And you're that teacher?'

'Well, that's up to you to say, Ms Rachel. For the moment I can take over the work. You can evaluate it. If I don't make a difference in a month's time you can get someone else.'

'I—don't like the way you said that.' She sat up in her chair and sniffed a tear away. 'You make it sound as if Mr Hendrix is——'

'Leaving,' he interrupted again. 'After a sincere talk, Mr Hendrix told me that he had worked long enough for the brand, and was going to quit.'

'Oh, my! He—you just discussed it and he——'

'Threw in his hand, as Zane Gray would say. Effective yesterday.'

'But—he's been working here a long time, and he ought to have a pension and retirement benefits, and things like that.'

He grinned at her, and leaned across the desk to where the account-books still lay. 'Mr Hendrix,' he drawled, 'has been collecting his retirement benefits for the past ten years or more.'

'I don't understand.'

'Those longhorns,' he said, tapping the book with one finger. 'I don't know when you bought them for fattening, or how long you've kept them, but they've been sold.' His big finger tapped the cover of the book. 'And I gather there hasn't been an entry made in the book. Mr Hendrix and his two friends kept the sale money.'

'But—that's——'

'You don't have any idea what you would get for twenty prime longhorns these days, do you? The longhorn is all lean beef. In this day of dieting, lean beef is the clamour from every supermarket in the country.'

'You're right,' she said. 'I haven't any idea how much money is involved.' So he told her.

'Dear God!'

'Exactly. Now, we could call the sheriff and have your Mr Hendrix arrested for theft. Or we could give him a good kick in the seat of his trousers and get him out of here. If we arrest him it will cause a good deal of scandal. If we boot him out, there'll be a lot less trouble.'

Rachel Hammond was not a girl who required much time to make up her mind. 'Do it.'

'I did.' Charlie rubbed the knuckles of his right hand. Rachel looked. The skin across that massive hand had been scraped.

'You didn't hurt him?'

'Not very much. He thought it was a great joke. Up until I carefully explained the whole situation. And then he got up and went over behind the barn to get his truck. As far as I know, he's halfway to Beaumont by this time.'

'And those other two?'

'Would you believe, they turned out to be cousins of his? They left at the same time. After I finished the argument with Hendrix, the other two didn't seem to want to argue any further.'

'I—you leave me with nothing more to say,' she commented as she leaned back in her chair. It was a relief she had seldom felt, this leaning back to allow the chair to take up some responsibility. Her mother and father had taught her to sit with straight back and feet flat on the floor. I wonder if I . . . ? she argued with herself. And then, 'Oh, the devil with it.'

She reached over and pulled out the top drawer of the desk. And then, with careful manoeuvre, put her heels up on the desk itself. The chair squeaked, she achieved balance, and suddenly the world was full of sunshine.

'I don't suppose you ever put your feet up on a desk?' she asked.

'Not when I'm wearing spurs,' he returned. That broad grin was back on his face, rubbing out those grim lines that she associated with him. It made him look—somewhat—attractive. If there really were such a thing as love, Hammond, she lectured herself, this might be the sort of man to begin it with!

'Now then, Boss, what would you like me to do next?'

Her feet came off the desk with a dismal thump. 'I thought we had straightened everything out,' she said. 'You're the foreman—and you'll figure out what's next. Won't you?'

The question at the end of the statement was said tentatively. She even managed to work up a tiny smile of encouragement, which seemed to set him off into a gale of laughter. Which she just could not understand.

When he finally quit the laughter he said, 'Yes. I'll figure out what to do next, but you're the boss. You have to put your brand on all the goings-on. Like, we need a couple of hands right away.'

'OK. Hire some.'

'I did. They'll be in tomorrow.'

'Then,' she said, 'we need to conduct a muster, to see how many cattle we really have.'

'Right on the spot,' he returned. 'Down in Texas we call it a round-up. For which we'll need a helicopter.'

'Rent one?'

He put his feet up on the corner of the desk. Rachel emulated him. It felt so good. Not that she had her feet up, although that was a—relaxing—postion. But rather because she was, for the first time, feeling totally relaxed. Nothing seemed to be impossible.

'To tell the truth,' he mused, 'I already have a chopper in the area. I suppose we could use it until we get settled down?'

'It has to be business,' she said. 'No borrowings, no gifts. Straight business.'

'Yup. Straight business.'

'This is all very nice,' she said in a brave tone of voice, 'but it's not the major objective of your visit.' He nodded as if he understood.

'When I said I wanted you to give me a baby I meant it.' His eyes narrowed. 'Of course, I meant it to be by artificial insemination!'

Charlie Mathers, caught unawares, almost choked as he lost his balance and his chair fell over on to the floor.

CHAPTER FOUR

THE ranch lay quiet for three days. Nothing stirred at the house. On occasion Rachel would come out to the stables, and Charlie would appear, unsummoned. Together they would saddle up, walk sedately out of the paddock, and then ride like the wind for as long and as far as her mare and his gelding would take them. On the afternoon of that third day Charlie borrowed her car and went off.

On the next day a helicopter circled the house a couple of times just an hour before lunch. The stabled horses snorted and jittered at the noise. Rachel came out of the office, a furrow on her face. A lesson in bookkeeping the night before had set her to searching this morning, and she did not like what she had read.

The noise of the chopper brought her outside, as the pilot searched for a flat place to land. The machine came down with a bump as a stray gust of wind struck the blades just at the moment of landing. The landing shocks squealed, the carriage absorbed the blow, and the giant blades lowered their pitch and finally came to a stop.

Even Mrs Colchester was brought to the scene by her own curiosity. She stood on the veranda with a mixing bowl and wooden spoon in hand, and nagged at her mistress, whose immediate response was to run out into the yard, not at all a ladylike response.

'Charlie!'

He climbed awkwardly out of the cabin and came over to her. 'You were expecting chopped liver?' He looked over his shoulder at the aircraft. 'Seventeen years,' he mused, 'and I still can't get the landings right!'

'Don't be like that,' Rachel said in her softest voice. 'I don't doubt that you're the finest pilot in the—in the what? I missed you.'

'One night and you missed me?' He chucked her under her chin and laughed. 'Air Force, lady. Air Force.' Henrietta came trotting out to meet them. He stooped to ruffle the dog's fur.

'The men ought to be along any minute,' he said as he walked them back to the house.

'They came already,' Mrs Colchester reported. 'Two men, two trucks, two trailers, two horses. And they are all Indians! Me, I am Indian too, of the Potowotami.'

Charlie stretched out and laughed. It was the first time he had seen even the tiniest crack in the housekeeper's stolid face. 'The horses are Indians too?'

'You know what I mean,' the woman said, demanding with her eyes that her dignity be restored. 'The men—they're not from any tribe around here.'

'Comanche,' he told her, and grinned as her black eyes grew rounder. 'Comanche warriors. You'd better hide, little Potowotami.'

'Don't tease her.' Rachel Hammond had grown immeasurably over the past few days. She had a better control over both her reflexes and her emotions. But still there was that glint of rock-hard character in her eyes. Flint-hill character? she asked herself. Am I like the rock of these hills? It's nice to have him back. Very nice. But that doesn't mean I have to tell him so, or let him read it in my face.

'Lunch in ten minutes,' she announced. Mrs Colchester cut off her smile. Look at that, Rachel told herself. She's been giving the orders for so long that she's insulted when I usurp her place. Or maybe it's when I regain the place that *she* usurped so long ago? In any event, the housekeeper said nothing, but set off for the kitchen, muttering, 'Lunch in ten minutes. Hah!' under her breath.

Charlie put his hands on Rachel's shoulders and turned her into the light. 'So. You look a lot better, boss. Been out in the fresh air?'

'And curled up with a good book,' she said solemnly. 'The station accounts. We seem to have holes in our fabric.'

'About as big as the holes in your fences,' he commented. And at that moment a heavy truck pulled up into the yard, hesitated for a moment, and went off up the hill. The sign on the side of the truck said Pontiac Fence Menders.

'A separate crew for the fencing job,' he reported as she turned to look. 'There's too much to do and cut a tally too. You know the old story, the West was won by colt revolvers and barbed wire fences? We don't need the revolvers, but we do need the fences. Are you friendly with all your neighbours?'

'Mostly. You'd better wash. There's been a revolution in the kitchen, but being on time is still important.'

He slid one of his big hands up behind her neck and positioned her head for a quick kiss on the forehead. He turned and walked down the hall towards the bathroom, while Rachel's eyes followed him. That long, loping stride, the cut of his square shoulders—everything a woman could ask for, she told herself, and then grinned. Because of course he wasn't. He wasn't exactly tall, he wasn't dark except for his permanent sunburn, and she was positive that she could find somewhere on his stripped torso some pure white. And he wasn't—well, that might be debated—handsome. He was very good at evading the issue in these parts. She brushed a hand across her forehead, where his lips had touched her. That was nice, wasn't it? Of course it was, you dope, she retorted, and went off to her own ablutions.

They were both back at the required time. Mrs Clochester had set the table rather formally, including a pure white tablecloth. The dishes seemed to be a little more fancy than he had become accustomed to. 'My grandmother's,' Rachel explained.

'Makes me suspicious,' he replied. 'Usually when a restaurant improves the chinaware it's because the food is getting worse.'

'Not worse,' she said, teasing him. 'But certainly different.'

And so it was. When Mrs Colchester wheeled in a cart of food, it contained a stack of hamburgers, a pot of steaming coffee, and a very small side-dish of vegetables. 'Wow,' he said.

'Wow indeed. Mrs C threatened to quit. Said it wasn't Christian to gorge yourself on red meat.'

'You pacified her? A rise or something?'

'Hey,' she said. 'I read the books. I understand your system. Hendrix wasn't the only one working a good thing around here. I told her if she didn't straighten up and fly right I'd fire her. Now, what about the proposal I made to you a few nights ago?'

'I have to eat,' he objected. 'And then I have a mile of work to do. You'll just have to wait, Rachel.'

She looked at him curiously. 'Are you *sure* your brothers and sisters all have big families?'

'Every one,' he said as he reached for a burger. 'God's own truth. Every one.'

'And you've never had any childhood—accidents?'

'Broke my leg once,' he answered innocently.

'Damn you,' she muttered. 'A broken leg wouldn't affect this! I *have* to have an answer!'

'All in good time,' he mumbled, his mouth full of burger. 'My, isn't this stuff a lot better than watercress?'

The work was hard. First a helicopter sweep around the entire perimeter of the spread, with Rachel and one of the workmen from the wire crew in the back seat. 'And there's another big one down there,' Charlie said. The chopper heeled over to one side and dived like an attack-machine. Rachel lost her arrogant cool and squealed, just before she lost all her colour.

'Do you have to do that?' Said petulantly, as she bent over to hold her stomach together. He casually turned around in his seat to look.

'Don't do that,' she commanded. 'Look where you're—flying.'

'I didn't realise you had stomach problems,' he half apologised. 'Did you get that location, Heinz?'

'Got it. That makes six. It hardly seems that there are any cattle at all on the spread. Most of them could walk their way to Topeka at the drop of the hat.'

'Not to worry,' Charlie said. 'There's good grass and plenty of water in the central area. Cattle may not be the smartest animals in the world, but they seldom walk off and leave good grazing behind them. Under their own steam, that is. Now, one more stretch, and we'll have it.'

'Then you wouldn't mind going just the least bit slower?'

He twisted around in his seat again and inspected her. Pale cheeks, perspiration, trembling hands. 'No, I wouldn't mind. In fact, we'll go straight back to the house. That's plenty for today. It'll be two or three days before your crew can get all that.'

'Three,' Heinz commented. 'We follow the old Spanish tradition, "*poco a poco*".'

'Which means?' Rachel managed to ask.

'A little bit at a time,' Charlie told her, and then concentrated on the approach and a gentle landing. He did a better job of it this time, but Rachel needed help to unglue her fingers from the steel arms of her seat.

By dinnertime Rachel was exhausted. It was not an unusual thing, but normally it was mental exhaustion. This time it was physical. She groaned as Mrs Colchester helped her into her chair.

'Some ancient and arcane Kansas disease?' Charlie came in, humming a little tune, and took the chair next to her. There are times, she told herself, when I deeply resent all that muscle of his. But then he wasn't down on hands and knees scrubbing the floor!

'House-cleaning,' she retorted. 'I hadn't realised how little cleaning has gone on in this house during the past few years. Mrs Colchester assures me that she's the cook, not the housekeeper. I ache in places where I didn't even know I had places.'

'I'll give you a good massage after we eat,' he promised.

'No, thanks.' She drew herself up straight-backed in her chair and glared at him. 'Another one of your secret skills?'

'Yes.' He gave a grand sigh. 'My last one, I'm sorry to say. Good chicken, this is. Local stuff?'

'Yes.' Her voice sparkled with pride. 'Except for the fresh vegetables, we grow most everything we eat. And what we don't grow—like flour, for instance—we trade for with our neighbours. This ranch ought to be self-sufficient.'

'Don't worry your head,' he said. 'Sooner 'n you can say "jump" it will be!'

The next day she volunteered to go out on the range with him. 'You won't like it,' he promised. 'Better if you stay at home. Most women don't exactly appreciate range work.'

'Well, I'm no candy-heart,' she said, and despite his objections she saddled her own horse and joined the crew just as the sun came up.

'The first thing we do,' he told her, 'is to gather a little herd together. The men built a corral out in the boondocks yesterday. Once we get the cattle into the enclosure, we'll go to work.'

'Seems to me the only work required is to move the cattle into the enclosure,' she said. 'What else can there be?'

'I...' He was almost ready to tell her, and decided not to. 'I think you'd better wait and see,' he said. So all morning long she rode trail as the men gathered in strays from the north section of the range. It wasn't as bad as she expected. From her reading, she expected a ride in a spit of dust. Here on the prairie, where the grass was as tall as a steer's stomach, there wasn't that much of a problem. By noon they had gathered in some fifty head.

She was glad when he swung down from his saddle and invited her to do the same. Mrs Colchester had appeared, driving a wagon that was to serve as a chuck-wagon. A fire improved the landscape. She hung on the rail of the temporary corral and looked at her bawling possessions.

'Not bad,' he told her. 'Take a good look. Those older steer look to be four years old. They're ready for market. Where do you ship them?'

'We generally move them by truck over to Holcombs,' she told him. 'The big slaughterhouse to the west of us.'

'So we'll sell off those twenty-two,' he said, whittling another notch on the tally stick which seemed to be always with him. 'Do you have any idea what they'll bring?'

'Not the slightest,' she said. 'I can quote you advertising rates for any page and size in our magazine, but ranch prices... Mr Hendrix always took care of that.'

'What an owner,' he chided. 'Those are all prime beef.' And he told her what price she might expect. Rachel took a deep breath. It was almost as if Santa Claus had scheduled a second visit to the hill country all in one year.

'And now what about those others?' She gestured at the rest of the herd that was gradually being segregated.

'I don't understand this,' he allowed. 'Normally when you buy young beef and fatten it, you don't have this sort of problem. But there are young calves out there. They need to be branded. And then...' His voice dropped, as if he didn't want her to hear.

'What?'

'Rachel,' he said, 'come get your lunch.'

'I'd like to know what's going on. It's my ranch.'

'It certainly is,' he agreed. 'But after lunch, shall we?'

Back at the chuck-wagon, Mrs Colchester had arranged a canvas fly-leaf which provided a little shade at the side of the wagon. They all moved into that shade, collected a plateful of food, and squatted down to eat.

'Don't you think this meal is a little too hearty?'

He looked over at her plate. 'We're not writing gossip stories,' he told her. 'Beef stew, with plenty of vegetables. Just right for this kind of work. Plenty of hot grub. Eat up.' Just this once, Rachel told herself, I'm not going to argue with him. He's been nice to me for a couple of days; I'll be nice to him.

She stuffed herself, and then added a little more. When the meal was done he walked over to the spring near where they were camped, filled both canteens, and came back. By that time the two cowboys were inside the corral, with a separate fire going.

'I want to see,' she insisted.

He pulled her down to the ground. 'No, you don't,' he said. She could smell the sizzle of hide as the branding irons were put to use. The heifers bawled and kicked up a fuss. Sitting behind the chuck-wagon as they were, she could see nothing.

'I thought that branding wasn't supposed to hurt them?' she asked anxiously.

'Depends on how thick the hide is,' he returned.

'Have you any idea how cruel that sounds?' she asked, exasperated. 'How would you feel if somebody came around and tried to put their brand on your—your hindquarters? That's no way to treat a lovely little cow.'

'You just aren't going to let go, are you?' he said wryly. 'Well, in order of questions, no, I wouldn't care to have my bum branded. Secondly, the heifers aren't the ones making all the noise.'

'That's enough evasion,' she snapped. For a moment she was Hammond, back again in all her regal glory. 'Tell me what's going on!'

'OK, lady, you asked for it. Some of those little beasts are male.'

'That doesn't tell me anything!'

'You're in the business of fattening cattle,' he said, sighing. 'The male is a fractious animal. If you want him to be fat and contented you have to——'

'Oh, my God, they aren't——'

'Yes, they are, ma'am. Would you like to go watch?'

Rachel certainly didn't want to go and watch. She didn't even want to stay where she was. She was up on her feet before he could offer a hand, dashing away from the wagon and the corral, in the direction of the spring. By the time he caught up with her she had lost all her lunch, and was hunched over in some misery, trying to comfort her upset stomach.

To complete her misery, she was still crouched down next to the spring when the two cowboys came out of the corral. 'All finished, Charlie,' one of them said. 'We're going to have a fine meal of prairie oysters tonight. Care to come join us?'

'Prairie oysters?' she asked.

'They're going to stay out here tonight,' he said. 'The trucks will be available tomorrow morning. After they load them up they'll round up another bunch, and do it all over again.'

'Prairie oysters?' she demanded. He had been trying to avoid looking at her. Now it was impossible. Her face was white, her eyes rimmed with red, and she was trembling.

'Take my word for it,' he said. 'Nothing is wasted at a round-up. You really wouldn't want to know.'

'Oh, my God.' She came up to her feet, looking for some place to run. Nothing appeared appetising, so she moved a tentative foot in his direction, and then ran at him as soon as he opened his arms to her.

Mrs Colchester had finished hitching her old piebald horse to the chuck-wagon, and started to bump over the prairie towards the ranch house. 'Come on,' he ordered.

Without protest, Rachel Hammond went with him to where their horses had been ground looped, and waited while he saddled them both. They rode back, a full hour of travel, without a word being said. When she dismounted at the stable she left him to care for the horses, and fled to the house.

At dinnertime Charlie was the only one to come to the table. Mrs Colchester grumbled and mumbled as she served him. A fine, full meal it was, but the cook was certainly not happy. About an hour later she came to him, on her way home.

'Ms Hammond, she would like to see you right away in her office,' she said. 'It was fun to be out on the range today. Missy didn't like it?'

'How right you are.' He pulled himself to his feet and finished off the bottle of beer at his elbow. 'Missy sure didn't like it.'

Despite the 'right away' he took his time, poured himself a second cup of coffee from the carafe on the side table, and only when that was finished did he stretch, and start down the corridor.

The office door was closed. He knocked peremptorily and went in without waiting for an invitation. The woman behind the desk looked up at him. Not exactly the Hammond of *Gossiper* fame, and yet not exactly Rachel, who was filled with fears and complexes.

'You wanted to see me?'

'Yes, I can't wait much longer, Charlie.' She nervously brushed her hair off her forehead, and planted both feet firmly on the floor. This time, she told herself, we're going to settle everything. Everything important, that is. He's not going to weasel out of it. It's not too late for me to go back to Libertyville and get the second man on the list.

Oh, isn't it? Of course it's too late. There's more to him than just being the father of my child. He's a multiple character, and somehow I seem to like all of him! Fool!

He dropped into the chair in front of her, draping one long leg over the chair arm. 'Now just what was that you can't wait for?'

'Don't give me that business,' she snapped. Strange how easily he brought the onslaught of tears to her eyes. But not this time, she told herself. Not this time. 'You know darn well I'm talking about—my baby! Now, are you in agreement?'

He hesitated, looking her up and down. 'Don't you think this is kind of crazy?' he asked. 'With your magazine and this spread, how are you going to take care of a baby? I'll bet you don't even know where to begin.'

'I can learn,' she muttered through clenched teeth. 'Other women have managed, without a lot of education. I can learn. There are books a-plenty. I can take courses at the University. What is there that's so difficult?'

'It's more than just changing nappies or filling bottles,' he said bleakly. 'You also have to love them. Not your strong suit, is it?'

She whirled around in her swivel chair so that her back was to him. But not fast enough so that he could not see the tear forming in her eyes.

Low blow, he told himself. Hammond may be impenetrable, but Rachel is as vulnerable as the day is long. She's not crying about a baby; she's crying about a life without love! For just a moment Charlie Mathers realised something that had been hiding away inside him. For all his years in the service, for all his large family, he was a little short in the loving field himself. He was about to add on to the conversation, when she wheeled her chair around, her eyes blazing.

'Damn you!' she exploded. 'I suppose you think you have a monopoly on loving?' He held up two hands in surrender, but she kept right at him. 'If I had a child, I could take care of him. Who would know better than me how hard it is for a child to grow up without love?' A pause for a surreptitious wipe at her leaking eye. 'And I'm *going* to have a baby!'

'Look,' he replied, 'I don't have any objection to your having a baby. As the last of the Hammonds, I suppose you owe it to your father and his father to do something. But tell me again why I should be the father of this child?'

'Because,' she sputtered, 'because you've been carefully selected by my doctor to be the perfect match. Genetically, physically, mentally, everything. And, I've already told you, I'll pay you well for the service.'

'Ah. You've been running a stud book on me?'

'You're darn well right,' she said grimly. 'This child is too important to me to be left to chance. And don't bother me with all those arguments about how millions of women managed to get it done without all this trouble. I'm not millions of people. There's only one of me—the last Hammond. I have to be careful.' A moment's pause, and then she added plaintively, 'And even with all this search and testing—I don't understand. You don't seem to be—you almost react as if you weren't the man we tested.'

'Sort of a mocking-bird egg left in the nest?' For just a second Charlie considered telling the truth about how he had come into the system by accident, short-circuiting the Hammond Search and Seizure programme. But only for a second. His uncle, before he died, had wanted mightily for him to come north and help this girl-woman. And Uncle Roger had been important in Charlie's growing up. He nodded.

'All right. I guess I could—theoretically—agree to the proposal.'

'Good! I'll get the medical team out here tomorrow, and they can get it over with in a jiffy.'

'Now whoa,' he objected. 'Just slow down. I said I can see this being a reasonable idea—in theory. But when you come right down to earth, I don't know that I can agree, not at all. Artificial insemination?'

'I can't believe you're saying that,' she told him. 'It's by far the most scientific way of doing it. The ranches use the technique all the time. That's why one bull can service a complete herd of cows. I can't see your objection.' She settled back in her chair. *So there!* she told herself. There isn't a better way to get this done. Not one!

'So tell me why,' he pondered, 'you would want to have one bull service a complete herd. Are there more of you hidden in some corner?'

'I—no.' Damn you! She was almost out of her chair before common sense took over. So he's playing hard to get?

'No, there's only me. That was only a metaphor. I'll up the price fifty per cent.'

'Sounds better and better all the time,' he answered.

He's weakening, she told herself. I've got him pinned down! 'But?' she asked. 'There was a *but*?'

'Indeed there was,' he said, rising. 'You've got the wrong bull—er—man, Ms Hammond. That's the trouble with all this research. Sure, artificial insemination is great for the rancher. Probably the cows don't mind in the least. But did anyone ever ask the bull what *he* felt about the situation?'

'You don't make a great deal of sense,' she commented. 'It's all very simple. I don't see why we have to introduce all this emotionalism into a simple business proposition. Surely you don't expect us to go back to the old-fashioned——'

'But that's exactly what I *do* mean,' he interrupted. 'If you want me to co-operate, ma'am, it's back to the old-fashioned groaning and moaning and sweat proposition. And there's no other way that I'm willing to co-operate.'

She was up out of her chair, her mouth formed for the usual Hammond roar, but no sound came out. What's wrong with me? she asked herself. I don't dare roar at him. He might walk out on me. So? So, said a deeper intelligence within her, I don't want to go through with this with some other man. Just with him. Which isn't logical! You might think I'm doing something emotional and stupid—like falling in love?

'Charlie, sit down. Surely we two logical human beings can reason our way through to a better solution?'

'None that I can think of,' he said. 'Look, ma'am. I'm tired. It's been a long, tough day, and I need some rest. That's my best offer. If you want me to father your child, then we do it the old-fashioned way.'

'But—that could take months,' she sighed. 'Although I've never tried it, I understand it to be very—vulgar. And there's no certainty of—being successful. There's no accounting for how often—I—surely you don't mean that, Charlie?'

'I surely do,' he returned. 'You have some very fine arguments, Rachel, about the cow and the crowd and the convenience. But I have to look at it strictly from the viewpoint of the bull. If you have some scientific survey that tells me the bull enjoys the hell out of all this, I'll rethink things. But until then, lady, it has to be the old-fashioned way. And now, if you'll pardon me, I'll get to bed.'

She watched his back as he stalked out of the room. An angry back, as if she had insulted him, she thought. And all I've tried to do is to get some common sense into this proposition. Surely there's no need to go through all that tangle of emotions that he seems to want? No doubt about it; I ought to go back to town and get my advisers to send me the number two man on the list. But—could they find a man who could take care of me *and* my ranch's problems? Could they find a man so full of humour and care and concern? Not just for me, but for everything and everybody? And if they could, would *I* be able to think about this new person the way I think about *dear Charlie?*

Wasn't that a dead give-away? '*Dear* Charlie'. I can't believe it. After all the years of lecture from my father, have I fallen off the bandwagon of stoic logic in just a couple of weeks? '*Dear* Charlie'? Come on now, woman, think straight. How does he rate such a salutation? Of course, I call Henrietta '*dear*' as well. A short form for affection, I suppose. And I *never* think to call Mrs Colchester '*dear*'. Doesn't that tell you something, Rachel Hammond? I wonder what he would say if he knew I'm classifying him in the same group as my dog? Now if I can only hold to that picture I ought to be able to break out of this problem about the bull! And now let's go to bed. 'Perchance to dream'?

Charlie started out for his bedroom, but detoured into the shower. One shower was not enough in the ranching business. He had a terrible itch in the middle of his back—and another one somewhere else. Neither could be scratched! 'Damn woman,' he muttered as he climbed into the hot spray and turned to get the right angle of attack. 'Why me, God?'

The hot water soothed. He applied a liberal dose of soap, massaging it in almost subconsciously, and thinking. Rachel Hammond. 'There's no doubt,' he muttered to himself, 'that she's one hell of a lot of woman. Point number one.' Another liberal soaping. 'There's no doubt that she wants—what? Not me, perhaps, but the service I can offer. And isn't that a terrible way to think about this woman? As if she were a cow, waiting to be serviced. But isn't that exactly what she keeps saying? Well, they're not going to fool around *my* family jewels with this artificial insemination business!'

Despite all his complaints, at this moment he found things were running out of control. He flipped off the hot water and let the cold run down his big frame. By the time he dried off he was still incensed, but somewhat calmer.

Why did this broad pick me up and proposition me? And who is this doctor that she keeps referring to? Somebody I *should* have met? The idea teased at him as he walked down the hall. Some fancy plan of Hammond's which came unhitched? Is there, somewhere in the wide, wide world, a big hulk of a man, looking for this woman? The idea tickled him so much that he was laughing as he passed Rachel's closed door.

Rachel, who was still awake, despite her every attempt not to be so, heard him come down the hall. His footsteps hesitated for a moment outside her door, and then he laughed and went on down towards his own room.

Damn the man, she thought. Double-damn him! She had pulled and pushed and tossed for so long already that her sheets were tangled around her and she had lost her pillow somewhere. Indignantly she squeezed herself off on to the floor, threw her blankets back on the bed and stomped over to her window. It was one of those clear, cool Kansas nights. The stars in their myriads were sparkling overhead. A three-quarter moon changed the whole outside world to silver. That wary coyote up on the ridge was joined by a partner, both wailing to the skies. A mating call? Rachel felt a shiver run up her spine. The last time she had thought of mating calls was when she was fourteen, watching an old Rin-Tin-Tin movie on television.

Disgusted, she fumbled around in the dark for her robe, and managed to wrap it around her. There might be peace out in the open. Certainly there was none to be found in her bedroom. She opened her door carefully, to avoid waking him, and walked down the hall to the kitchen door.

A cool, almost cold wind was blowing when she stepped out of the house. She closed the door as quietly as she could, then walked around the corner of the veranda to where the lounge chairs waited. Rachel Hammond, restless in body and soul, tried to discipline herself, without any luck. She paced back and forth for a time, then returned to the chairs and dropped into one of them.

There were incidental noises from the barn. The chink of some sort of metal, the casual stomping of a stabled horse, and the sound of water, flowing from the little spring that provided water for both house and barn. Somewhere in the distance she heard a mournful birdcall. A loon? The wind ruffled her hair. She relaxed for a moment.

Her left hand was hanging down, almost touching the floor. A cold, wet nose thrust itself into it. 'Blue?'

Not the puppy, but the mother. 'Henrietta?' Her fingers were licked in acknowledgement. 'Only us women keeping the night-watch?' Her dog gruffed an agreement. 'Well, we deserve each other, don't we?' Another agreement.

'Am I being a fool, dog? I know all there is to know about running a gossip rag; why the devil am I dreaming of remaking myself into a rancher? Instead of using that psychologist to find me a man, I should have used some man to find me a psychologist!'

Her dog snorted in disgust and lay down to sleep. 'And that,' Rachel told herself, 'is just what I need too. Tomorrow I will put on the whole armour of innocence—lord, where did *that* phrase come from?—and completely neglect this Texas cowpoke. I'll get another good week of rest, and then go back to the magazine. Maybe I'll leave him out here to run the ranch. He seems to be pretty good at what he does. Horses, cattle, choppers—now don't say that didn't surprise you, Rachel Hammond!'

She squirmed around, trying to make herself comfortable in the lounge chair, but the wind was rising, the temperature dropping, and neither her nightgown nor her robe did much to alleviate her feelings.

So stop playing the heroine, she told herself, and go back into the house for something warm. She pushed herself out of the chair, waking the dog in the doing, and stopped for a moment to apologise. By the time Henrietta was finished with her objections, Rachel was really chilled. She fumbled for her slippers, but could only find one. It was a hop and a skip routine across the wood floor of the veranda, until finally she came to the door. Henrietta was close behind her.

Rachel fumbled for the knob. The door was old, the knob was older, and it normally required a considerable slam to open it. So, without thinking, Rachel gave the knob a hard twist, and pushed against the door with her shoulder. And nothing happened.

'Oh, lord,' she muttered. She knew without looking. The Yale snap lock had closed when she came out of the house, and there was no way in the world that she could get back in. Except to go around the house and tap on Charlie's window. And that, she told herself, I will never do. So back she went to the lounger, invited Henrietta to come up with her to share the heat, and prepared to spend the rest of the night consorting with the stars.

'But you see,' she told herself, 'if I were on good terms with Charlie, all of this would be a laugher!' It was a good moral lesson, but did nothing towards keeping her warm through the night.

CHAPTER FIVE

RACHEL failed to make an appearance at the breakfast table. Mrs Colchester, coming in with the syrup for the pancakes, shook her head. 'Very bad,' she said. 'The nose runs, the eyes weep, the throat coughs. I don't understand it. She spends all night on the porch, you understand. Something about worshipping the stars. I don't know this worship. She says, after you have break-fasted, would you please to come by her bedroom for just a moment?'

'Yes, of course,' Charlie replied as he dug into the succulent pancakes. 'If she's not coming, I suppose I could eat all of this by myself?'

'It would make me very happy,' Mrs Colchester said with a little giggle. 'Always she worries about the food. Waste not, want not, she says. And things like that.'

'Well, I'm glad somebody's happy around this place. Run along now, child.'

'Not a child,' the woman replied firmly. 'At sixty I am not a child!'

'Yes. Yes, of course you're not. Sixty, huh? How long have you been on the ranch?'

'I came when I was young. With the grandfather, you understand. Maybe I was—oh—thirteen then.'

'And you never had the chance to finish school?'

The woman turned around to face him. 'Always this question,' she said. 'Why should I finish school? Do they teach you how to live, how to ranch, how to find a husband? Nothing. My father said I must learn more.

Poor Indians are always poor if they have not the education. But Mr Hammond, he says a woman only needs to know house and home and kitchen. So, he offers more money, and I stay. I send it all back home, and my father, he don't argue any more. *You* finish school?'

Caught unprepared, Charlie blinked at the attack. 'Well, I guess I'd have to say yes,' he confessed. 'I finally finished college. It took me six years to do it, but it's done. Can't you see that I *look* smarter now?'

The woman giggled again. Charlie shook his head, disgusted at his own action. A giggle, from an Indian woman, did not mean what it meant to a white woman. It meant she was embarrassed by the subject.

'Foolish talk,' she returned. 'Going to school does not show on the outside, only on the inside. You don't forget, Ms Rachel says come to see her?'

'I won't forget. A very educational conversation, Mrs Colchester.' The woman giggled again and fled. Charlie turned back to his plate to give the pancakes the greeting they deserved.

Rachel Hammond sat up in her narrow bed, two pillows plumped up behind her. Her nose was red and sore, her eyes were blurred, and she had a massive headache. All emphasised by her sense of having been ill-used. Nevertheless she was dressed, if one might call it that, in one of those frilly nightgowns that her Aunt Harriet had bought for her, back in the days when her brother Jimmy was still the heir apparent, and little Rachel was just a happy-go-lucky girl. The clothes were still stuffed in the back of her cupboard, and she hadn't heard from Aunt Harriet in almost ten years. But today, for some reason, she had ordered Mrs Colchester to dig this rag out for her. A pure white cotton gown, almost transparent, that covered everything from chin to ankles, and yet left everything exposed. She could barely see herself in the mirror on the opposite wall, but she tried to preen. That was the moment he came through the half-opened door with his usual casual approach. Unless one studied his eyes, one would think he had not noticed the gown at all. Damn the man, Rachel told herself.

'I hear you're not feeling too well?'

He took the chair beside her bed, without even an invitation. I don't know why I bother, Rachel thought. He's not the least bit conformable. If I take up with this man, he'll have to be house-trained!

'I'm well enough to conduct business,' she muttered, and then coughed a time or two to prove it. 'Hammonds don't all go soft just because they have a little head cold!' Two more coughs, and a vain attempt to blow her nose without applying that hurtful pressure to it, without success.

'I have a feeling,' he drawled, 'that now I'm going to find out that it's all my fault.'

'It is,' she snapped. 'Among the dozen or more things you repaired in the past few days was the lock on the kitchen door!'

'It needed it,' he agreed, trying to maintain a neutral position. He knew by the set of her eyes that he was sailing, like the ancient Greeks, between Scylla and Charybdis on a wild sea.

She threw him a quick glance. 'And locked me out in the cold. But that isn't what I asked you to stop by for.'

'Oh?' He crossed his legs.

'I wanted to tell you,' she said hurriedly, 'that I've decided to agree to your terms.'

'You agree to——?'

'You either have the worst memory or the lowest sex libido of any man I've ever met,' she snapped.

'Oh, that.' A moment's pause as if he was thinking something over. She glared at him, trying to compel him by the sheer power of her thoughts. Don't, she told herself, almost screaming. Don't introduce half a dozen other qualifications. Just say——

'Yes,' he said, interrupting her thoughts. 'OK, then.'

'That's it? Just "OK"? Something as important as this, and all you have to say is "OK"?' It was hard to control rage, Rachel discovered in that moment, when you were feeling as bad she was at that moment. I think every muscle in my body aches, and even some of the aches have aches! And this imperious—cowpoke—all he can do is slouch there and say 'OK' on the most important decision in my life!

'Well,' he said cautiously, 'that seemed to be the important thing to say.'

'And when,' she asked, in a very unsteady voice, 'can we arrange to get this—show on the road?'

'Most any day now,' he allowed as he stood up. 'It's not the sort of thing you can do when one partner is sickly, you know.'

'When, damn you?'

'There's lots of things need doing around this spread,' he told her. 'Some more trouble with the cattle, for example. I plan to ride out to the tally and see what the problem is.'

'And then there are, I suppose, half a thousand other things more important?'

'Matter of priorities, ma'am.'

'Don't call me ma'am!'

'Yes, ma'am.' He was out of the door before her dirty coffee-cup smashed against the wall about six inches from his head. He whistled as he went down the hall, which only added to Rachel's tremendous headache.

The headache persisted throughout the day, made worse when Charlie bustled in at lunchtime, still whistling, and failed to come by the sick-room to report. Rachel fumed and fussed and tossed and turned. She wanted to ask him what was going on. She wanted to ask *somebody* about the editorial for this week's *National Gossiper*. She wanted to ask someone why her head hurt so much. She wanted to be somebody's little girl, allowed to climb up into somebody's comfortable lap and seek solace. She wanted to—murder that man?

Mrs Colchester came in twice. Once to take her temperature, all the while muttering that she was hired to cook, not to run a nursing home. The second time with a large glass of hot lemonade, 'Which is what my mother used all the time for colds, before Kansas was full of doctors. Quacks, the lot of them. Now see if you can drink the whole thing down.'

Rachel managed the dose, and much to everybody's surprise fell into a uneasy sleep. When she awoke it was dark outside, and she was feeling as miserable as a girl could possibly be. So much so that she was unable to stop the shivering and the sobbing.

Charlie had spent the evening in the business office, where the paperwork was helping him develop a headache of his own. He walked quietly down the hall on his way to bed, when he heard Rachel crying. It was just the sort of thing he would never have expected from Hammond. He stopped by her door for a moment, and then went in.

By the feeble light of the night-lamp he could see that Rachel was tossing and turning, her nightgown rumpled up to her thighs, her blankets all over the floor. She was mumbling. He tiptoed over to the bed and touched her forehead. It was warm and dry. Too warm. As well he knew, the nearest doctor was thirty-five miles away. Decisions, he told himself. Take her to the doctor? Bring the doctor to her? Compromise?

It was long after Mrs Colchester had left the farmhouse, so what must be done lay entirely in his hands. First, she had to be made more comfortable. He searched the kitchen and came up with an enamelled wash-basin, which he filled with warm water and then carried back to the sick-room. 'Rachel?'

She moaned something that he was unable to interpret. He shrugged his shoulders and went to work. Stripping her was no easy thing. The nightgown fitted just a little too closely everywhere. Once, during the exercise, she mumbled, 'What are you doing?' He recited some doggerel that satisfied her, and when the nightgown was disposed of he gently laved her from head to toe. It was remarkable what effect the gentle washing had on the patient. And on him.

Rachel gradually settled down and accepted his ministrations. He himself required a considerable amount of discipline. She was a great deal of woman, and he was a man with a hair-trigger in the sex line. But, with all the handicaps, he finally managed to finish the job, change the sheets, and tuck her into a simple man's shirt to serve for the rest of the night.

During all of this she had managed to grab at his hand and hold it. Now, when he tried to break away, she stirred uneasily and refused to let go. 'Don't leave me,' she muttered. And then, more loudly, with a sense of panic, 'Don't leave me!'

'I won't,' he told her. That was before he assessed her narrow little bed. 'I don't intend to sit up all night,' he murmured.

'Don't leave me,' she said, more clearly this time.

All of which seemed to leave only one alternative. He slipped his arms under her dead body-weight and picked her up. 'That's nice, Daddy,' she whispered in his ear. Like a face full of water, that statement. Very suddenly he lost all his wild male responses, and managed to carry her back to his own room almost as if she were a child, kicking the door shut behind them.

Charlie had never disputed his room asssignment. It was probably the biggest bedroom in the house, with an immense, old-fashioned brass bed big enough for three. He overcame the difficulty of opening up the bed by balancing her weight on his knee while he pulled the blankets back. Throughout all this he kept crooning to her—fragments of songs that he had used for years when night-riding a herd of cattle. When finally he managed to get her down on one side of the bed, he chuckled to see that she was quiet, and wearing a big smile on her face.

He touched her forehead one more time. After an initial period of perspiration while he was bathing her, her temperature seemed to have dropped. And now what? he asked himself. It had been a long, hard day out on the range. Never had he known a more cantankerous herd. And one of the newly repaired sections of fence had come down and had to be repaired.

Accident? Poor installation? His wire repair team had come well recommended, but *seeing* was better than *thinking*, as his father used to say. Get to bed. Either the problems of the night would go away, or they wouldn't. There was no reason to stand in the middle of the bedroom in the developing chill.

Back to the bathroom, feeling his way along the wall to avoid putting on more lights. It gave him a chuckle. He and Rachel were the only two living things left in the house, give or take a mouse or two. A quick, warm shower relaxed his muscles. His mind wandered. This wasn't what he had planned when he came out of the service. There was a small ranch over by Nogales way that hadn't paid in over a decade. He had planned to change that situation.

But now Rachel had his promise. Fathering her child was not a one-night stand. Or even a nine-month stand. If she bore his child, he meant to stick around to help raise the little fellow. Yes, it would be a boy—Hammond would, some way or another, see to that. And she would expect, once the child was born, to give him a certificate or something, and see him to the door. 'And *I'll* see to *that*,' he grumbled as he shut off the water.

A heavy rub with the big bath towel, and, wearing only the towel around his waist, he walked back down the corridor to his own bedroom. There was a little bit of light from the east windows, luckily, or he would have fallen over his own boots. Another moment of contemplation, looking down into the darkness where she lay. Well, he told himself wryly, she's been inviting me into her bed for a long time!

He climbed into the bed, trying to be quiet, and not succeeding. His two hundred and nine pounds were somewhat more than the old springs were prepared for. They complained. He froze in position, half up and half down. Rachel stirred and muttered something. He hardly caught a word. Something to do with the magazine—a dream from the heart, he told himself. And then he relaxed the rest of the way. He flipped the towel off on to the chair next to the bed, made himself a little nest as far away from the sleeping girl as he could, and closed his eyes.

Just after midnight, as restless as the cattle which had made up most of his life, he came awake. The girl had moved closer to him, turned on her side facing him, and her head was resting on his shoulder.

Not quite comfortable, she wiggled a little further in his direction. He managed to put his arm around her shoulder for comfort's sake. The firm cones of her breasts, separated from his skin by only a sheer cotton shirt, bore into his chest. Charlie Mathers barely contained himself. Trapped in position where he lay, he could neither come nor go. All he *could* do was lie still and hope she wouldn't awaken and demand an explanation.

She made some delightful noise, and then giggled. Try counting sheep, he advised himself, but being a true cowhand he ended up counting steers. One after the other, counting the north ends of Texas longhorns going south through a hole in the barbed wire fence. Maybe there's some symbolism there, he told himself. Even he could hardly stand it. The tension wore him down, and eventually he went to sleep.

Rachel Hammond woke up at about eight o'clock. Late for her, but things were in such a jumble. To begin with, there was a man in her bed, and her head was resting on his shoulder. It took a lot of Hammond courage not to scream. There *has* to be some logical explanation, she told herself, as one of her fingers gently caressed his chin.

Man. Of course it was a man. He needed a shave. His hair was tousled, giving him a boyish look. There was a tiny scar just on the height of his right cheekbone.

There was another below his right ear. Rachel shook her head. Not boyish—piratical! Be more careful in your judgements, woman!

Edge away from him. Get out before the volcano erupts! Obediently she edged. He made a muffled groan of protest, and the arm under her shoulder tightened, and then relaxed. But his other arm came over, landing one huge hand on her capacious left breast. Landed, cupped, coddled, and weighed. Another sigh—of enjoyment? Disgusted with herself, Rachel tore herself away with one quick roll, landing on the floor for her efforts. Or rather on his boots, set upright on the floor next to the bed, with his spurs next to the boots. Not the sharp-pointed rowels which could penetrate a horse's thick skin, but the round, blunt kind. Rachel's soft bottom had not the staying power for this or any other type of spur. She landed on them—sat on them, to be truthful, and this time it hurt. She screamed.

The bedroom door slammed open. Mrs Colchester and her broom stood there. 'What's going on here?' the woman yelled as she crossed the threshold with her broom raised to the attack position. The noise was too much for Charlie. He came awake, thoughts reverting to the war he had been fighting not more than six months before, and came up out of the bed, totally naked, ready to fight.

Mrs Colchester screamed again. Rachel, not willing to be left out, struggled to her feet, gently comforting her punctured bottom.

'Charlie!' Rachel yelled, and motioned towards the bed. He took one look at his display of maleness and vaulted back under the covers again.

'I am not,' Mrs Colchester stated firmly, 'going to continue working in this den of iniquity. Not one moment. How could you do this, Rachel Hammond? What would your father say? What would your grandfather say? Shame! Shame!'

'I haven't any idea what father would say,' Rachel said gently. 'As for Grampa, I suspect he would have said something like "It's about time, girl!" He wasn't the saint you try to make him, Mrs Colchester.' Despite her ire, the cook pushed a chair over to her. Rachel fell into it, strangely relieved. I'm tired, she told herself. As weak as a kitten. What in the world has happened to me? Her eyes strayed to where Charlie was sitting up in the bed, his bottom half covered by the sheets, his top half, muscles and all, nude. Rachel drew a quick breath. Is that what happened to me? she asked herself. They say it's a very physical activity. He's worn me out, and I didn't even know it! Damn that man.

'That's enough, Mrs Colchester,' she ordered. 'There's nothing of which Charlie or I should be ashamed. If you don't feel you can continue here, then pack your bags. I'll figure your wages right away.'

'Well, of all the nerve,' the cook sputtered. 'Turning me off without a minute's notice after I've served your father and your grandfather—all those years?'

'I didn't turn you off, you quit,' Rachel told her. 'I'm sorry that your strict sensibilities have been bruised, but I can't help that. I can't even promise that it won't happen again. Now, are you going or staying?'

'That does it. I'm leaving. Immediately. At once!'

'Your pay cheque will be on the desk in the office,' Rachel told her. The woman glared at them both as she started out of the door. 'You'll be sorry,' she said. 'The Lord punishes sinners!'

'If it is a sin, it's a very tiny one,' Charlie responded.

'You are all,' Mrs Colchester said in a prophetic voice, 'going straight to hell and damnation!' She slammed the door behind her. Rachel could hear her feet pounding down the hall.

'Well?' Charlie asked.

'Perhaps.' Rachel sighed. 'You make a great deal of trouble for just one man. I'd better get down to the office and figure out her pay.'

'First things first,' Charlie said. 'She can wait. My stomach can't. Why don't you zoom down to the kitchen and whip us up some breakfast?'

'I would,' Rachel Hammond said as she used one hand to push her hair back in place. 'The only trouble is that I've never learned how to cook!'

The two of them gathered in the kitchen an hour later, prepared to do battle. 'Me, I can cook steak,' Rachel offered. 'Mrs Colchester likes to have help, but only for fetching and carrying. She guards her cooking secrets, you understand. But I spied long enough to cook a steak.'

'Well, I can do steak and eggs,' Charlie chimed in. 'Standard range food. Lord knows there's always plenty of beef available on a cattle ranch. I hear chickens every morning somewhere around here.'

'Which Mrs Colchester always looked after,' Rachel added glumly. 'Out behind the barn there's a big chicken coop. I have no idea how many birds there are. Mrs Colchester feeds them grain once a day. She gathers the eggs in the morning. Sometimes there aren't any eggs. When a hen goes for too many days without eggs, then we have a chicken dinner. The grain is in a big sack out in the barn.'

'So I guess, Rachel, that you'll have to take over all that part of things until Mrs Colchester gets over her peeves. Does she do this often?'

'Counting this time?' she asked. He nodded. 'Well, in that case, she's blown up like this once in my lifetime.'

He shook his head, with just a touch of a grin on one corner of his mouth. She glared at him. She had donned one of her prettiest outfits in honour of the occasion. A red and white dirndl blouse, low and square-cut, offering a fine view of the tops of her breasts, matched with a calico skirt that swirled when she moved. He had already noticed the view. She had caught him at it the moment he came into the kitchen.

'Let me explain,' she said, hiding her temper with a great deal of difficulty. 'I was raised to be the editor of a magazine. I do that work very well. I live in a penthouse apartment at the Sheridan hotel. The hotel has a kitchen. When I order things they appear, already cooked. My dad said you only have so much room in your brain, so don't try learning things you don't need to know. I didn't need to know cooking. I still don't!'

'Well said.' Charlie chuckled, which caused Rachel to lose just another bit of her temper. 'So we'll have steak and eggs today. You scoot out and find us some eggs. I'll get the beef—we *do* have a side of beef ageing?'

Rachel shrugged her shoulders. 'In the cold room in the back of the house,' she suggested. 'I think we'd better hire somebody, or go back to the hotel.'

Those eyes of his followed her, pinned her against the serving counter as if she were a butterfly in his collection. 'We don't quit at the drop of a hat,' he said. There was a hardness in his voice that she hadn't heard before, and she flinched away from it. 'You talk about self-reliance, raising a baby all by yourself, but you can't see your way clear to spend a couple of weeks without kitchen help? Come on, girl.'

'I can't eat steak and eggs for breakfast,' Rachel complained. 'The eggs are all right for occasional meals. The steak is too heavy. I need roughage. Cereals, milk, things like that.'

'That stuff is easy to prepare,' Charlie said. 'Cereal comes in box. You put it in a bowl, and add milk.'

'I don't think we have more than a pint of milk,' she told him.

'And we don't have any cows in season?'

'Pasteurised milk,' Rachel insisted. 'After all, we have to be careful. I'm eating for two now.'

He came around the table and stopped about a foot in front of her. What did I say? she asked herself. Did I sprout horns or something?

'Milk. Pasteurised milk,' she repeated.

'The milk part I understand,' he drawled. 'Oh, hell. So somebody has to go into the town for food? How far?'

'Thirty miles. Down to Beaumont. Once a week. Mrs Colchester used to go. I can find an old shopping list.' Rachel backed away from him. That stern look was still in control of his face. The little scar seemed to be pulsing at her like a beacon. She stared at him, hypnotised. It took more than a minute for her mind to respond. When it did she was both humiliated and angered. He's treating me like some dumb kid, she told herself.

It was just enough to pull her back into herself.

'Of course,' she said. 'I'm a good shopper. I can go in the car. I'll call the city and have—no, that won't do. I'll have a car brought out for our use. I can drive a car.' And I'm talking like a frightened child, she told herself. Get a grip on yourself, Hammond!

'Beaumont,' he said, and scratched his head. 'Plenty of flat places down at Beaumont. The helicopter is sitting out there behind the corral. We'll both go.'

'I forget you can fly that machine,' Rachel said. She ducked her head to hide the harried look that flooded her eyes. She remembered vividly her last trip in *his* chopper, and wasn't sure she was prepared for another wild ride. But he was waiting, watching, daring her to make a commitment.

'Of course,' she said. 'Right after breakfast. You're cooking, Charlie.' He smiled at her then, a genuine, gentle smile. As both sides of his mouth curved upward, she could see a little dimple developing at his left cheek. Altogether a fine man, she told herself. Why was I in such a panic? And then she blushed at the thought. He saw that, too, and treasured it.

Both Rachel and Charlie were sitting up late after a strenuous day. 'I'm beginning to feel pretty ancient,' Charlie said as he put down yesterday's paper. 'A full day down in the big city? Just suppose we had three or four kids along with us. They never stop saying "why?"—or "why not?" Why do you suppose kids talk like that?'

'It *was* nice,' Rachel responded. She was sitting opposite him on the big lounger, with a mass of yarn sprawled over her feet. 'And no, I haven't any idea when they stop saying those things. But I suppose I'd better give it some thought. You've had a lot of experience with children? Darn this stuff!'

'More than I'd care to recall. I can't exactly recall how many nephews and nieces I've had to deal with over the years. But then, being away in the miltary for so long, one tends to forget. What are you doing?'

'Can't you see? I'm knitting.'

'Oh? I would have sworn that was one of the things you seldom did.'

Her full mop of hair had fallen over her eyes. She pushed it away to look at him. 'Sarcasm?'

'Sarcasm? Not from me. I don't know a thing about knitting.'

In the lamplight his face had softened, and somehow she believed him. It takes a lot of doing to believe him, she told herself, but I'm going to do it regularly from now on. After all, he's done a great thing for me. I wonder why I didn't enjoy it? You don't suppose I'm one of those frigid women?

'Neither do I,' she said. 'But so many people knit that I figure I could learn if I applied myself to it. But——'

'But—no?'

'But no.' Her mind reverted to her favourite subject. 'You were away a long time?'

'Off and on,' he reported. 'Enough to lose track. Long enough for some of the younger ones to forget who Uncle Charlie was.'

'That must have hurt?'

'Only temporarily.' He chuckled at something he remembered. 'Too bad. I wish I could do something to help. Say, come to think of it, Juarez Joe knits—or crochets, or something.'

'That great big Indian guy? The one with all the scars? He knits?'

'Or something like that,' Charlie said. 'He was in my squadron in the war, and was wounded. I don't suppose you'd know, but in many military hospitals they have people come around to teach patients all sorts of things they can do while they're recuperating. In my last incarceration I had an old lady come by twice a week to teach me to hook a rug. Down home in Texas I've got me some dandy rugs.'

She put her needles down and stared at him. It wasn't the idea that he might hook rugs that interested her, it was that other thought. He had been in the war and had been wounded, and that was how he learned. Wounded? A little corner of her heart responded. Without bothering about her rules of logic, Rachel Hammond said something stupid. 'You were wounded?'

'A time or two,' he admitted.

She drew in her breath sharply, making a hissing sort of sound. 'You were wounded a time or two? Dear God! How can you be so blasé?'

'Well,' he said, 'I don't think He exactly had a hand in it. I went into harm's way, and got my—er—body kicked. Nothing serious. I still have all my arms and legs.' He lifted up each member to illustrate. 'Flying in wartime is a dangerous profession. I heartily recommend to everyone I meet that they not try it.'

'But—you're a hero!'

'Not exactly.' He lay his newspaper aside and gave her his full attention. 'Heroes are people who give everything they have in order to save someone else. Me, I'm just a fellow who was near by when a lot of heroes did their work. But why should you worry?'

'Because I——' She barely caught herself. Because I've come to care very much about you. Because the more I see of you the more I want. Because I—because I think I'm in love with you, Charlie What's-your-name!

'And speaking of heroes and such,' she said, 'don't you think it's time for you to tell me what your name is?'

'Name? It's Charlie.'

'Come on now, I'm not a little girl looking for lollipops. What's your last name?'

'Oh, that? Well, I was baptised Charles Albert Mathers. A common enough name, isn't it?'

'I suppose you're right.' I know you're right, she told herself, but there's something strange about the name. No, not strange, unusual. What is it?

'I—there was once a Mathers family that lived in these parts. Are you related?'

'I wouldn't be surprised,' he said, chuckling. 'The family have always been wanderers. I don't doubt that some of their seed landed in Kansas. And Nebraska too, for that matter.'

'One man by the name of Borgen,' she said cautiously, 'lived in Libertyville. He died a little time ago. Roger Borgen? You might know him?' She squinted, and examined his face from the side. 'I know it sounds silly, but you look like him.'

Charlie looked away to break her concentration. So I look like Uncle Roger? he asked himself. Hardly possible, but if true it's a real compliment. But she's only guessing. Let her keep on guessing.

'Lots of folks in our family were named Roger. Goes all the way back to the Roger Mathers who was a corsair, back in the 1600s. Hung in chains at Bristol dock, he was.'

Rachel shivered and shook her head slowly. He said so much and yet didn't say so much. He'd make a great corsair, too, wouldn't he? A swashbuckler of the first water!

'I know what it is,' she said. 'Albert. My grandfather was named Albert. Did you ever meet him?'

'No, ma'am. I have a brother and several cousins of that name, but they're all my generation.'

He's not going to admit anything, she told herself. Change the subject and try again another time! 'So tell me, how were you wounded, Charlie?'

He grinned at her, that big devouring grin that swept all her suspicions away. 'Not much to say about that, either,' he explained. 'I was flying an F-111 on an intruder mission, when half a dozen MIG 23s came up at me. Towards the end there I was zigging when I should have been zagging, and the first thing you know all the alarms went off. I think my elbow hit the ejection button, and blew my seat right out of the aircraft. Can you imagine that?'

'I can't really.' But she couldn't help matching his grin. There was something about this man that tugged at her conscience. 'Zigging, huh? A likely story, Charlie Mathers!'

'My grandfather always taught me, when you get your story made up, stick to it every inch,' he returned. 'So now, that entitles me to ask *you* a question, doesn't it?'

'Just one.'

'Why the devil are you taking up all this knitting? Why the devil do you keep talking about eating for two?'

'Why...' It was hard to talk about the subject without blushing. She turned a beautiful blush-red, but stuck to the course. 'I'm knitting for the baby,' she said. 'All prospective new mothers knit. And I have to watch what I eat for the same reason.'

'Perhaps I'm missing something,' he drawled, his face as straight and sober as a judge.

'I don't see why. After all, you're the cause of all this.'

'I am—I'm the cause of all what?'

'You know. Last night.' She picked up her needles again. 'But I still don't understand why I didn't enjoy some of it. All my books say that there's a—good feeling about it.'

Charlie shot up out of his chair and moved a foot or two away from her. 'Look, Rachel, I don't exactly know what you're talking about. Last night you were a sick little girl. I washed you off and carried you back to my bed because you didn't want to be alone. Your fever broke, and you fell asleep on my arm. It's still aching, by the way. And that, ma'am, is *all* that happened last night!'

'You mean that you—didn't?' She dropped her needles again and folded her hands in her lap. 'You mean that I—that you——'

'Nothing else happened,' he said firmly. 'Nothing.'

'Then I'm not——'

'Then you're exactly what you were before,' he insisted. 'I told you we'd take care of that other item when both of us were ready for it. If you think I would run around and do that to a sick woman, you're crazier than I thought you were!' With that Charlie walked out of the room, leaving Rachel huddled over herself.

God damn the man, she shouted at herself. I thought it was all over with, and it hasn't even begun. I am going to *get* that man, and I'm not going to wait around until the cows come home. I'm going to *get* that man and then throw him out on his—ear! Damn the man! Both her fists clenched. She could feel the bite of her nails as they scarred the palms of her hands. A tiny drop of moisture formed in her left eye. A moment later Rachel Hammond sat there alone and cried.

CHAPTER SIX

CHARLIE went to bed at eleven o'clock. The ranch world had changed with just a few minutes of conversation, and he was not sure he liked the change. And after Rachel had gone to bed he spent an hour or more pacing the porch.

Rachel. He pulled her out of his imagination for study. A beautiful woman, raised with a narrow need and an even narrower education. What kind of a father could the poor kid have had? A bigot, for sure, who'd then proceeded to pass the heritage on to his daughter. Her life at the ranch during these past days had been a great awakening for her. And now, he told himself, I'm sure what Uncle Roger wanted to tell me. He wanted me to take a hand with this girl and free her from all those thousand and one inhibitions and weird ideas. Like having a baby. Lord, the woman was no more than a child herself. *Why* would she want a baby?

Immediately, when he posed the question to himself, a dark cloud seemed to flow through his logic channels. A cloud bearing the picture of that evil old man hanging on the wall. Hammond, she called herself. And there was the answer. How long had her father and grandfather pounded it into her? Hammond. Rachel was the last of the line—unless she produced a baby. The only way she could be free of her ghosts was to continue the Hammond line.

And you, turkey, he told himself fiercely, you've been elected to be the proud father. Or rather, you've been elected to service the poor kid, and then you're out of sight, lad!

And that, he told himself, is where I have to draw the line. There's not going to be any child of mine running around the middle of Kansas without a father. Not on your fat, ever-loving life, Rachel Hammond!

With all those thoughts in mind, it was no wonder that sleep eluded him. And when the handful of pebbles rattled off his window, all thought of rest disappeared. He struggled out of bed and padded over to the window. It opened, but only after the application of his muscle. 'Joe?'

'Me, boss.' The big Comanche was standing outside the window. His horse waited patiently at the end of the veranda, ground looped. 'Thought I'd better ride in. There's motors runnin' down outside the fence line near Colter Springs. Trucks, I reckon. Not more'n two or three men. You comin'?'

There was no need to ask. Charlie was already pulling on his work clothes and heading for the front door.

It was difficult to walk quietly in the dark down a long wooden corridor while wearing boots, and Charlie won no prizes. So when he came along to Rachel's door it was open, and the girl was standing there in the shadows.

'What?' she whispered.

'Dunno,' he responded. 'Five'll get you ten it's cattle rustlers. Joe and I will ride out and investigate.'

'They're my cattle.'

'True. But I'm in a hurry, Rachel.'

'They're my cattle. I'm coming.'

In the dark he could barely see the white sheen of her nightgown. He had ridden a lot of fence lines; he had ridden with a lot of women. But never the two things at the same time.

'You mightn't be able to keep up,' he groused.

'Perhaps. My cattle, my fences, and I'm coming.'

'Stubborn woman!'

'You'd better believe it.'

It was easier to give up than to try to argue her out of anything. He shrugged his shoulders and headed for the door. 'You get dressed. Something warm. I'll go get us a couple of horses.'

With Joe to help, the two horses were quickly ready. They had waited no more than two minutes when Rachel came out of the house wearing boots, blue jeans, a heavy sweater, and a wind jacket. Without a word she swung up into her saddle.

She handled her horse in true Western fashion, slouching in the saddle for the long ride, rather than stiffening her backbone. Horse and girl seemed to be welded together. Charlie gave a grunt of approval. The wind came up slightly, blotting out the noise as steel-shod hoofs hit the ground, as leather and steel chattered when they rubbed across each other. Not absolute silence, but close enough.

'Frankie, he cut through the fence and circled around,' the cowboy explained as they rode stirrup to stirrup. 'Looks to be twenty-five good beef critters there. A nice evening's haul.'

'When we get there,' Charlie ordered, 'you slip across and get on the far side of the fence-cut. Me, I'll stay on this side——'

'And I'll stand fast in the middle of the gap,' Rachel interrupted, 'and see that none of them break through.'

'The hell you will,' Charlie said, trying to keep his voice down. 'Should have stayed at home. This is no place for a woman. I want you to—what the hell is that you've got?'

'Don't panic,' she returned. 'It's a .44 calibre six-shot revolver. You've never seen one before?'

'I've seen one,' he growled as he kneed his horse over beside her. 'I've seen one,' he repeated, 'in the hands of a young fool who thought he knew something, and ended up dead. Give me that thing.'

'Damned if I will.' Rachel swore two well-rounded oaths at him, and then squeaked as he snatched the weapon out of her hand. 'Give me back that gun.'

'As you say,' he lectured solemnly, 'damned if I will.' She snatched at it, to no avail. 'If you *had* to carry one out on a ride like this you certainly wouldn't have a shell under the hammer. I thought Hammond didn't raise any idiot children, but I can see I'm wrong.'

'Give me that revolver,' she said. Every word was accented, deliberate, reinforced by her anger.

'I said no. I mean no. We're the good guys, Rachel Hammond. Even if I gave it back to you unloaded there's no way of telling what the other side would think if they saw it. No Guns. All capital letters.'

Rachel could see that he meant every word of it. Yet the Wild West movies were all she knew of rustling cattle. 'Then how in the world are you going to stop them?'

'With this,' he muttered. Slung on the far side of his saddle was a lariat. He uncoiled it for a moment, letting her eyes follow by moonlight as he built a loop. 'Twenty feet of good, solid rope. It used to be rawhide, but today it's nylon.'

'But I don't know how to make one of those things go,' she wailed.

'Shush,' he whispered. 'We're too close already. Act like a mature woman for a change, Rachel.' He was too far away for her to hit him. She would have liked to. But of all the other men Rachel Hammond knew, none would have hit her back. This fellow... There was enough of a *maybe* about him for her to kick her mount and move a safe distance away.

The men at the parked truck felt very sure of themselves. They were talking up a storm, and setting up a floodlight, as if they thought the world belonged to them. Charlie reined in and dismounted, and the others did the same.

'What the hell?' Charlie said under his breath.

'We set up a decoy camp about twelve miles that a-way,' Joe returned. He gestured vaguely towards the south-west. 'I learned something from the military, Major.'

'Don't Major me,' he said softly. 'You go ahead across to the other side of their fence-cut.' A mournful whippoorwill cried from the far side of the fence.

'That boy never learns,' Joe commented. 'Makes a whippoorwill sound like a crow. But he's over there—in back of them.' And with that, the Comanche slid down and disappeared in the thigh-high prairie grass.

Charlie moved over to the nearest fence post and hunkered down. Rachel came up beside him and did the same. Close enough to talk, but not close enough to touch. I'm no fool, she told herself, and if he whacks me it'll be a real whack. Besides, I want at least a hundred more answers.

'Major?'

'Just an old custom,' he told her. 'They called my grandfather "General" for years, and him just a country preacher.'

'General?'

'Yes, General.'

'Why?'

'Damn it, Rachel Hammond, will you kindly button your lip? We aren't out here to have a social tea.'

'I want to know!'

'My Gawd. If I tell you, will you shut up?'

'Yes. For the moment.'

'OK, they called him General because he was a brigadier general.'

'But——'

He shut her off by putting his big palm across her mouth, and not too gently. 'You promised,' he hissed, 'and here they come.'

And here they came indeed. The two cowpokes who had ridden off with Hendrix after that big argument. One carried a big pair of wire-cutters. The other stepped out of the way to avoid being hit, as the first man cut the upper strand of wire, and then the two below it. 'Got to make the cut ten feet wider. Don't drag it too far,' one of them murmured. 'Just enough to let us bring them through. What's the matter?'

'Lost my other glove,' the other man grumbled. 'I better go back to the truck and get another pair. Don't wanna get all cut up on that barbed wire.'

'I mighta known you'd find some excuse. The barbs on this here wire ain't hardly sharp enough to...' But his partner had gone. Mumbling to himself, the first man moved the cut strands of wire a few feet and then stepped across the fence line.

Rachel just could not keep her cool. It had been a long night, filled with bitter argument. The long ride in the cool air had added something to it all. And now, as she shifted her weight, Charlie's hand came down on the top of her head and actually pushed her down into the prairie grass. She rolled over, ready to put up a fuss.

But over her head she could hear the humming of his lariat as he ran out a loop. The cowpoke was a standing target, outlined by the searchlights. He did manage to get out one, 'What the hell——?' when the loop dropped over his head.

The other end of the lariat was still attached to the pommel of Charlie's saddle. And his horse knew just as much about cutting out cattle as his rider. As soon as he felt the tension on the rope, the horse backed up. The rope tightened. The man flopped over on his back. And with the speed and practice of a rodeo rider, Charlie was on him with two pegging ropes in his hands. He might not have set a rodeo record, but it was time enough. Their prisoner, tied hand and foot, was towed back into the shadows, gagged, and re-tied with a fresh rope. Before Rachel could bring up word one of her protest, Charlie was back beside her, recoiling his lariat.

'Always carry two,' he whispered in her ear. 'This one's for throwin', the other's for tying.' She started to protest. His heavy hand on her shoulder kept her locked in place. 'Don't you dare move a muscle,' he warned her.

There was a place for indignation, and Rachel Hammond knew that that place was not here. One man had been taken out. Two remained. And how those two were to be enticed out into the open she had no idea. So when the hand on her shoulder pushed, she relaxed flat on the ground, almost as if she were four feet down in the water, with the prairie grass weaving in the breeze high over her head. Somewhere over her head there were man-noises.

'Lou? Where the hell are you, Lou?' And then, at a lower rate, almost talking to himself, 'Shoulda known he'd skip out. Always avoiding the work and claiming the pay-off.' The noises, the mutterings, all went by them, and then she could feel Charlie come up to one knee and make that looping lariat whistle as he built up a rotation. Then another moment of silence, and an inarticulate cry from somewhere beside her, over where the cattle were bedded down. And then that sequence of sound. The whir of the rope airborne, the quick tug backward as the horse took up the slack, a jingle of spurs as Charlie went after this second man, and then a drag and a bump as another helplessly squirming body was added to their pile.

Rachel came up to her knees, a move that brought her head almost clear of the grass. Another form was slithering towards them. In the light of the searchlight she could see the tops of the grass move. Juarez Joe came up out of the grass and said noncommittally, 'Don't need me at all,' he murmured. 'I could have stayed in my sleeping-bag for all the good I've done.'

'There's one more?'

'Nope. The kid got him from the backside a couple of minutes ago. It's that Hendrix fella. Now what do we do, boss?'

'Take them in to the sheriff,' Rachel said excitedly. 'Caught red-handed.'

'If we had a tree I suspect you'd want to lynch them,' Charlie said, chuckling.

'Well, why shouldn't we? They were caught rustling cattle, weren't they?'

'Have to prove it in court,' he returned. 'Lawyers and courtrooms and legalities. We couldn't prove a thing at the moment.'

'My lord, you don't suppose we have to turn them loose? I'll be darned if——'

'Rachel, you are surely your father's daughter. Calm down now.' At that moment the younger Comanche came riding into the circle of light, a man walking in front of him. Hendrix, out of breath but too proud to accept defeat, glared at them and then hunkered down, the rope still around his shoulders.

'You ain't smart enough to make this stick,' he muttered. 'You might just as well turn us loose.'

'Maybe you're right,' Charlie agreed amiably. 'We certainly couldn't prove intent if there aren't any of our cattle inside your truck.' A moment of silence, and then a laugh from Hendrix.

'Well, there ain't,' the man yelled at them. 'You can't prove a thing.'

'Probably not,' Charlie admitted, as if he had not a care in the world. Both the Comanche ranch-hands had disappeared. In a moment there was the sound of cattle being awakened against their will. After a few seconds they quietened down again, settled in. Twenty minutes later the two cowboys walked back into camp.

'Three head of beef in that truck,' Joe reported. 'All of them with our fresh brand on them. I got instant photographs of them.'

'That's a damn lie,' Hendrix yelled as he came clumsily to his feet. 'We never laid a hand on them cows!'

'Probably not,' Charlie said. 'Probably they just up and climbed that ramp, looking for something good to eat.'

'You can't make that stick,' Hendrix muttered, but he was perspiring in the coolness of the night, and his hand was shaking.

'I don't doubt you're right,' Charlie agreed. 'I'll tell you what we'll do. We'll bed down out here with things just the way they are, and one of us will go round up the sheriff and bring him out.'

'Hah! He ain't gonna come all the way out here just for a few cows.' Hendrix, feeling things go his way for a change, settled himself down into the grass and relaxed. 'Must be more than forty miles from here to the sheriff's office.'

'Yup,' Charlie replied as he got to his feet. 'And it's almost eight miles back to the house and our helicopter, so Ms Rachel and I had better be on our way.'

'Helicopter?' Hendrix yelped.

'Yup. Progress has come to the Kansas plains. And while we're gone we'll leave you in the hands of two of the finest Texas Indians.'

'What tribe?' Hendrix gasped.

'Comanches,' Charlie returned. 'Unreconstructed Comanches. You boys be sure you're good, 'cause there's no tellin' what they might decide to do. C'mon, Rachel.'

She automatically put out her hand and he pulled her to her feet. As they walked the fence line towards their mounts, she tugged him to a stop. 'You're really not going to leave them at the mercy of those Indians?'

'Exactly what I have in mind, lady.' He pulled her closer, until she stood chin to chin with him. Well, not exactly that. Her chin was some six inches lower than his. 'I'd think by now, Ms Rachel, that you wouldn't be so quick to judge people. Juarez Joe is a graduate of Texas Aggie. My family actually owns six ranches down in the Panhandle. Joe is the general manager of the corporation that runs them all. He's come all the way up here just to do me a favour. And the kid is his oldest son.'

'Well, I never——' she started to say, when he lost his temper.

'No, you never do,' he snapped as he swung her up in his arms. 'Never think, that is. Do you know what your trouble is?'

'I—no, and I don't want to hear,' she said.

'I'm damn sure you don't,' he told her as he stalked over to the horses. 'Spoiled damn brat. You seem to think that nobody else but you has any rights. You'd do better if you could run this ranch with robots. Then you could put them away in the barn with the horses every night and forget about them.' He set her down none too gently at the side of her mare. 'And now, lady, if you could condescend to put a foot in the stirrup?'

He didn't wait for her quiescence. He picked her up again, hands around her waist, and forcibly thrust her left foot into the deep stirrup. Before he could think of anything else, she told herself, I'd better move!

Her graceful body swung up, but so full of fear was she that she almost went over the mare's back and down the other side. Almost, but not quite. He still had a hand at her waist. The horse was hardly three years old, and not accustomed to all the excitement. She sidled away from him, pranced a step or two, and then responded to the spurs and was off into the darkness.

'Damn fool woman,' he muttered as he mounted up and went on after her.

'Look at them go,' Joe commented to his son. 'Crazy disease, love. Don't catch it.'

'You needn't worry,' the kid returned. 'I'm immune. Had it six times already.'

'And only nineteen,' his father groaned. 'Listen to them go. Any minute now, one of those animals is gonna put a foot in a pot-hole and they'll end up ass over tea-kettle. C'mon, boy, let's get us some shut-eye.'

It took just that amount of time for Charlie to catch up with Rachel. He grabbed at a rein and pulled both mounts to a walk. 'I didn't say break your neck,' he growled at her.

'Keep away from me. If I had my quirt,' she yelled at him, 'I'd——'

'Didn't your father or mother ever spank you?' he interrupted.

Her mare danced around in a circle, fighting his hand on the reins. His own animal, like any good quarter-horse, moved with the mare, always keeping his head in her direction.

'No!' she half screamed at him. 'And don't think you're going to do anything of that kind.'

'Not me,' he said gruffly. 'You're far too old for that. But believe me, I've got to do something.' His hand on the mare's reins forced that animal to come up side by side with his own. He dropped the rein, leaned over in her direction, and swept her out of the saddle.

'Don't you dare!' she roared.

'Oh, I dare.' It started out to be a punishment, but not more than a second after his lips touched hers all thought of punishing flew out of his head. Soft, warm lips, stiff when first he touched them, but quickly relaxing under his probe. A moment of defence as she blocked access to her mouth, and then the barrier went down under the assault of his tongue. The penetration was gentle. His arms tightened around her, but she hardly felt their pressure as Rachel Hammond surrendered, for the first time in all her almost-thirty years. Surrendered, and threw her arms around his neck as she tried to worm her way deeper into his grasp. She had closed her eyes when the attack began. Now she opened them, and stared into his, so close and so commanding. Wide-open eyes, his. Startled, wide-open eyes. He broke away from her and took a deep breath.

'That ain't exactly the way it was supposed to be,' he muttered. She managed to free one hand from around his neck and wiped the perspiration running down off his forehead. 'What the hell are you doing to me?'

'Don't ask me,' she replied wryly. 'I'm the one being punished, aren't I?'

'And you damn well better not forget that.' He had to do something to maintain his position. Be angry, he told himself. Be mean. Be prepared to do it again! But mind overcame emotion. He kneed his horse over beside the mare and, almost as if she were a fifty-pound sack instead of a one-hundred-and-twenty-pound woman, swung her back into her own saddle.

'And now ride,' he ordered. 'Not like Paul Revere. More like the US cavalry, who took their time and tried never to have the horses break a leg!'

'I wish I were a horse,' she mused.

'What in God's name for?'

'I notice you treat all the horses in a very gentlemanly manner.'

'But they deserve it.'

'And I don't?'

'You could say that.'

Fury came fastest when summoned. Rachel had trouble with her reins. Her hands were shaking too much. The mare hardly knew which command to obey, and ended up by doing none. 'Now look what you've done,' she muttered.

'What? Me?'

'You indeed,' she said, touching the animal's side with her heel. The mare broke into a canter, and the gelding joined just alongside. 'I just don't understasnd you,' she said reflectively. 'We took so much care.'

'We?'

'My two doctors and I. You have no idea what trouble we went to just so that everything would be perfect.'

'And I've failed? I'm not perfect.'

'Well, that's one of the problems,' she said. 'You're better than perfect. And then on the other hand, not so good at all. You just don't meet my ideal. I guess that's what I want to say.'

'I'm sorry to hear you say that, but an honest opinion is the best thing in the world. And how about you?'

'Me? There never was any attempt to measure me. I am what I am. There's no possibility that I'll change.'

'What a shame,' he retorted. 'Somebody should have measured you a long time ago. Somebody should have taken you in hand and got your engine running straight.'

'And you're that somebody?'

'I could have been.' He pulled over his stetson and wiped his brow. 'I could have been, but your crazy needs got me to staggering around the hay barn. What is it that you want? To continue the Hammond dynasty?'

'I'll admit that. My father left no doubt that he wanted a boy; when he lost little Jimmy he went full speed ahead to make me *think* like a man, even though he thought there were lots of man-things I couldn't do. So yes, this child I want is to serve my father's memory. And——' She broke off, turning her head into the wind. There were a multitude of things she wanted to tell him, but did not dare.

'And?'

'And I don't think any of that is important to you. Leave it.'

'Not if you want me to be this boy's father. It has to be a boy, I suppose.'

'Of course,' she said bitterly. 'I'd hate to think about having a girl, and then having to do it all over again.' Another moment of silence as the horses continued their steady lope towards the house. 'Well, in any case, it shouldn't bother you. Obviously you're not up to doing it. After we settle this business with the rustlers, I think I'll go back to town and take up with the magazine until we can find a better candidate than you.'

'And what happens to me?'

'Just write it down as an experiment that didn't work. You might, if you wouldn't mind, look around and find me another foreman. Unless you might consider staying on yourself?'

'No. There's no way I could just hang around. Once we leave, the party's over, Ms Rachel. I suppose I could find you a foreman without any trouble. Unemployment is way up, all over Kansas, Nebraska, Wyoming. I'll put out the word. And in the meantime, Joe could look after things for you.'

'And you, Charlie? What will you do?'

'The things I came up to Kansas to do, I guess. I have to take over my uncle's place, execute his will—things like that. He had no children. I'll bet things are all run down. My uncle was an invalid for the last six months of his life. Things can go to pot under a hand that's bedridden for that length of time.'

'I can see that. I have to thank you, Mr Mathers. You've taken hold and made some marvellous improvements in the ranch. Absentee ownership isn't something that makes the cows grow, is it?'

They had just turned into the yard, and approached the silent helicopter, its rotor blades turned the length of the fuselage and lashed down, chocks under the wheels to keep it from rolling, lines pegged out fore-and-aft to secure against the wind.

They drew rein beside the beautiful white machine, and he swung out of the saddle. 'Want to come with me?'

'I—don't think so,' she said cautiously as she stepped down from her mount. 'I think we've said everything that needs to be said.'

'Well, not quite,' he said as he walked around his mount and came to her side. 'There's probably a million things that ought to be said. Like, for instance, you're one hell of a lady, Hammond. But after all this work you've put into this baby proposition, you're just going to give it all up?' She backed away from him, as if he were a lit stick of dynamite. His voice rose, and he gave her a little shake. 'You're just going to walk away at the first real obstacle? You really didn't mean it, after all, did you?'

'I meant it,' she cried indignantly. 'I haven't given up the project, I've just given up on you! I'll find a way, believe me. And another man, if need be.' Her voice fell to a whisper as she ducked her head. He must *not* see her crying!

He put his hands on her shoulders, and looked down at her. In the darkness she could no longer read his face. 'I wish it could end differently,' he said. There was a shadowed sound in his voice, real regret. She shivered. 'Like—oh, hell.'

He snatched her up in his arms again and gently, possessively held her. It's not something I really want, she lied to herself. He's not going to dominate me and turn me into a house-mother with ten kids. I'm fully in command of my own needs and wants, and there's no way he can take me over and try to remodel me. Some cowpoke from Texas? The ony thing going for him is that he *does* take a bath every day. And for the rest of it, I can do without him.

That was all thought out *before* he kissed her. Afterwards she had no real memory of what went on when his lips sealed her off from the world. Riots of coloured fireworks seemed to be shooting off, high in the sky. But not so high that she wasn't still higher. She flew among the wispy clouds, looking down at the green and gold and red of the rockets, played against the silver and white of the fields, all bathed in the rays of a weak little moon.

Her body shivered from head to toe. There was no control she could institute against the feeling, so finally she just lay back against his arms and let it all happen.

Somehow it ended. Somehow she found herself still six inches or more above ground. He let her down, regrettably. The arches of her feet seemed to have difficulty accepting the reality of weight. But by then it was done. His hug lasted a moment longer, a moment to savour as she leaned her face against his shoulder. His hand came up and riffled through her hair, almost as if he were giving a benediction.

'Goodbye, Hammond.' Softly said, with a definite tinge of regret.

'I won't see you again?'

'No reason to, lots of reasons why not. No, I'll get the sheriff's men out to the camp, take care of all the paperwork. What you ought to do is get a good night's sleep and then get back to your magazine. Right?'

'I guess,' she said, and then shivered as she squared her shoulders. Rachel Hammond had disappeared. Now it was just plain Hammond. 'Come by the office some time, and I'll pay you off.'

'No need,' he assured her. 'I didn't do anything. There's no need to pay me off. We'll just call it quits, shall we?'

Yes, she told herself as she backed off a few feet. We'll just call it quits. Why should it hurt so much? She tried one of her father's prescriptions. Straighten up, freeze all your muscles in position, adopt a glare—even though he can't really see it in the fading light of the setting moon. Do it, Hammond. Don't ever let this man see you're crying, because if you do he'll think it's just a farce we're playing!

In the gathering darkness he could barely see her hand waving slowly.

He turned and went over to the chopper. Habit led him to unfasten the lines, pull the chocks, make his walk-around inspection. Training took him into the pilot's seat to complete his engine run-up and the electrical tests. Memory held him as the rotors turned gently. Memories of what might have been. At which point he shook himself like an old sheep-dog and did his best to force her out of his mind. He turned on his navigational lights, revved up the engine, and the lovely white chopper set itself and vaulted into the sky, marking its movement only by the red marker-lights on the fuselage.

Memories. A wonderful, bitter, maladjusted woman, who needs a man like me to marry up with. But she doesn't want to marry. A child would be nice, but not its father. What kind of a racket is that? He shook his head again. The flight instruments glowed blue and green at him. The altimeter said two hundred feet. He set the controls to 'hover', turned on the radio, and went about contacting the sheriff's department.

CHAPTER SEVEN

Rachel Hammond looked around her pyramid office and sighed in disgust. Everything that she had seen since that day of her return from the ranch left her with a dyspeptic stomach.

'Look, Elmer,' she said, trying to hold her voice in control. 'I've gone over every issue you've put out since I left. They all feature the same subject.'

'What's that, Hammond?' Elmer Chatmas had been editor of the magazine since her grandfather's day. He knew a thing or two—or three.

'Boredom,' she screamed at him. 'Plain out-and-out boredom. Do you realise that our circulation has dropped eight thousand in the weeks I've been away?'

'Holidays,' he said. 'Summer-time. People are out of town. Our kind of readers don't take the *Gossiper* along with them for summer beach parties. We're not the *Digest*, you know.'

'I know that,' she snapped. 'But still the front page is filled with boredom!'

'See,' he gloated. 'Just what I told you. You've been away just a couple of weeks and you've come back loaded for bear. What do we do next?'

'I'll tell you what we're going to do,' she insisted. 'We're going to prove to all the world that the *National Gossiper* has still got a sting in its tail. Now, for next week, I want you to tear down whoever we have for the front page, and run up as big a campaign against him as possible. The works. Theft, women, May and December relationships——'

'Embezzlement,' Elmer interrupted. 'That always goes over well!' The idea caught her fancy.

'Yeah. That's just it. As big a balloon as we can run. Why in the world didn't I think of embezzlers before? Our readers always go for the money bit. Who got what, that sort of thing.'

'Because, love, your mind doesn't run in those channels. You're really a very nice girl.' Elmer needed a smoke-screen. He defied all the office rules by pulling out his pipe and lighting up.

He must have commented along those critical lines for the past three years, and always received a mild reaction. But this time she blew her skull. 'Nice?' she roared. 'I'll give you nice! I want this next issue to be so raw that *nice* never ever comes to mind when he—when they think of us.'

Elmer almost choked over his pipe. 'You mean—rotten?'

'I mean rotten!'

'No matter who it is?'

'I don't give a damn if it's the Archbishop of Chicago.' And then a quavering pause, and a question. 'It isn't the Archbishop, is it?'

'No, but——'

'Don't tell me. I don't want to know. Next Monday I want to open the paper and be so thoroughly surprised that I'll think it's a good run no matter what the story is. Make it big. It's going to be the last gossip issue that we ever run. After this we're reorganising into something more literary. I'm tired of being known as the queen of smut. Got it?'

'You mean that? You don't want any sort of a hand in the production of the magazine for next week, and you want it to be as rotten as possible?'

'That's exactly right.'

He got up clumsily. Sixty-five was a difficult age. Knees no longer bent on command. Elbows had a tendency to jam up. Minds had a tendency to cloud over. Make it as rotten as possible? That wasn't hard to do, but the little lady was going to be shocked all the way down to her shoe inserts. And like a Hammond she would have to bear up under the shock, even if it killed her. Elmer Chatmas headed for the door. 'And what are you going to be doing as I create this—spectacular magazine?'

'Getting ready for the change-over. The first thing we need to do is streamline. We won't be making much of a profit for the first six months. I'm going to start an investigation,' she told him, a fierce grin on her face. 'Haven't you noticed that every time you see a figure around this office, it's always rounded off? Our circulation is 630,000? Come on, now, exactly that, or do we throw away a bushel of other, real figures instead of all those zeros?

'I get payroll accounts twice a month. Always they come out in nice round figures. Nobody ever enters dimes and quarters and nickels, and I'll bet there are a tremendous number of them!

'Every time we do a big story, all the victims come out in round numbers! And all the detectives are heroes. Well, let me tell you something, Elmer! This month will put an end to all that. I'm going to go through every department in this building and shake it by the neck until it gets away from round numbers!'

'Yes, well.' Elmer sucked on his pipe, and then let it go out. 'Don't overdo it,' he told her. 'You and I, we can't put out this magazine all by ourselves, you know. Push a few people too far and they'll up and revolt, my dear.'

'If they do, that's my business!'

'As you say. If they do, that's your—business.' He closed the door and was gone before she could add to her last statement. Who was it on that ranch? he mused. Somebody got to our Hammond, and left her on half-cock, ready to fire at a moment's notice.

Rachel walked over to the window and looked out down Main Street. Traffic was slow, with reason. Two blocks away on Eisenhower Avenue a bus and a truck had run into each other. A police helicopter came in out of the smog from the west, and circled the site.

The craft's appearance jolted her heart. *He* flew a machine like that. A chopper. And she hadn't seen or heard from him in a week. Not since he had crammed himself into his machine and flown out of the Bar Nine ranch.

Rachel had come back to town more sedately, in her limousine. She intended to avoid helicopter riders for a lifetime—or maybe two lifetimes. She had caught her heel on the rug as she tried to get out of the car. It was just the time and place for Charlie to be there to catch her, she'd told herself. But he wasn't, and her chauffeur had had to do the catching.

Still fuming, Rachel had rushed into the pyramid building, doing her best to avoid the tears.

'You need a handkerchief?' her secretary had asked, and had her head bitten off. The word had quickly spread that Hammond was back, and in no good spirits. The rest of the staff had made themselves hard to locate until the boss went off to her apartment at the Sheridan.

Where, alone in her apartment, with the doors closed and locked, she had thrown herself on the massive bed and had a good cry.

Charlie Mathers made intermittent trips back to the ranch for the next three days, to set things up. Two new, young hands, well recommended, had appeared on the scene, as well as a foreman, an elderly, retired master sergeant from the brown-shoe army and Fort Riley. And a promise from Juarez Joe and his son to 'hang around in the neighbourhood until they get their feet on the ground'. Then, shaking the dirt of the Flint Hills from his boots, Charlie took his helicopter back to Beaumont and rented a car for the trip to Libertyville.

'Just what in hell are you up to?' Frank Losen, Charlie's lawyer, threw himself down into the depths of the super-sofa, and twisted to pick up his glass. 'You've had yourself a nice vacation. I don't know anything you'd like more than a chance to run a ranch.'

'Bull feathers,' Charlie snorted. 'Good time? With Holy Rachel at hand? Good lord, that woman could convince you without any trouble that the sun rises in the west!'

'Oh? It doesn't? Lord, this is lousy Scotch. Where the devil did you get it?'

'Where else? Across the line in Missouri. You know they have drinking laws in Kansas. Drink it and start talking. What have you learned?'

Losen pulled a sheaf of papers out of his briefcase. He shuffled a couple of them to the top of the pile. 'Now, then. It's all one corporation, Hammond-Borgen, with two divisions. One is the magazine, the other is the ranch. Over the last fifteen years the ranch hasn't made a penny.'

'So the magazine supports everything?'

'That's the story. Now, your grandpa held fifteen per cent of the whole shebang, but when Rachel's father took the magazine into pornography——'

'Pornography?'

'Well, that's what your grandpa called it.'

'So he sold all his stock?'

'Lord, no. He loved the ranch, and he wasn't about to separate from it. He just—well, he just segregated the stock, took his name off the company books, and put his shares into a blind trust. He made believe that the magazine just didn't exist!'

'I—wait a minute. What are you telling me?'

His lawyer laughed at him. 'What I'm telling you is that you have just inherited forty per cent of the Hammond-Borgen Corporation from your uncle Roger.'

'And Grandpa has another fifteen per cent in some kind of a trust? Do I understand all this? If I could get the old coot to vote with me, we could take over the entire corporation! Throw the rascals out, so to speak? But he wouldn't, would he? He wouldn't be caught dead having anything to say, good or bad, about that rag!'

'Never a chance,' Frank retorted. 'He wouldn't! You know your grandfather is as strait-laced as they come. No, dear friend, if you have some hanky-panky planned, you have to make up to the trustee who controls the blind trust.'

'Who is?'

'Is this really the best Scotch you have?'

Charlie walked over to the head of the sofa. 'I'd better warn you, Frank, I'm not in any cheerful mood!' He paused for a moment, rubbing his chin. 'Frank—yes, I have a bottle of Chivas Regal, forty years old. I could probably remember where I put it. Maybe I—no, I'm sure it's here somewhere.'

'I'd kill for a drink like that. Your grandpa thought I was an up-and-coming young man, a real churchgoer. "Set your mind to run this magazine straight and decent," he told me.'

'Frank, don't try my patience!'

'Of course not. I'm your grandpa's trustee.'

'Ah. That bottle is upstairs in my bedroom. And I believe I'll join you.' He was back in minutes, waving two bottles in the air, rather than one.

'Before we begin the festivities,' Frank Losen said very seriously, 'the only thing you could do, holding the majority of the stock, would be to vote her out of office.'

'I know that.'

'Then be sure you know that being the boss of that corporation is all she lives for. Throw her out on the street and she'll crack up for sure.'

'Yes, and I know that too,' Charlie said. And then a pause for consideration. Rachel Hammond, broken into little pieces? All that beauty smashed? Good lord! 'Come on, pull the cork out of that thing and let's get down to some serious drinking.'

So, what with the morning after, and a multitude of little things that needed to be done in his own little bailiwick, it was Monday morning before he took to the streets of Libertyville to wander, restore his memories, and think what next he might do about Rachel Hammond. He had long since given up the option to do nothing.

He didn't need a great deal of planning. His lawyer caught up with him shortly after twelve o'clock in the

Barbecued Beef, a downtown restaurant of strange repute.

'You're going to eat in this place?'

'You bet. I can see you're in good humour today.'

'But—they keep half the light bulbs unscrewed so you can't see what you're eating. The salad's made in downtown Hamtramck by a bunch of laid-off auto workers!'

'You've got the wrong idea, Frank. If you come out for salad, go to a salad place. This place serves beef. It's the best beef in the world, my friend. And when they cook it they do a minimum amount of damage to the thing, and all you have to do is cut it—with a fork, mind you—and chew it down. Now, did you come to ruin my lunch, or do you have something else on your so-called mind?'

'I came to invite you out to the ball game. Kansas City is playing at home this afternoon. We could hop over in that little chopper of yours, see the game, and then explore the Kansas City night-life.'

'Well, that's very kind——'

'But I'm not going to, man. Coming in the door, I spotted a copy of the *National Gossiper*, and all hell broke loose.'

'What do you mean?'

'Here. Take a look.' He passed the magazine over, upsetting Charlie's coffee-cup.

'Look, I don't have time for magazine studies. I've finally made up my mind about this Hammond lady. Too much pussyfooting's been going on in these parts. I'm going over to lay it straight on the line.'

'You'd better look first, buddy.'

'One thing at a time,' Charlie said. 'I'm not smart enough to look in two directions at the same time.'

'So you're going to track down Hammond, and you're going to tell her something. What?'

'I'm going to tell her we're going to get married. And that's all there is to that!' Charlie pushed his chair back and tipped a salute to his lawyer and went out into the sunshine on Custer Avenue. Frank remained at the table and watched as his client stepped out smartly into the sunshine.

'Sure. Get married,' Frank muttered. 'Then you'll need two lawyers. Or maybe three!'

'What I need before I see this woman is somebody to hit,' Charlie muttered as he came opposite the *Gossiper* building. 'Somebody big.'

'Hot damn!' The exclamation came because those two big bodyguards were still standing at the downstairs door of the *Gossiper*, just as they had been not three weeks ago. Male! Big! Hittable!

'Gentlemen. Are you employees of this magazine?'

'We are. Haven't we seen you somewhere before?'

'Have you read this rag today?'

'Who, me? I wouldn't touch it with a ten-foot pole.'

'Me neither,' the other guard said. 'Lousy. Full of lies, innuendo, all that stuff. I don't know what keeps them out of jail for so long.'

'Oh, lord,' Charlie grumbled. He smacked one fist into the other palm. How in the world can you beat up someone who agrees completely with what you have to say? 'Excuse me,' he said as he walked around them to go in.

'Hey, you can't go in there. The place is closed. And I understand Hammond has hired a couple of extra guards.'

'I just hate to do this,' Charlie chortled, 'but I'm going in. Are you stopping me?'

'I'm stopping you.'

'Wait just a minute,' the second guard said. 'Haven't we played this song before—with this same guy?'

'Come on, stop me,' Charlie insisted.

The two guards stared at each other for a second. They must have had a corporate communication system in their heads. They both turned to Charlie. 'Stop you? Not a chance. If you want to go in, Mister, you just go right ahead.'

'Damn,' Charlie said. He rocked back and forth on the balls of his feet. 'Won't change your minds?'

They shook their heads. Charlie shook his too, then reached forward to open the door. A helping hand was there before him. 'You just go right ahead.' A second later they added, 'Sir.' The two of them managed a little bow and stepped out of the way.

Disgusted, Charlie erupted into the ground-floor lobby like a tornado looking for a place to touch down. There was not a soul in sight. A lift door hissed at him and opened. Still pounding his hands together, he moved into the lift and scanned the directory. Every office had a name, and he knew none of them. But finally there was one discreet little button labelled 'Penthouse.' He pushed it so hard that the machinery shuddered before it shut its door and started upward.

It was a slow lift, which gave Charlie Mathers plenty of time to organise his 'mad' and get it steamed up. The lights blinked at him, one floor at a time. When he had counted ten, the machine he was riding stumbled to a stop, then hitched upward another inch or two before it opened its door.

He was facing a blank wall, and a closed glass door. The title on the door was just what he had expected. 'Hammond', it said. 'Damn woman,' he muttered as he palmed the knob. The door slammed back on its stops. A woman at the desk facing him gave a little squeak of alarm, and pressed the little red button on her desk.

'You needn't squeal,' Charlie said calmly. 'I never eat blondes before supper. Where's Hammond?'

'She's—not here.'

'And you go to church every Sunday?'

'I—you think I'm lying?'

'I know you're lying. Where's Hammond?'

'She's not here. They left just a few minutes ago.'

'*They* left?'

'His name is Olsen. He won a contest. That's all I know!'

By God, Charlie told himself, another contest winner. I didn't work out, so she's got someone else to take my place! And I'm jealous as hell, that's what I am. I could kill both of them, and that's for sure.

'They've gone out to the ranch?'

The middle-aged woman before him looked petrified. 'N-no,' she stammered. 'Hammond would never go back out there. Something happened on her last visit and she swore she would never go back there. Never!'

'Yeah,' he snapped. 'That I'll believe the next time a week comes up with two Tuesdays.'

The lift doors out in the hall whooshed open, and a pair of very large-looking young men fought each other to get out into the corridor. A moment later the office door opened, and they came into the office one at a time.

'What's wrong, Ms Sally?' The bigger of the two looked as if he might be two hundred and fifty pounds, and stand six feet five. The little fellow was more likely one hundred and ninety-five, and six foot even. The woman at the desk had pushed her chair back and stood up.

'This—er—gentleman was just leaving,' she said.

Charlie took another look at the pair of them, and considerd. I could, he told himself, take either one of them without any trouble. I could probably take both of them—well, make that a seventy per cent chance. On the other hand, since I was just going anyway—what the hey!

'Like the lady says,' he agreed amiably, 'I was just leaving. Excuse me?' He stepped around the pair of them gingerly, doing his best to avoid touching either of them. Safely out in the corridor, with them forming a wall between him and the secretary, he called, 'You won't forget to tell Ms Rachel that I called? And that I was very perturbed about the last issue of the magazine? And that I'll see her in court very very quickly?'

The lift door was still open, waiting restlessly for a patron. He pushed the lobby button, the machine activated itself with a groan, and the double door swung shut. None of the three he left behind offered a comment of any kind.

The machine disgorged him in the silent lobby. Across on the other wall was a bank of pay-telephones. How did you go about finding the big boss's address when she didn't want to be found? He grinned as he thumbed through the directory for the personnel office of the corporation, then dropped in his coin and dialled.

'And you're who?' the elderly lady at the other end demanded.

'William Two Feather,' Charlie said. 'I'm Mrs Colchester's son. My mother is very ill, and as a former employee of your firm—they've cancelled her medical insurance. Would you believe that? Forty years working for the Hammonds and they cancelled her medical insurance. So I have to get in touch with Hammond, and I forgot where she's living in the city. Some hotel, I believe.'

There was a moment of silence as the clerk on the other end of the line consulted her computer. 'Yes, Mrs Colchester. Forty years service and Hammond just——'

'Turned her out of house and home. Can you beat that?' Charlie slapped a big paw over the telephone transmitter. He had almost said, 'turned her out into the snow'—it seldom snowed in Kansas in August. He was beginning to like his part too well, but there was no room for humour.

'A shame,' the voice from Personnel said. 'It's against company policy to give out any information on Hammond, but I see that Mrs Colchester——'

'My mother,' Charlie said mournfully.

'Yes, your mother, Mr Two Feather. She formerly lived in the penthouse suite at the Sheridan Hotel, on Broad Street. You can find the place?'

'Easy,' Charlie said. 'Easy. I thank you. My mother thanks you. The entire Potowotami Nation thanks you.' He dropped the handset before the clerk could gather her wits, and was out on the street in a hurry. The two door guards kept a respectable distance.

'Missed Ms Hammond,' one of them called after him. 'She just went out the back way when you came in.'

'Thank you,' he yelled as he dived into his rented sports car and started the engine. 'There,' he lectured himself, 'all done with smoke and mirrors, and not a fist laid on anyone. Diplomacy, that's what! The way of the future.' He was whistling as he drove off.

The Sheridan was one of the new residential hotels on the outskirts of the city. Set back in its own enclave of fences and trees, and discreetly guarded against all comers, it boasted valet parking. Charlie left his prize vehicle in the hands of the attendants and rushed into the lobby.

'I have an emergency message for Ms Hammond,' he announced to the desk man. 'Can I go up?'

The desk clerk looked him up and down. In the heat of the day Charlie had abandoned his suit coat and tie, unbuttoned the top three buttons of his shirt, and had rolled his sleeves up above his elbows. Obviously the desk man thought him to be not quite the type to be admitted.

'Not without authorisation,' the haughty clerk retorted. 'I'll call and see. Your name is?'

'Mathers,' he said. 'Charlie Mathers.'

It took but a moment for the connection to be made. The telephone buzzed once and was picked up at the far end. The clerk handed him the phone. With one set of fingers crossed, he used the others to push down the plunger, thus disconnecting the line.

'Hello,' he said into the dead handset. 'Rachel, this is Charlie. Yes, Charlie Mathers. I have that information you wanted. Yes, come up right away?'

He dropped the handset back on its cradle. 'She says "come up right away",' he told the house clerk. 'Which way?'

The clerk's face looked curdled, his lips pinched in, as if what he had to say tasted bad. He still believed that Charlie Mathers could not possibly be welcome in any of the suites of *his* hotel, but the customer was always right.

'The lift in the corner,' he said. 'It's an express directly to the penthouse.' He gestured towards the line of lifts in the far wall. 'Car number one, the penthouse,' he murmured, and then brushed his jacket off with both hands, as if he had been dealing with something undesirable.

'Pontius Pilate,' Charlie said, grinning at him. 'You know, wash the hands after anything as disagreeable as all that. Thank you.'

The clerk fumbled for something to say, but by the time Charlie reached the lift all he could muster was a cold, 'Thank you.'

This lift knew its business. Its door closed without slamming, and it zoomed upward at high speed. Charlie, standing in the middle of the car, reached desperately for one of the wall-mounted brackets. The thing stopped the same way it had started. With enthusiasm. And the door opened on a dimly lit green corridor. There was only one door in sight.

The doorbell could be heard. Discreetly heard, of course. The door opened without a single noise. A hotel maid shrugged her shoulders at him, as if waiting for him to display his card from the plumbers' union. She sniffed at him and elevated her nose.

'And me too,' he said sincerely. 'I'm Charlie Mathers. Is Hammond here?'

'In the living-room, but she has company already.'

'I know. I think I need to see them both.'

'Then I'm supposed to announce you.' The little maid walked down an interior corridor ahead of him. A pair of double doors were closed. She knocked briefly, opened one door, and said, 'Mr—er—Charlie Mathers is here, ma'am!'

There was a squeal of rage from inside. The maid gestured Charlie in through the door, and then shut it behind him. She had obviously been working for Hammond long enough to know when to get out of the range of fire.

Charlie leaned back against the closed doors. In front of him, in the sunken living-room, there wasn't an ounce of joy.

Rachel Hammond was rising from a pouffe at one side of the room. Across the low coffee-table from her was a large young man, who looked to be one of those people who could easily win the Mr America titles. He was dressed in blue shorts and a grey T-shirt, and evidently had spent a long time cultivating his tan and his muscles. His hair was cut short, a butch cut, shaved closely on all sides. His face was square-set, with a bulging neck. Altogether, Charlie thought, the kind of nice young man I wouldn't care to meet too often. Except for today.

Rachel, on the other hand, appeared as if she had just come out of the shower. Her hair glistened. The lace collar of her négligé was belted firmly under her white robe. The robe was buttoned up, from neck to hem, which stirred briefly about four inches below her knees. She was also wearing a face he remembered, fully flushed with anger, eyes piercing him like daggers.

'I thought I made it plain,' she said firmly. 'Our business venture is concluded. I have hired this gentleman to take your place. Edward, would you please . . . ?'

The 'nice young man' stepped around the coffee-table, looking altogether too eager to do whatever was required. Charlie watched him move—slowly for such a well-built young man.

'Rachel, I don't think you ought to do this,' Charlie temporised.

Hammond looked as if she didn't agree. Edward paused to look over his shoulder for confirmation. 'Get rid of him,' she snapped. He began to move forward again.

This is just what I need, Rachel told herself. The trouble with all this anguish is that it hasn't had a firm conclusion. Edward will surely destroy this—this—— She fumbled for words. Plain, honest Charlie. Not by any means the handsome young stud she had wanted, and yet he was—damn it, why do I whiffle about him? 'Get to it, Edward,' she repeated harshly.

And then her eyes widened and she took a couple of protective steps backward. Her nice young man had advanced up the two stair levels to where Charlie stood, and then, for some reason that Rachel could not quite see, he had fallen down. 'Edward!' she yelled.

The nice young man struggled to his feet and rubbed his stomach as if it hurt. He looked around over his shoulder again, and Rachel offered him an encouraging smile. He turned back towards Charlie, made some slight motion, and fell down again!

'You know, Rachel,' Charlie said, 'this poor young man is liable to get hurt. In fact, I think he's already hurt. Poor kid.'

'What are you doing?' she gasped. 'You——'

'Exactly,' Charlie said. 'You sent a boy to do a man's job. And now look what we've done. I had to hit him on the jaw. I think I've broken a knuckle here. And it's all your fault. Going to get up again, son?'

Edward mumbled a word or two. There was something wrong with his jaw. 'I know,' Charlie said compassionately. 'Women! They go through this routine all the time, looking for the "parfit gentil knight" to slay a dragon for them. Especially this one. Here, let me help you up.'

Edward cautiously accepted the offered hand, and mumbled something again.

'Yes, I know,' Charlie said. 'Look, the plain fact of it is she's trying to make me jealous. I have the job—a firm contract. And all you can get is trouble by scabbing. Say, look. Take a cab over to the hospital and let them fix you up. Everything is on the house. The Hammond-Borgen Corporation. Hammond here will call ahead and OK the bills. Right?' He turned around and glared at Hammond, who had suddenly become Rachel again.

'I—yes,' Rachel muttered as she circled around the room, keeping at the furthest distance she could from him, and found the telephone. Meanwhile, Charlie slipped an arm around the young man and helped him out of the door.

The maid was huddled in a corner, eavesdropping and enjoying it all. 'See that he gets downstairs,' Charlie ordered. 'And he'll need a cab to take him to the hospital.' After which he left the pair of them, went back into the living-room where Rachel waited, and closed the door behind him.

CHAPTER EIGHT

'WELL,' Charlie said as he did a mock-washing of his hands. 'That certainly made me feel better.'

'Barbarian,' Rachel muttered as she tried to squirm further away from him, into the depths of her couch. 'You could have hurt the boy.'

Charlie laughed. 'Why don't you listen to what you're saying?' he asked. 'Boy indeed. But old enough for your purposes? I think I hurt my knuckles more than his jaw.'

'I don't care to talk about it. Violence appals me. Please go, before I call the police.'

'Ah. What a good idea. Why don't you call them? They're probably looking for you anyway.' He took a quick, jerky pace up and down in front of her. 'You don't abhor violence, Hammond. You abhor *physical* violence. The world is full of other kinds. I'm surprised you don't recognise that. You've suffered more mental violence than most anyone else I know!'

She came to her feet with a startled look on her face. 'Don't you start now on my father. He was a good man, for all his little faults.'

'Little faults? My Gawd, woman, what do I have to do to make you see the light? Well, the police will be along soon enough.'

'Looking for me? I didn't do anything.' Indignation fits her, he told himself. Just that little bit of colour to her cheeks makes all the difference between austerity and beauty.

'That may be, lady, but *somebody* did *something* with that so-called magazine of yours. You'll be happy to know that we've taken out an injunction against you and your dirty rag, and I don't doubt that my lawyer has arranged for a dozen or more cops to find you and serve the writ. You certainly blew your top this time, lady.'

'I don't know what you mean. I haven't seen today's issue yet.' She drew that haughty cloak of the imperial Hammonds around her, swathing herself as if she were the Statue of Justice on top of the capital building. And that too, he told himself, is something we've got to settle some time soon. But that's not first priority.

'I haven't seen today's issue yet either,' he assured her. 'But my lawyer tells me that it's bad, even for you. Tell me, why did you bring in the boy?'

'You know why,' she said bitterly. 'Just because you reneged doesn't change anything. I still wanted that baby. Time is running out for me, and I can't do it all by myself. If I could I would, believe me. You don't know anyone who hates men worse than I do.'

'Tell me,' he chuckled. 'Did the boy go along with your proposal for an *in vitro* fertilisation?'

'Of course he did,' she snapped. 'I raised the offer to four thousand dollars.'

'That's certainly a good price,' he agreed. 'But the terms? Yetch!'

'I'll get it done, Mr know-it-all, in spite of you and your friends. I *will* get it done. I need this child!'

'*You* need the baby, or is it your father who needed the baby? And him dead and gone these three years or more.'

'Damn you. You think you know everything, don't you?'

'No, I'm far from knowing everything, Rachel. All I know is that you're frozen inside that shell of ice you've grown, and headed hell-for-leather down the road to Hades!'

'If that's my final destination,' she flung at him, 'at least the ice will be melted by the time I get there. Why are you badgering me? Your part in my troubles is over and done with. Did you want your money? Is that why you came?'

'For that piddling amount? Come on, Rachel, you know me better that that!'

The goading succeeded. She launched herself across the room at him, both hands extended like claws, the red gleam of her nail polish threatening death and destruction. 'I'm going to——' she gabbled, and then lost control of her voice.

Charlie was no fool. He knew how dangerous claws could be. He stood still until she was almost within range, and then his longer arms snatched her wrists out of the air and pinned them to her sides.

Rachel made a couple of attempts to break loose, and then her strength failed her. For a moment she wavered back and forth, and then she bent over past her point of balance and collapsed.

Before she could hit the floor he caught her, and cuddled her, sobbing, against his chest. He carried her over to one of the overstuffed chairs, and sat down, holding her in his lap.

'There, now, Rachel,' he coaxed. 'Cry it all out.'

She tried to struggle on, but had not the strength. The tears flowed like rivers. She ducked her head into the softness of his shirt and cried her years of anger away. Poured out her anguish on to shoulders broader and stronger than her own.

Charlie Mathers was not the world's greatest planner. The crying he had hoped for, but once it started he ran out of ways to guide it. Psychology I and II had been part of his freshman education, and a good many rivers have gone over a good many dams since that time. Not knowing what to do next, he shifted her weight, ran one hand through the tangle of her hair, and hoped for the best. But the softness of her, lying there in his lap, introduced thoughts once held in thrall by his anger. Controls he had thought to be imbedded in steel suddenly turned to jelly. His suddenly clumsy fingers tugged at the two top buttons of her robe, and brushed it open. Without any particular instruction, his hand slid down into the opening, touched and cupped her breast, and gradually massaged its tip.

The woman stopped crying. 'What are you doing?' she gasped, and sniffed a tear or two away.

'What you've always wanted,' he murmured. There were three buttons still fastened on the robe. He lost his patience with them. As he tugged, the remaining fasteners snapped off one at a time and went sailing across the room.

'Tell me to stop,' he rasped. 'It's your last chance.'

'What I've always wanted?' Not a remonstrance, but a question asked in awe, as if a sudden need had come upon her and she could not understand what or why.

'What you've always wanted, woman.' A tender smile crept across his craggy face, and then a look of surprise. 'You never wear a bra?'

'I—never.'

'Yes. I can see why,' he murmured, his concentration now on the mounds of white flesh before him. A man would be a fool to ignore it all, he told himself. He stood up and carried her to the couch across the room, and stretched her flat on her back.

'Charlie?'

'What, sweetheart?'

'I—you mean that?'

'Yes. We're going to get married, you and I. Want me to stop?'

'I don't know, do I?'

Charlie Mathers dropped to his knees in front of the couch. His eyes absorbed all the glorious womanhood of her, standing proud and firm. Gently he lowered his head, and allowed his tongue to possess one of those hard brown tips.

There's nothing new to all this, Rachel's analytical mind told her. I've seen movies of it being done, I've read books describing it. Nothing's new, but everything's new. The moment his mouth surrounded her nipple she had felt the involuntary contraction that brought her entire body into play. Nothing new? She drew a desperate breath, then locked one of her hands in his hair. Not for punishment, not for control, but rather to give herself something of him to hang on to while her world began to go around in circles.

Sweetheart? He called me sweetheart. Or is that just the normal line that a rampaging male uses to bring a woman to compliance? Probably that. Probably—but at that moment he surrendered his claim at her breast, and moved gently and slowly up her throat, across her chin, and up to her lips.

Leaving behind? A sort of regret that he had stopped. A coolness where his lips had been, as the air in the room absorbed the dampness he had left behind. A slight chill quickly replaced by his massaging hand as it climbed the mountain.

Lips. Gentle, caressing lips, touching once gently and moving on, then coming back again to seal her entirely within herself. Without thinking, she closed her eyes. His tongue moved against her lips, nuzzling, seeking admission. Which she granted without protest. The lips pressed more fully, the tongue sought—something. And a violent ionic charge ran up and down her spine. She wiggled closer, but by the time she found the better position his mouth had moved on. Back down to her breast, a momentary halt, and then further down into the soft roundness where her waist constricted, and her navel attracted.

Somebody in the room moaned in excitement. Rachel heard the sound, felt the excitement, and her whole body quivered.

'Rachel? Shall I stop?'

She heard him as if from a distance, as if he were standing by the top of an empty barrel, and she were inside on the bottom. A hollow sound that reverberated around the barrel and into both ears at the same time. She was entirely confused.

'Rachel?'

'I—don't know,' she gasped. And then, desperately, 'Don't stop!'

A hand and arm slipped under her at the knees; another balanced her from behind her back. He lifted her up as if she weighed nothing. Strange, she told herself through the confusion. I feel like nothing. Is it possible to float? Magic?

Somehow he opened the double doors of the living-room without shifting his hands. Somehow, although he had never been there before, he found the turning and opened her bedroom door. Somehow he stretched her out gently on her bed and knelt beside her. Throughout all of this Rachel Hammond had kept her eyes closed. Now she opened one eye.

His face was inches from hers, his eyes open and staring. There was an expression on his face that she had never seen before on any man. It was hard for her to study it with just one eye, but she dared not open the other, or surely the whole affair would disappear—fade away and disappear. So she searched his face carefully.

Desire? Yes, much of that. There was a darkening under his normal tan, and she could feel the heat arising even at this distance. Confidence? As if he knew he was doing what she wanted. As if he *knew* something that she did not know—as yet.

Love? She had never known love before, and could not judge.

And then he moved. Her robe slipped off her shoulders under his questing fingers. Her négligé followed. The room was cool. She shivered.

'I know, love.'

His mouth again, at her breast, while one hand roamed up and down from neck to waist, searching for—all those little spots that caused her to quiver. Searching as if he were a hunter who knew where to go. And then, using his fingers like little soldier's legs, he marched one hand slowly down across her breast, into the deep declivity of her stomach, and then paused.

She was wearing a pair of very utilitarian white briefs. The Rachel Hammonds of this world paid no attention to things that others did not normally see. His fingers disappeared under the rim of those briefs. Rachel gasped and put her arms around him, trying to pull him closer.

His fingers stopped for a moment. Her briefs disappeared. He drew back. Disappointed, Rachel opened her eyes and wished for one wild moment that there might be mirrors on the ceiling. Which was an impossible dream. But she could see herself, a pale white nude, stretched out on top of the blue and white spread that covered the bed. Something moved in the corner of her eye. She turned to look. He was standing by the bed, completely nude himself.

Startled, Rachel turned away, and he laughed. A humorous, teasing laugh. 'Well, we can't all be as beautiful as you.' It was a lie, she told herself, because he's as beautiful as I am. Not the same, but beautiful. She turned back, forcing herself to look.

He loomed over her while she searched him out. There was a T-formation of light hair across his chest, left to right. From its midpoint another segment of hair marched down his flat stomach and into—oh, my, she told herself and shut her eyes. Oh, my!

Rachel stiffened from head to toes, her arms rigidly beside her, the fingers bent into fists, her nails biting into her palms. The bed under her swayed as he settled beside her. She could feel the touch of him all along her body. He's going to do it, she told herself fiercely. Hang on tight. Maybe it won't hurt!

'Relax, woman.' His head was at her ear. She understood the words, but could not believe them. Nowhere in any of her research had she come across a time in these exercises where one should 'relax'!

'For God and England?' he murmured in her ear. What in the world is he talking about? she asked herself. Get on with it. Why doesn't he get on with it? He moved.

But not in any manner that she might have conceived. He chuckled again, lay down at full length beside her, and began to draw little circular diagrams across her exposed body with his index finger. Gentle drawings, up hill and down dale—pausing at the top of the hills for a moment, then moving down and down as if he meant to jump into the canyon between her legs.

Rachel summoned all her strength and forced herself more frigidly into an unmovable statue—for about thirty seconds. His fingers moved again, over the cliff, into the canyon. She had never dreamed such excitement could exist. She had never known that that one little spot was there. He touched it gently, and Rachel Hammond screamed in excitement, bounced in the bed and snatched at him as if she were trying to completely absorb him.

He moved then, nudging her legs apart and moving in between them. 'Ready, Rachel!' She was shaking with excitement, and he wanted to talk! I'll kill him, she told herself—just as soon as he's finished!

'I—I——' The words would not come. Perspiration was pouring from her forehead.

'I understand,' he said. Gently, still using one hand to tease her breasts, he settled his weight and entered her. Rachel's world dissolved. Multi-coloured fireworks were flashing around her head. Some fool was yelling, 'Faster, faster!' That same fool reached madly for him, trying to force him deeper when he was in his withdrawal cycle.

His huge hands slipped under her buttocks, synchronising her movements with his. He pounded at her for a wild moment, and then took her with him up to the climax of the Little Death. After which he collapsed on top of her, panting, out of breath. As was she.

More than one minute passed, but Rachel was unable to measure time exactly. Her mind was still disconnected from the rest of her. He seemed to weigh a ton, but when he tried to move she clutched him tightly and murmured a frantic 'No.' More minutes. She could no longer feel the fullness of him inside her. Regret washed her mind clear. She opened her eyes and grinned at him.

'And is that,' she asked coyly, 'all there is to it?'

'Why, you little vixen,' he said, laughing. He rolled off her, but not so far away as to be out of touch. 'Yeah, that's all, lady. Thirsty?'

'As if I had been in the desert,' she assured him. 'You?'

'The same.'

'There's a little refrigerator in the corner,' she suggested. He rolled away from her, landing on hands and knees on the thick carpet. A moment later he was back with two iced glasses.

'What is it?'

'Bourbon and branch water,' he said, laughing. 'Well, I guess you don't have branch water in these parts. I salute you.' He raised his glass. Rachel did the same. One sip to moisten her bone-dry lips, another to wet her throat, and then she held the glass up and played with the droplets that beaded its rim.

'It was—something different,' she said with a sigh. 'Has this been going on for very long?'

'Thousands of years,' he returned as he finished off his drink and climbed back on the bed. 'Thousands of years. God said "increase and multiply". So he made the sex game the most enjoyable item in all the world.'

'But—so many people seem to have trouble with it.'

'Yes. But not you and I, Rachel, thank the lord. Yes, it's the only game that rich and poor alike can enjoy.'

'Poor better than rich,' she commented with a grin. 'The poor people seem to do so much better at it than the rich.'

'That's because they don't have as many hang-ups as the rich,' he said. 'Now then, I've had a hard day, and I could use a little nap. Drink up.'

She did. He lay back in the bed and pulled her up against him. And before she could think of the rest of the stuff she wanted to talk about he was fast asleep. She left him that way for about a half-hour.

Is that all there is to it? she asked herself. Lord, that was enough! She had never in all her life had such a physical reaction as during that last climactic moment. And there he lay, sprawled out on his back, making little noises as he breathed in and out. Not a handsome face, she reminded herself, but good enough to go the route. A sturdy head, full of all kinds of thoughts, able to do a million and one things that needed doing in this world. A chest that moved up and down as he breathed—and a scar just above his right nipple. Four inches or more of scar. She caught her breath as she watched it. So recent as to be still inflamed. Battle wounds?

You know so little about him, she told herself. So very little. And you want to know so much. If my—she patted her soft stomach and blushed—if my baby looks like his father, wouldn't that be—nice?

He was stirring uneasily at the moment. She was leaning over him, so close that one of her breasts was rubbing across his mid-section. Purely accidental, she told herself as she straightened slightly. Is that how he's turned on? Could he possibly do it again?

It didn't seem so. Could he do it again? Recklessly she leaned over and extended a hand to just—touch, that's all. Just touch.

His eyes popped open. 'What the hell,' he muttered as he rolled over on top of her. Dismayed—and yet pleased with herself—she discovered that he could.

'Now that's not the type of afternoon I had planned,' he said, leaning back in one of the lounge chairs in the living-room. 'I hadn't expected to—have things explode in my face. Are you all right, Rachel?'

'All right? I couldn't be better. Well, that isn't exactly right. I can see I'd be better off if you had shaved this morning.'

'My apologies. I usually get it done in the morning and, if I'm going out with a lady, again at night before we go. A hard business, being a man.'

'Yes, I can see it must be,' she giggled. 'Very hard.'

'Don't rub it in, woman. I've got more than one scratch on my back that I didn't put there. You were like a wildcat in that second session. Whatever happened to the sweet demure Hammond girl?'

'I wouldn't know,' she told him. 'I'm a little—sore—in one or two places. Somebody bit me—right on my—right there somewhere. But I'm glad we were able to do it. You really were the man I wanted.' Her face turned brilliant red. I can't imagine doing—that—with Edward, she told herself. Or any other man I've ever met. Only with Charlie.

'And so that part of it is concluded,' she said. There was just a little wistful touch in her voice.

'Concluded?'

'Well,' she said, 'once might be a miss, but twice is certainly going to achieve my goal, isn't it?'

'Oh, lord, do you still have that on your mind?'

No, I hadn't, she told herself. From the moment he touched me, I haven't even thought about the consequences. But now that we are back to the rational, I can force myself to think. The baby is on the way, I've managed to get one project going down the road, so why shouldn't I boast about it?

'Is that really what you were thinking?' He had walked across the room and was standing directly in front of her, glaring down.

And now he's angry, she thought. I wonder why? We've both played our part, and the play is over, isn't it? Of course not, her conscience told her. Of course it's not over. He's a fine man, the kind of man my father would have just loved as his son.

As his son. The phrase stuck in her mind, wiping out every other thought. As his son. My father. My grandfather. In the end, Rachel Hammond, you have ended up by doing just what all those men wanted. Damn this male world!

'Yes,' she said as she stood up gracefully. 'I've got what I wanted.' She patted her stomach to emphasise her mood. 'Everything has turned out fine, and I enjoyed myself considerably in the doing. I do have to thank you for all that, Charlie.'

'And now? Don't thank me so damn casually. We're going to get married, you and I, and between us raise this little fella the way he should be raised.'

'Why, there isn't any "you and I",' she said recklessly. 'I thought you understood that. I needed you desperately for the laying of the keel, but from now until the launching I can take care of things myself.'

'You think so?' he asked harshly. 'You think you've got everything sewn up, and now you can go off about your business?'

'Why, of course.'

His face quivered, and then he smiled at her. Not a pleasant smile, but rather a cold thing, cold enough to freeze the Missouri River. 'Don't be too sure about that,' he said. 'It's been known, lady, that it takes more than a couple of quickies before a woman becomes pregnant.

You may find that nothing's working. Then where will you be?'

Oh, God, she thought, that couldn't be. We were a perfect match, he and I, and—no, the lord wouldn't do a thing like that to me. He's just trying to frighten me. She plucked up her courage. There was no way in this world that she could do such a thing with anyone except Charlie, and he was getting up on his high horse!

'That's not possible,' she told him, her eyes flashing the danger signal. 'I'm sure it's not possible. I'm sure you've served your purpose.'

'And we won't be needing each other any more?'

'And——' She didn't want to say it, but anger carried her forward. 'And we won't be needing each other any more,' she said. 'Come by the office tomorrow, and I'll pay you off.'

'The hell you say,' he muttered. He took one step in her direction. She backed off. So did he. There was a perplexed expression on his rugged face. 'Look at me, Hammond. You've only heard it a couple of times in passing, and I'll wager you don't remember. What's my full name?'

'Why—Charlie,' she replied. And then puzzled through her mind, trying to remember the rest. Yes, he had said it one or two times out at the ranch, but now, for the life of her, she couldn't remember. 'I—it just seems to have slipped my mind.'

'Mathers,' he told her. 'Charlie Mathers. And there's no way you're going to avoid me or my name, love. You and I are going to be married. Sooner than later, because my grandfather isn't one to put up with that later business. Have you got that?'

'But——' He had used all the right words, Rachel told herself. No, I could possibly raise this child all by myself, but—I don't want to! I want Charlie Mathers. Day and night till death us do part. Even though he means to be the boss? her conscience asked. Even if, she thought. Even if.

He knew what she was thinking. Her flexible face had raced through all the emotions of her internal argument. 'We're going to get married,' he repeated.

Rachel found herself wrapped up in the middle of his arms. 'Yes,' she murmured. The pressure of his arms increased for a second, and then relaxed. His lips came down on hers and sealed her to the bargain. For aeons the wild, exhilarating kiss ran on, until finally he broke it for lack of breath.

'There,' he said, inhaling deeply. His arms opened and Rachel, totally exhausted, dropped into the nearby lounge chair.

'There indeed,' she said. There hardly seemed to be anything else to say. Married, she thought. Like thousands of other women throughout history. I never thought it could happen to me. And happily ever after?

Charlie seemed to shrug all his muscles, and managed to relax. Marriage, he thought. I've been avoiding it for years, but now I've chased this woman until she caught me. Who would have thought? In need of movement, he walked over to the occasional table sitting by the couch. A copy of the *National Gossiper* was lying there, face down. The back page reminded him of what Frank had said at the restaurant. He flipped the magazine over so its cover could be seen. The story attracted him. He picked up the publication and began to read.

'Lord,' he muttered. 'You people are giving this poor soul a hard time. Embezzler, crook of the first water. Who the devil is this man? Story on page four.' He flipped through the pages. 'Ah, here we have it.' And a pause, while his anger built. 'Dear God! Roger Borgen!'

He whirled around, folded the magazine neatly in quarters, and put it down carefully on the table. Rachel could see the rage rising in his eyes, the anger reflected in his carefully enunciated words.

'There's not a word of truth in this,' he said harshly. 'Don't you people ever check *anything* before you print it?'

Rachel looked up at him for a second, frozen in time. Then all her training took over, and it was Hammond who responded icily, 'I haven't read this issue. But I'm sure that it's been investigated with our usual thoroughness. Who was the gentleman, did you say?'

'I'll say.' His voice had dropped to a whisper. 'The finest man I have ever known. Roger Borgen. You've just bet me a million dollars that there isn't a word of truth in this rag.'

'I—Uncle Roger?' She drew herself up to her full height, her head spinning. 'I don't remember making any such bets with you!'

Charlie looked down at his watch. His big hands were trembling. 'By this time my lawyer will be down at the court-house, filing a million-dollar suit against you and your paper. That's our bet, lady. I'm going to bust this filthy magazine of yours. When I get through with it, you'd better damn well pray I don't wreck your ranch as well.'

'Others, better than you, have tried. None of them succeeded.'

'Then listen carefully,' he said. She shivered. His voice was deep, vibrant, threatening. 'My name is Charlie Mathers. Charlie Mathers. And you're going to be seeing a lot of me, Hammond. You've stepped beyond the bounds of decency this time. The reason why nobody has ever beaten you before is because they didn't have enough money and enough evidence. This time you've bitten off more than you can chew. I've got the money, and I'll get the evidence.' He flipped the magazine over, face down, and shoved it at her. And then he turned and walked away, slamming doors as he went, leaving her frozen, trembling.

Her mind whirled. He had come to ask her to marry him, and he had left with a death wish in his mind. The headline said,

> Millionaire philanthropist might have been embezzler. Famous Libertyville tycoon being checked by the Gossiper Spotlight Team. Details on page four.

The magazine slipped from her fingers and fell to the floor.

'I suppose,' she screamed in hysterical panic at the door which had slammed behind him, 'this means the wedding is off?'

'I was beginning to wonder what happened to you,' Frank Losen said. He was sprawled out on Charlie's favourite couch, in the middle of Charlie's favourite apartment. 'It's been a busy afternoon.'

'You can say that again,' Charlie said as he closed the door behind him. 'I'm exhausted.'

'Oh? How did you make out with Hammond? Did you ask her?'

'Yeah.' Charlie made for the bar and poured himself a shot of rye. 'I asked her, and then I read that rotten magazine cover!'

'And then?'

'Luckily there was a husky young man there I could use for practice. After I read that magazine I was almost sick to my stomach. I guess the wedding's off.'

'You only guess?'

'Hey, you can't just turn off the tap,' Charlie muttered as he refilled his glass. 'Can you love a woman and hate her at the same time?'

'Damned if I know. Say, I managed to get a few things done,' his lawyer told him. 'First of all, the injunction was a cinch. The judge took one look at the headlines and signed the writ right away. We've locked up the garages, and all the trucks are under guard by my private agency.'

'That's OK for next week,' Charlie agreed. 'But I want something—I want to smash that woman. Tomorrow.'

'We might just do that, too.' Frank Losen pulled up his briefcase and set it on the table. 'I've managed to get a call out for a special meeting of the stockholders. For tomorrow, it's set. Over in the boardrooms at the pyramid.'

'I don't quite—my mind's a little disturbed.'

'It means that you can go into that meeting with enough proxies to toss her out on her ear, that's what it means.'

'But hell, Frank. I can't run that magazine. If we throw her out the whole place will collapse.'

'Maybe so, maybe not. There's Elmer Chatmas, you know. He's been in harness for so long I don't think he could ever quit. Elmer's a sensible man. He's been the power behind the throne for a long time. And I'm sure there must be one or two other people around who could help out?'

'I wouldn't know,' Charlie said. 'God, my head aches.'

'Another afternoon at the bottle?'

'No, lord, no. I wish it *was* that.'

'I don't believe it. You, Charlie Mathers, *wishing* for a hangover?'

'There are some things, Frank, that you lawyers don't know. Shoeing a horse, for example, or——' He stopped at just the right moment. How would Frank ever understand the rest of the statement—*or loving a woman*?

'I suppose you're right,' the lawyer said as he gathered up all his papers and stuffed them back into the briefcase. 'I'll see you tomorrow, then. Ten o'clock?'

'Ten o'clock.' Charlie walked him to the door and showed him out. And then he went over to the window and looked out over the city. 'Libertyville, Kansas,' he murmured. 'Home of cows and printing presses and tornadoes and indomitable ladies.' He shook his head dolefully. 'And I don't know just which one of them makes for the biggest problem...'

Back to the cabinet, where he refreshed his rye and added an ice-cube. Rachel Hammond! He settled back in his chair and considered. Out at the ranch she had been beginning to change. Oh, there had been times when she slipped back into her old form. But certainly there had been change. And now, to come back to the city and find her not only as bad as she had ever been, but even worse. If that were possible.

Tomorrow, he told himself, I'm going to rush into the meeting room and bring the whole house down around her head. And then? And then I'm going to go back to Texas and have a month of drink and destruction.

And then?

And then I'll scoot around and see if there's any country aching for a fight, looking for a competent fighter pilot! And with that he played chug-a-lug with his glass and threw the empty container at the artificial fireplace.

CHAPTER NINE

TOMORROW! Rachel Hammond eased back in her chair and sighed. Outside her office on top of the pyramid, a worker was cleaning the streets of the city, pounding water down on the mid-Kansas town as if there were to *be* no tomorrow. 'So what are the possibilities?' She turned to look around the circle of her senior staff.

'Two different kinds of problem,' Elmer said. 'The injunction and the court suit are a problem, but not one that we haven't seen before. We go to court. We stall. We tell them that we have reason to believe—and all that junk. Then we offer to settle. In our next issue we publish a retraction—on the last page of the magazine, and in small print. If they persist we offer them money.'

'And if they won't compromise, and they won't take the money?'

'That's what Zimmerman is for,' Elmer said. 'That's why we keep him on retainer. What say, lawyer?'

Alfred Zimmerman sat in the middle of the circle, a small, neat man, precise in all ways, wearing a pair of gold-rimmed spectacles. He cleared his throat, and tried not to look at Hammond. 'I thought it was the policy,' he said, 'that all stories of probable risk would be reviewed by my staff? I didn't see this issue of the magazine until this morning at breakfast. I must say that you spoiled my meal.'

'But it sold a lot of copies,' Hammond said harshly. 'Get on with it. What do we do next?'

'Well—as far as the injunction goes—we really need to find out who's behind all this. The court record indicates Frank Losen is suing, as trustee for the estate of Roger Borgen. Now, Mr Losen is as shifty a lawyer as ever came out of Dodge City. But I can't believe that Frank is acting for the estate out of the goodness of his heart. I wish I knew who's backing him.'

'And if we find that out?'

'Then we turn loose our team of investigative reporters and get a profile on this man. Who knows? *He* might be susceptible to all the foibles of mankind. A little adverse publicity might make him see reason.'

'Dirty pool,' Elmer chimed in. 'That's what got us in this situation in the first place. More of it might croak us.'

'But it's an angle, and we'll try it anyway,' Rachel decided. 'Next?'

'As for the other problem?' The lawyer set back in his chair and brushed his decidedly thin hair with one well-groomed hand. 'We have a great deal more to fear from the meeting of the corporation than we do from the judicial system. Given the fact that everything possible is against us, I could still string out the court case for four or five years—maybe more. But the corporation?'

Rachel rubbed her forehead. It ached. All of her ached. But for good reason, she told herself. What a wonderful afternoon! Yes, Charlie left in anger, but I'm sure that once I get this problem with the magazine straightened out I can get Charlie back into focus. A great deal of man, Charlie. And I can't do without him!

Zimmerman was still droning on. Whatever he said went right past her ears and over her head, ignored. Charlie. She leaned back in her chair and closed her eyes.

Charlie on his gelding, riding through the prairie grass, a man in charge of a man's destiny. And if he could make the ranch pay she wouldn't need the *National Gossiper*—not for anything. She rubbed her hand over her forehead again. The ache persisted. But the conversation around her did not. Her eyes snapped open. They were all staring at her, waiting.

'Restate the problem,' she ordered. Zimmerman shrugged his shoulders and fumbled back through the packet of papers he had before him. 'Slim it down,' she added. 'I'm afraid that you've got into the habit of telling me more than I care to know.'

Zimmerman was not the kind of man to blush. From an old German family, his folk had come to Kansas when it was still caught in the throes of the slave wars, the dark and bloody ground. But he *was* perturbed. He paused to clear his throat again.

'Simply stated, Hammond,' he began, 'you do not have absolute control of the stock in this corporation. Nobody has. When Roger Borgen died, he held some forty per cent. You held some forty-two per cent, and the rest—we just don't know where the rest of the stock is.' Another stop to clear his throat. He reached into his waistcoat pocket and found a lozenge which he placed on his tongue.

'We have carefully avoided a corporate meeting for several years. In that way the legally elected board of directors could continue to function. Now, we are setting sail on a stormy sea——'

'Please, no rhetoric,' Rachel said. 'Can somebody find me an aspirin?'

A half-dozen hands moved to produce the pill. Rachel selected a couple and gulped them down.

'I don't know how you do that without water,' Elmer commented.

'I don't know how you do that with alcohol,' she said grimly. 'Now, Mr Zimmerman?'

'We could call a meeting,' the lawyer said, just as grimly as she, 'and find out that the holders of this missing stock could show up—and vote against us.'

'Hmm.' Hammond tapped her pencil on her desk top and suddenly noticed it was in disarray. It was something she hated. Desk tops should be neat, tidy. And hers was not. She shut out the staff members and their comments and began to restore order to the scene in front of her. The staff grew quiet. They all knew what was going on. Even a paper-clip out of order was usually the source of a maddening comment. But this time Hammond had nothing to say; she just sorted and shifted and pushed until things were as they should be. And only then did she turn back to her staff, most of whom were consulting their watches.

'So it's late,' Rachel said. 'And you're all tired—as I am. Well now.' She ticked off the things to be done.

'You, Mr Zimmerman, go back into court and see if you can get this temporary injunction lifted. Lie, cheat, steal—I don't care how you do it. I want the trucks to move tomorrow and the presses to roll.' The lawyer nodded, replaced his papers in his briefcase, and started to get up.

'And you, Elmer. Take another press-run of today's magazine, and move it to the rail-head for shipment. I have the hunch that this thing will sell double our usual subscription list.'

'No changes?' Elmer asked.

'Changes? Why changes?'

'I think,' Elmer said, 'we ought to add a little cover-box saying that people have got an injunction seeking to suppress this issue.'

'Yeah,' Hammond said, coming to life for the first time. 'Freedom of speech. Freedom of the Press. Right on the first page. Fourteen point type. Go!'

They all moved to leave. A collective sigh could be heard from all around the room. The wall clock behind her struck eleven. 'All but you, Harry.'

The young man who was the magazine's auditor stopped and turned around with a question on his face. 'Harry,' she said softly, as the others hustled out, 'I want you to spend the night or the week or the month, and get me a list of all those other stockholders. Name, address, telephone number. And call me the minute you know something, whether I'm at the office or at home. Don't fail me.'

He smiled an acknowledgement and went rushing from the room. Hammond always rewarded those who did well for her. And who knew what sort of reward the Ice Lady might possibly distribute?

Rachel Hammond, who knew exactly what that grin intended, smiled herself and slumped back in her chair. Whatever the young man thought his reward might be, it wouldn't be what he hoped for. She leaned her head back in the big swivel chair and, not expecting to, she fell asleep.

It was a sleep filled with dreams. The same dream, actually, running through her mind as if it were a tape spliced in a circle for continuous running. In that dream she came up to the ranch house in her limousine, and climbed out, dressed in a pure white wedding gown. It was a full-figured gown, sweeping down from her hips to her feet in a wild explosion of silk and satin and orange-blossoms. She twirled a couple of times, but no dust dared to rise. The bodice of the dress, reaching upward from waist to choker collar, consisted of a single layer of transparent silk. It came upward to her neck, where a tiny rosebud was tucked into a frill of lace. Beneath the skirt were two cotton petticoats that rustled whenever she walked; above the skirt, under the bodice, there was nothing but Rachel Hammond.

In her dream she walked towards the veranda; Charlie came down the stairs, almost tripping over his spurs. He was dressed in black dress trousers, a handsome pair of dark brown boots, and a big smile. Just the sight of him excited her. Her breasts kept coming to attention, pushing outward at the transparent silk. He reached out his hands to her; she ran in his direction. Only when they were but an inch or two away did his grin disappear. 'Mathers,' he said grimly, and then the rest of him seemed to fade away, like the Cheshire cat of literary fame, but leaving behind that terribly grim face. Until that too disappeared. A moment of blackout followed, and then the film began to run again.

Rachel awoke and screamed. The night cleaning lady pushed in the door of her office and flipped on the light. 'You still here, Ms Rachel? I thought everybody had gone home long ago. Child, it's two o'clock in the morning!'

'I—I must have been over-tired,' Rachel stammered. 'Everybody's gone? My chauffeur too?'

'Everybody gone, Ms Rachel. I could get you a cab real easy. There's a couple of them park right outside the door most nights.'

'I'd like that.' Rachel stood and stretched. It was true. Every bone in her body ached—especially her hip-bones. He was a heavy man, she reminded herself, and giggled at the thought.

'You really must be tired,' the cleaning woman said. 'Here, let me help you to the door, and then I'll call downstairs to the night guard. He'll look after you—you need someone to, anyway.'

Rachel readjusted her blouse and shook her skirt free. Wrinkles did not matter, not tonight. With her eyes only half open, she kept her right hand extended to the wall. The touch steered her—and reassured her. The little lift waited for her. She climbed in and pushed the button. The car started, stopped, and started again, moving so slowly down the shaft that she almost fell asleep again. 'I must get this thing fixed,' she said, just as the lobby door opened.

'Does need some overhauling,' the guard ventured. 'I got one of those cab drivers waiting for you, ma'am.'

'Don't call me ma'am,' she said, but gently. 'Call me—Rachel. You're Foster, aren't you? What are you doing working the midnight shift? You've a wife and two children at home, I seem to remember.'

'Three now,' Foster said. 'Night shift pays more money. Here you go. Slide into the cab and he'll take you straight home.'

'I feel—as if I'd been on a wild drinking party,' Hammond told the busy driver moments later. 'But I haven't had a drop of alcohol. What do you suppose it is?'

'Release of tensions,' the cab driver told her. 'Happens all the time. I get all these big shots who come off the airplane filled with their fears and tensions, you know. And then, after the meeting's over and they're still employed, they just fall back in the seat of my cab. Some of them start singing.'

'You wouldn't want me to sing,' Rachel said. 'Even the cows can't stand my singing. But Charlie, he sings like a bird. Well, at least the cows like him.' A pause for reflection. 'And I do too.'

'And here's your hotel, ma'am. Not to worry about the fare. I run a tab for the *Gossiper* people. You sure work strange hours. And let me give *you* a tip. When you go in, they've a fine indoor swimming-pool. Take a dip, then call—Charlie, was it?'

'Yes. Charlie.'

'Call Charlie on the phone and tell him you love him!'

'What a good idea,' she murmured as she wandered into the lobby and took the lift up to the penthouse.

Waiting outside her hotel is the most stupid thought of the day, Charlie Mathers told himself. So you blew your top. What else did you expect of a wandering cowpoke? Yes, she was wrong. No, you were right, Charlie, boy. And look what being right gets you. She comes back to her hotel at two in the morning, looking as if she were three sheets to the wind, and you're parked over here for the past three hours, hoping you don't have to explain to the beat cop why you're there.

Why *are* you there? Here? Charlie shifted restlessly in the driver's seat of his Porsche. No matter where he searched, he couldn't find a cigarette. Not even an old butt stuffed in the back of the glove compartment. His nerves were aflame. And that's what you get when you give up smoking. Nothing seems to be coming out right with Rachel Hammond. A lovely woman. And instead of marrying her you give her a one-night stand. One-afternoon stand. Whatever.

Why didn't you say something like, 'Rachel, I love you. Let's you and I get married'?

Why didn't you? Because she would probably have said no, and had you thrown out on your pretty little ear!

He stopped his fidgeting. A light had appeared in the window of the penthouse. He watched it, fascinated. At that distance he could see nothing more than the light. What could she be doing? What had taken her so long to get upstairs? Damn! He pounded with one fist on the steering-wheel of the car.

'You waitin' for a street car?' A heavy voice at his ear, with a heavy Scandinavian accent.

'Oh, hello, officer. I was just——'

'Talking to yourself,' the burly policeman said. 'I've been watching you on and off for almost twenty minutes.'

Think fast, Charlie Mathers told himself. Think fast. 'Well you see, officer, it's this way. I'm a writer. Novels, you know. And I found myself stuck with one of the scenes in my manuscript, so I came out into the night air to talk my way through it——'

'And of course you've got a tape recorder to keep track of all that?'

As it happened, he did. His car had one of everything, as he pointed out to the cop. 'And so you've solved your problem, and now you'll be on your way, right?'

'Well—I do have a couple more scenes to work out,' Charlie said.

'But you'll do that at home, won't you? This is a restricted residential district, and we don't like strangers parked on the odd streets. Sir.'

'I—yes. I was just going.' He looked up to the lighted window one more time. The window had been half opened, and now there was a shadow, as if someone was standing just inside. Damn, he told himself as he started the engine. Like some puling schooboy. So I love the girl, no matter what the devil she does, I love her.

'I wouldn't wait too long,' the officer reminded him.

'No. I won't.' He shifted into gear and roared away from there like a dragon late for a fire-storm. Behind him the policeman grinned as he tucked his complaint book back into his pocket.

Two blocks from where he started, Charlie Mathers finally came to and took his foot off the accelerator. Moving at something much closer to the speed limit, he found his way across town safely. Luckily.

His mind was not on driving. Not at all. His mind was on a beautiful, strong-willed woman, lying beside him on a wide bed, smiling at him. But he did get to the underground garage at his apartment house, and took the lift up to the seventh floor. As he fumbled with his door keys, he could hear his telephone ring. Speed compounded the fumbling. When he finally got the door open he dashed across the living-room to pick up the instrument—and heard only the dialling tone. Whoever it was that was calling had given up the ship. And it *might* have been Rachel, he told himself disgustedly. Maybe she would call again?

He went back to close the outer door, then stripped, article by article, in the living-room. But no amount of slow motion helped. The instrument remained silent. Maybe I should call her?

He looked at his thin gold wristwatch. Three in the morning? No time for calling now. It might be just the last straw if I got her out of bed at this hour. Drooping, dispiritedly, he administered a double Scotch and found his way to bed.

* * *

Well, why not? Rachel told herself as she strolled across the lobby of her hotel. Cab drivers are all graduate psychologists, aren't they? The indoor pool was in a separate room just off the lobby. Lighted by small green bulbs along the waterline, it beckoned to her. She held a locker, with several swimming-suits. It took but a moment for her to change. The warning sign cautioned. There were no life-guards on duty after eleven o'clock. But Hammond was a woman very sure of her skills, and willingly took risks. She walked up to the deep end and dived in.

Thirty minutes later, completely refreshed, ready for almost anything, she wrapped herself in a bath towel and rode the main lift up to her own floor. Neither the night clerk or the lift operator had a thing to say. Life was often like that when all around you knew the approximate size of your bank account.

She almost rang the doorbell, until she remembered that her maid would have long since fallen asleep. So instead she fished with wet hands through her capacious handbag and found her own key. Moments later, dripping on the carpet but not caring, she flicked on the lights and made herself a daiquiri.

The telephone set was positioned on an occasional table against the wall. She went over and opened one of the sliding windows and looked out over the city. Nothing was moving, except for the police car parked just at the edge of her view.

'What you ought to do, Hammond,' she said conversationally, 'is have a nice drink, and then call him up, and tell him how very sorry you are for making a world-class fool of yourself. Like the cab driver said, he can't know you love him if you don't tell him, right?'

She sipped the sweet cocktail in her hand and shuddered. It was too sweet for the occasion. She pulled out the telephone directory. It took hardly a moment to reach the telephone exchange of his apartment building. She fumbled with words, making a dozen or more statements, any of which might do the trick. She could hear his phone being rung.

'Mr Mathers doesn't answer,' the operator told her.

'Ring him again,' Rachel said, suddenly no longer relaxed. With the telephone in one hand and her drink in the other, she paced back and forth nervously.

'He still doesn't answer, ma'am.'

'Please,' she stammered. Suddenly this telephone call had become more important than anything else in all her life. 'Please—one more time.' She could hear the feedback of the ringing. On and on and on. A tear formed in one eye, and then another. 'Oh, God, what have I done?' she muttered to herself as she hung up and went off to bed.

The minute her head hit the pillows she was asleep. An awkward, troubled sleep, with that same dream running through her mind, over and over and over.

Until her maid came in and woke her to the bright sunlight of her morning.

CHAPTER TEN

THE boardroom at the *Gossiper* building was ornate but small. The huge mahogany table seated only eight people. In the corner by the president's chair was a mahogany podium and lectern, complete with microphones. Frank Losen nudged his client. 'Like the British Parliament,' he whispered. 'Fifty members and only eight seats. That tells you something.'

'Oh? What?' Charlie Mathers settled into his seat and tried to get comfortable. In honour of the occasion he was wearing an off-white suit, complete with a white shirt and a string tie. His lawyer, perhaps showing more knowledge, came in a pair of jeans and an open-necked shirt. The meeting had been called for eleven o'clock. They had arrived at ten-forty-five, and no one else was in the room.

'That shows you that Hammond-Borgen are not encouraging a large number of stockholders to have their say.'

'I wish they'd turn their air-conditioners down,' Charlie mumbled. 'I didn't get a lot of sleep last night. I could catch up on some here if it wasn't so darn cold.'

'I hear that Hammond likes it that way.' The lawyer opened his stuffed briefcase and handed Charlie a set of forms. 'Your voting certificates,' he said. 'I get to vote your uncle Roger's stock, since the will has not yet been probated. You get to vote this proxy for your grandfather's shares in the blind trust. Altogether, we're sitting on a majority. You can vote Hammond out in one ballot.'

'Yeah,' Charlie said as he hunkered down in his chair. What was that you told yourself yesterday? Voting Hammond out is the same as breaking her will-power. If I do, she'll collapse. And probably hate me for the rest of her life! How's about *that* for a cheery little vote?

Just to change the subject he asked, 'How did things go in court today?'

'Not bad, not good,' Frank said. 'The judge refused to dissolve the injunction, but he also refused to make it permanent. And then he asked for supporting documents. You wouldn't believe the number of papers the corporation filed. It would seem that our sole interest in this suit is to stifle the free Press. That's a classy counter-action. They submitted so much material that it took the entire session just to identify the papers.'

'That sounds like a big-time job,' Charlie retorted. 'Can they get away with it?'

'It's all a ploy,' Frank told him. 'On our way out of the court their lawyer cornered me. He wanted to remind me how long such a suit could last. Then he said, "I suppose I could talk Hammond into a settlement." And he walked out.'

'Settlement?'

'No, huh?'

'I—really don't know, Frank. I'm not much for these things. I need to be outdoors in the fresh air. And damned if I don't think I'd get along better with cows than with people. Hey, here they come.'

Here they came indeed. A phalanx of people, all armed with briefcases and papers, marching in smartly to what were designated seats and standing areas, and clustering there. Including the two right behind Charlie, who gave him a dirty look, as if he had stolen their seats. He chuckled to himself, shrugged, and sat up taller than before. 'Pull in your gut, Frank,' he whispered. 'We're on parade.'

'Not me,' Frank said as he slumped just a little further down in his chair. 'I left the Army twenty years ago. You don't put me back in harness by a little side-show.'

An elderly man near the head of the table was obviously counting heads. 'That's Elmer Chatmas, the editor,' Frank whispered. The counter seemed to be satisfied. He turned and nodded to a hulking man standing in the far front of the room. 'And that's one of her guard dogs,' Charlie whispered back.

The bulky young man opened the door. 'No clash of cymbals,' Frank whispered mockingly. Rachel Hammond was standing at the door. 'For effect,' Frank added.

'Oh, shut up,' his client told him in an undertone.

He didn't want conversation. He just wanted to look. Or perhaps get up and run across the room and sweep her up and——

And at that moment Hammond came into the room. There was a hushed murmur of approval. Rachel Hammond had put off her business uniform. No navy blue skirt, no frilled blouse, no suit coat. Instead she was dressed in as simple a dress as woman could find. An A-line, lily-white, with insets of bunches of little gold flowers embroidered around the hem. Charlie took a hissing deep breath. His companion, smiling, turned to stare at him.

She looks sweet enough to eat, Charlie thought. Magnificent. Beautiful. Thirty? Not possible. Twenty-one at the most. Simple, innocent. None of her tortured soul showed through the smile she flashed at him. There was some sort of message in that smile, only Charlie Mathers was in head over tea-kettle, and the message escaped him.

Rachel Hammond was smiling, indeed. But it was a smile she had to hold on her face with all her might, for fear that it would slip away and be carried down in a flood of tears. He looked so grand. Neat enough to grace any boardroom—or bedroom, she told herself. Isn't it strange? There isn't another person in the room. Not anyone. How easy to fall in love; how hard to do anything about it!

She walked over to the head chair in her usual graceful movement, swaying slightly, sending her skirt into a gentle arc. His eyes followed her every step. Her eyes were glued to his. If only he would smile.

And when he did her own smile became broader and more natural. She beamed at him, almost ignoring Elmer, who was holding her chair. The editor cleared his throat, bringing her back to reality. She offered him a smile as well, and slipped into her chair.

A throne, actually. Her father had had it specially built for her, with some four inches of extra height so she could look down at most other people at the table. Most people. Not him. His crinkly little smile indicated that he spotted the deception and acknowledged it. Rachel blushed and lowered her long eyelashes.

The chairwoman's gavel lay just within the perimeter of her sight. Nudged by Elmer, she picked it up and whacked it resoundingly on the block. It made an echo run through the room. There had been little sound before; now there was absolute silence.

'The secretary will read the purpose of this call for a special meeting of the board,' Rachel said.

Halfway down the table a young lady, not more than twenty herself, managed to stand up nervously. 'Madame Chairwoman, the board is in receipt of a letter from Mr Frank Losen, holder of record of forty per cent of the voting stock of the Hammond-Borgen Corporation, acting as executor of the estate of Mr Roger Borgen. The calling makes reference to the issue of the *National Gossiper* of Monday last, and asks that a vote of no confidence in the present administration be taken.'

'And that's all?' Rachel managed to keep her voice as cool and composed as usual. Somewhere in this room disaster lurked, and she had a good idea in which corner it was to be found.

'Yes, ma'am.' Rachel motioned for her to be seated. The girl dropped in her chair as if a huge weight had been taken off her shoulders.

'Discussion?'

Elmer Chatmas got up and was recognised. 'In every magazine there are some bobbles and breakdowns,' he said. 'Yet you will notice that over the past three years, while Hammond has been at the controls, the net profits of this corporation have increased more than fourteen per cent. And that in a falling market. I can't believe that the needs of the organisation can be best served by replacing Ms Rachel.' He sat down in a spurt of polite applause.

Frank Losen looked over at Charlie; he nodded negatively. Frank got up and was recognised. 'Madame Chairwoman,' he said, 'we have not come here to measure how many dollars and cents this administration has made. We are here to defend a reputation. Most of you knew Roger Borgen well. He was a good, sincere man. In the last issue of our magazine we turned on him like a pack of wolves, cutting him up into little pieces.

Uncle Roger—most of you called him that—was not an embezzler. He was not a crook. Instead he was a man of great and good proportion, a churchman of good repute, and a wise adviser. The only derogatory thing I ever heard said about Roger is that he was a lousy golfer. Acting for the estate of Roger Borgen, I demand a vote of no confidence in the existing board.' He sat down. Only one pair of hands applauded. Charlie Mathers. And then silence.

Rachel stood up. 'I know it's not proper for the chairwoman to enter the argument,' she said softly. All in the room leaned forward to catch her words. 'Mr Borgen—you were right, Mr Losen. Uncle Roger—Uncle Roger was the sweetest and kindest man I ever knew. Only, my father hated sweetness and kindness. And he taught me the same. The issue of which you speak was ordered by me. I ordered it, and then failed to check it. It said exactly what I wanted to have said. In every little detail.'

There was a brief pause as she looked around the room.

She stabbed at her leaky eyes. 'I am my father's daughter,' she continued. 'And I have never been more ashamed of myself than I am today.'

A rustling of papers indicated the surprise of all the participants. Rachel seized the bevelled edge of the table to steady herself. 'You have seen the last issue of the *National Gossiper* in its present form. It is the determination of the present executive body to convert our magazine to a more gentle form. A magazine for women, without all the vitriol.'

She stopped for a moment to wipe a tear which had escaped. 'We will undoubtedly never again make the profits we have in the past. But profits are not everything.' Another tear missed her handkerchief.

She slammed the gavel down. 'Vote,' she demanded. There was a croak in her throat as she wiped the tears and fell into her seat.

Elmer Chatmas stood up again. The dumpy old man looked confused, but he went about his work with a flat voice and a neutral face. 'The administration votes forty-two per cent of the outstanding stock of this corporation. Our vote is "No".'

Frank Losen sprang to his feet. In comparison to Elmer, the lawyer looked fit to fight. And he said so. 'I vote the forty per cent stock of the estate of Roger Borgen. I vote "Yes".'

The people at the table looked at each other uneasily. Rachel bowed her head and let her hair fall over her eyes. An occasional sob still broke through. It was the only sound in the entire room.

I know he has the rest of the stock, Rachel thought as she scanned Charlie's rugged face. I know he has it, and I know he'll vote against me. And then what will I do? All of my life, all of my being are tied up in this corporation—and I have used that power vindictively. I deserve to be fired, she told herself angrily—only—what shall I do afterwards? Return to the ranch which I've already proved I don't know how to run? Abandon Kansas and go east? There might be something I can do—but I don't know what it is! Unconsciously, her hand dropped to her stomach and gently caressed the 'perhaps' in her life. And that was the moment that Charlie Mathers stood up.

Every head in the room turned in his direction. He looked at them all slowly, one at a time. 'A great wrong has been done, and it must be righted,' he said. Faces fell in all directions. Only Frank Losen was smiling. Grinning, actually.

'But,' Charlie said in his deep voice, 'this is not the way to make things right. Eight-two per cent of the stock has been voted. I hold the proxy for fourteen per cent of the remaining stock, owned by my grandfather, Brigadier General Frank Hammond, and made a part of his blind trust.' Another pause while he looked down at the papers in front of him.

'Madame Chairwoman,' he said, 'I abstain.'

There was a scream of noise. Everyone in the room had something to say—to their neighbours, to their opposites, to themselves. But when Charlie Mathers dropped back into his chair, Frank Losen studied his face. 'So that's the way the cookie crumbles?'

'That's the way, Frank.'

'It's your cookie. I've got another court appearance this afternoon. See you around, shall I?'

'Sooner or later. Thanks, old buddy—for everything.'

Frank Losen got to his feet, stuffing his briefcase with unused papers. 'No thanks necessary,' he said, chuckling. 'Wait until you see my bill!'

Losen was the last to go. Except for Rachel, who was still huddled in her chair, and Charlie, who was just getting up to walk to the other end of the table. He disturbed the symmetry of things by pulling Elmer's chair over beside the huddled woman.

She looked up when he took her hand and began to caress it. 'Why, Charlie?'

'Because that's the way I think things ought to be,' he murmured. 'Because there is no one in this state who could run the corporation better. Because you have finally come out from behind your Dr Jekyll disguise, and into the real world.'

'Not without help,' Rachel said. 'Not without help. Only now I feel as if there's nothing more for me to do.

I don't really want to run the magazine any more, Charlie.' She looked up at him. Tears had ruined her mascara, and she didn't care. He whipped a massive handkerchief out of his inside coat pocket and offered it to her.

'There's no real need for you to run this darn thing,' he said finally. 'I'm sure we could find someone else we could hire to keep it going. But not until we get an apology out for Uncle Roger.'

'The apology is easy,' she said, working up a little smile. 'But what is all this "we" business?'

'Not the royal we,' he said. 'The partnership we. You and I, Rachel. We are going to get married, and then we are going to—raise a few more members for our partnership. You don't mind?'

'Get married? I hadn't ever thought about that lately,' she said. Only all of last night, and the night before, and perhaps a week or more out at the ranch. 'But the more I think of it the better it sounds. We? The two of us? You don't plan to dictate to me the way my father did to my mother?'

'Not a chance.' He leaned over and, almost as if it were simple, picked her up and settled her in his lap. 'Not a chance.' She shifted around until she was comfortable, and then turned her face up to him. He needed no further invitation. The door opened about halfway through the kiss.

'Oh. Excuse me.' Rachel sat up, embarrassed. It was the same cleaning woman who had interrupted her the evening before. 'There,' said the beaming old lady, 'I told you so, didn't I?'

'You surely did,' Rachel said, smiling.

'Told you what?' Charlie asked.

'None of your business,' they told him simultaneously.

CHAPTER ELEVEN

WHEN they came back from their ride Rachel was red-faced from the wind, and happy. They stabled both horses, wiped them down, and gave each of them a pail of oats. 'You know,' she said as they worked together, 'you never did tell me what happened to Mr Hendrix.'

'Your old foreman? He comes up for trial on the first of September, charged with rustling and embezzling. The other pair of riders that worked for him, the judge gave each a suspended sentence and told them to get out of Kansas. Satisfactory?'

'I don't know,' she said, sighing. 'Mr Hendrix worked for our family for so many years.'

'So when the trial comes up you can be his character witness.'

'You're teasing me!'

'Not a bit. A good word from a good woman could work a lot of good for him when he's being sentenced.'

She thought for a moment, nibbling on her lip. 'Then I will,' she said, and took his arm for the walk back to the house.

But there was more to worry her and, being by nature a worrier, she picked at him. 'You're sure that the Reverend will be here on time?'

'That makes six times you've asked,' he said. 'The answer is still "yes". He's bound to be!'

'But it's a long way from Texas, love.'

'Not to my grandfather. Juarez Joe is flying him in. Or didn't you notice that we've cleared an air-strip in back of the house?'

'Oh, I noticed, but—it's a very important day, Charlie.

'I know, I know. And you were the woman who didn't want to get married.'

'That was before I found out how much fun it would be. You *have* enjoyed it, haven't you?'

'Very much so.'

Mrs Colchester, who had begged to be returned to work, came into the room carrying a little white plastic container.

'Keep it at room temperature for thirty minutes,' the cook said.

'Good.' Rachel moved over to the table where the light was the strongest, and set up a little chemical laboratory of her own.

'And may I ask?'

'None of your business—yet,' she told him. 'Move out of the light, please. And be careful of that container! Good lord, you gave me the darnedest scare. Spill that and I'd have to get a new kit and try it again tomorrow.'

'Oh?' He picked up the little container and sniffed at it.

'Don't do that,' she snapped at him. 'Put it down. You can't imagine how much trouble it was getting that into the cup.'

'Well, I can see it would be hard,' he sympathised. She gave him another sharp look.

'You know what that is?'

'Yes, I know what that is. No, I don't know what you're up to with it. But go ahead anyway.'

'Charlie!'

'What have I done wrong?'

'You just don't say that kind of thing. It isn't—isn't done.'

'In the Air Force it's done all the time,' he told her, and grinned as he did. 'Don't be so sensitive, love. People have bodily functions, and those functions have names. Blame the problem on Queen Victoria. She's the one who cut all those useful names out of the language. After we get three or four kids around the house, you'll find that you need some short little word to use. Have you ever tried to teach a two-year-old kid to say "Urinate"? Nonsense. So what are you going to do next?'

'Men,' she muttered. 'I don't know how I'm going to get along with you. Now if you'll stop bothering me, I have to follow the directions carefully. Let me see, now. First I take the test-tube with the white powder in it, and I use this dropper to soak up some—fluid. And then I squeeze the fluid in with the powder.'

'No trouble there,' Charlie said. 'Even I could do it.'

'They have them in the high schools now,' Mrs Colchester contributed. 'Kansas is a very advanced place.'

'Well, then, Doctor?'

'Then I take this little plastic gadget with the two little bulbs in it, and put that in the mixture, and use it to stir things around until the powder all dissolves. After which I leave the bulbs in the liquid for fifteen minutes.'

'All very educational,' he said. 'Just what are we supposed to learn from all this?'

'Why don't you read your paper?' Mrs Colchester suggested. She brought it to him, gave him a little push, and settled him into the over-stuffed chair.

'Well, thank you,' he said, as he reached for the sports page.

'You're really not interested?' Rachel asked.

'Of course I am,' he said sarcastically. 'And I know you'll tell me all I need to know when you get finished there.'

'You know, you're a pretty obnoxious man.' Rachel checked her watch and went back to her little laboratory. Mrs Colchester picked up the directions and read them to her.

'First, to wash off the bulbs in cold tap water. Do not touch the beads with the fingers.'

'OK. Next?'

'Next you take the cover off the tube with the colourless liquid, then you put the beads in that tube—and leave them there for fifteen minutes.'

'I wish I'd had dinner,' Charlie grumbled.

'Keep talking and you'll get nothing but bread and water,' Rachel told him. 'Look, Mrs Colchester, only five minutes and already there's——'

'Fifteen minutes,' the cook insisted. 'We can't do this by guesswork. It works like a recipe. I tell you what. I sing you a little Indian song, huh?'

'So why not?' Charlie commented. 'She sings better than either of us.' He slapped the paper down on the table. 'Would you believe it, the Royals baseball team lost another game. That means six losses and one win in the past two weeks. What they need is some young blood.'

'You said it,' Rachel yelled, holding up the tube with the two little bulbs within. 'You said it! We did it!' Both women shouted their glee and danced each other around the table.

'Would you mind telling me what this is all about?' Charlie asked. 'I'm really getting hungry.'

'Settle back,' Rachel told him. 'Get a good grip on yourself. Ready?'

'Of course I'm ready,' he grumbled. 'I'm a former fighter pilot. Nothing really surprises me.'

'Thank God for that,' Rachel told him solemnly. 'Charlie Mathers, you are about to become a father!'

'What?' Charlie Mathers, experience and all, stumbled to his feet, swayed slightly, and reached out to lean on his wife-to-be. 'What?'

'Coward,' she told him, and then squeezed him gently. 'This is one of those early pregancy tests. See, the lower bulb has turned green.'

'And so has Mr Charlie.' Mrs Colchester giggled.

'And don't for heaven's sake tell my grandfather about the baby,' he told her as they watched the two-engine Caravan circle the landing-strip. Rachel was already in her wedding gown, a dainty white lace and silk concoction that fell barely to her heels. It hugged her from neck to waist, and then swept out in a voluminous skirt, fleshed out by a pair of starched cotton petticoats that provided the necessary rustle as she moved. The collar was high, Edwardian, with her hair carefully put up to match, and held up by a crown of orange-blossoms. On her bosom she wore his wedding gift, a sparkling star sapphire, and on her right wrist was a bracelet of flowers. All in all, Rachel told herself, I feel very—bridish?

'That makes four times you've told me,' she said mischievously. 'And don't you tell him that you and I have been living out here for the past two weeks, either. I think that might be too much for an elderly Methodist minister.'

The welcome was effusive. All of them walked back up to the house, where the old man allowed that he would love a cup of coffee, and then he sat down in the most commanding chair in the kitchen. 'Now,' he said, 'you're a cute little thing, Rachel Hammond. So when is the baby due?'

Behind his grandfather's back, Charlie Mathers choked on his own coffee, and spilt a copious amount of the hot liquid over his hand. 'Oh, I don't exactly know,' Rachel said nonchalantly. 'Perhaps in seven months. Something like that.'

'If it's a girl,' the old man said, 'I hope it turns out to be as pretty as its mother.'

'And if it's a boy?' she asked.

'Then,' he said, 'you'll have to try again.'

Rachel managed a nervous smile. This tall old man, inches taller than his grandson, and only slightly bent with age, was a force she dared not trifle with. And yet there was something he had to know. 'About the magazine,' she offered.

He shifted his weight in his chair and half turned in her direction. 'Yes,' he said. 'What about the magazine?'

'Well,' she stammered. 'I've—given it up.'

'There's one good step.'

'And Elmer Chatmas will run it.'

'And that's another good step.'

'And we thought—well, we won't take out the man from Mars thing, or the UFOs. But we thought we'd turn it around towards humour—and modern women. Kansas has a thousand writers with a good sense of humour. We're going to hire some of them, and let them go whichever way they want.'

'And that,' the old man said, 'is another good step.' There was a bustle in the living-room as the rest of the guests arrived. Grandfather Mathers stood up, tall and sturdy in his eighty-seventh year. 'Come on,' he commanded, 'let's get this show on the road.'

The living-room had been decorated—swamped, the word should have been—with all the flowers the Kansas summer could provide. A good half-dozen women from the magazine had undertaken the decorations. Mrs Colchester had drafted help from the Potowotami Indian nation, who arrived *en masse* with piles of food.

'I hope I do this right,' Mrs Colchester murmured. 'I never been a bridesmaid before. What do you think about that?'

'Don't ask me,' Rachel said soberly. 'I've never been a bride before.'

'Nervous?' Frank Losen was the best man. They were standing together in a little group at the entrance to the living-room.

'Scared to death,' Rachel said, and bit her lower lip to hold on to her courage.

'About what?'

'That's the problem. I don't know what I'm scared about.' I need something, she told herself desperately. I need some word, some phrase, some idea that ties us all, Charlie and I and all the others, into a viable, loving whole. What can I say?

Grandfather Mathers came into the room at that moment. No longer the big, casual man, but clothed now in his robes, his face calm and solemn. 'So that,' the good Reverend said, 'leaves all the rest of it to us.' He managed to drive the four of them into a group at the improvised altar. Almost it seemed as if he was herding them, as if they were a quartet of heifers. Then he stepped around in front of them, inspecting everything with an eagle eye. He shrugged his shoulders and managed to stand an inch or two taller, fingering the bible he had used for seventy years.

'Dearly beloved,' he said.

Yes, that's it, Rachel Hammond told herself excitedly. Dearly beloved! She looked up at the man who stood beside her, and he returned the look. His lips moved without speaking. 'Dearly beloved,' he mouthed. Rachel Hammond, all her doubts resolved, squeezed her man's arm and turned back towards the preacher.

Those opening words floated out over the crowd, leaked through the windows, and blessed the house and all who would be its inhabitants. Rachel Hammond missed all of the words that followed. There seemed to be a protective blessing over the house and all the hearts that would live in it. A blessing which released all her real and fancied tensions, which erased all the memories her father had pounded into her, so she could even think of that man with equanimity.

'And I now pronounce you man and wife.' The final curtain. Rachel Mathers turned to look up at the huge man standing beside her, drawing her to him with the strength of his eyes alone. Promising the world and all its appurtenances. The flower that was her heart opened and burst into blossom. That's it, she told herself excitedly. My dearly beloved.

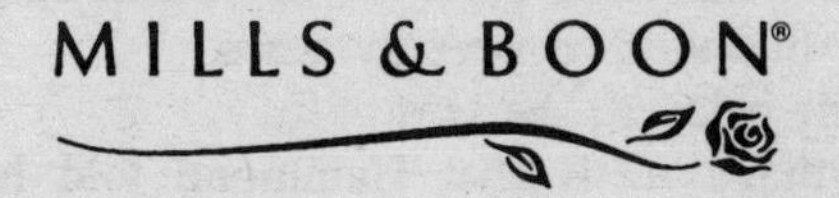

Look out for

Lynne Graham's

new romance:

THE RELUCTANT HUSBAND

Available in paperback in April 1998

Frankie was horrified to discover that her marriage to Santino Vitale hadn't been annulled—and now her intended to claim the wedding night they'd never had! He insisted they be together for three weeks, after which they would divorce and go their separate ways. But Santino hadn't reckoned on them falling for each other all over again...

Here's a preview!

THE RELUCTANT HUSBAND

'Francesca...?'

Gooseflesh broke out on her arms, her every muscle jerking painfully tight. That name she never used, that voice...the soft, mellow syllables as smooth and fluid as honey yet as energising for Frankie as the siren on a police car riding her bumper. There was a whirring in her eardrums. Slowly, very slowly, her feet began to turn, her slender body unnaturally stiff as she fought her disorientation, refusing to accept her instantaneous recognition of that voice.

Santino Vitale fluidly uncoiled his long, lean length from behind the table in the far corner and moved silently out of the shadows. Her tongue welded to the dry roof of her mouth. Her skin felt damp and clammy. For a moment she seriously doubted her sanity and the evidence of her own eyes. In an exquisitely cut silver-grey suit, an off-white raincoat negligently draped across his shoulders, Santino looked shockingly alien and exotic against the shabby backdrop of scarred tables and grimy walls.

'Would you like to join me for a drink?' Dark eyes as stunningly lustrous as black jet whipped over her stilled figure. Smoothly he captured her hand, warmth engulfing her fingertips. 'Ah...you're cold,' Santino sighed, shrugging off his coat to drape it slowly and carefully round her rigid shoulders.

Frankie stood there like a wax dummy, so overpowered by his appearance, she could not react.

Shattered, she couldn't drag her gaze from him either. At six feet four, he towered over her in spite of her own not inconsiderable height. Devastatingly handsome, he had the hard classic features of a dark angel and the deeply disturbing sexual charisma of a very virile male. Without warning a tide of remembered humiliation engulfed her, draining every scrap of colour from her cheeks. Everything that Frankie had struggled so hard to forget over the past five years began to flood back.

'*This* is the La Rocca hotel,' Santino murmured.

'This place?' Complete bewilderment and the sense of foolishness that uncertainty always brought made Frankie sound shrill.

'And you are here to meet a Signor Megras?'

'How do you know that?' Frankie demanded shakily. 'Just how do you know that? And what are *you* doing here?'

'Why don't you sit down?'

'Sit down?' she echoed, dazed green eyes scanning him as if he might disappear in a puff of smoke at any moment.

'Why not? I see no Signor Megras.' Santino spun out a chair in silent invitation. The proprietor hurried over to polish the ashtray and then retreated again. 'Won't you join me?'

A faint shaft of sunlight pierced the gloom, highlighting the tattered posters on the wall and the worn stone floor. Every natural instinct spurred Frankie to flight. She reached the door again without the awareness that she had even moved her feet.

'Are you afraid of me now?'

Frankie stopped dead, nervous tension screaming through her rigidity as a rush of daunting confusion gripped her. For an instant she felt like an adolescent again, the teenager who had once slavishly obeyed Santino's every instruction. She had been so terrified of losing his friendship, she would have done anything he told her to do. But no, Santino had not taught her to be afraid of him...she had had to learn for herself to be afraid of the frighteningly strong feelings he aroused inside her.

Was it *his* fault that she hated him now? She didn't want to think about whether or not she was being fair. Instead she found herself turning to look back at him again, somehow answering a need within herself that she could not withstand. And inexplicably it was like emerging from the dark into the light, heat and energy warming her, quelling that sudden spurt of fear and making her bite back her bitterness. Slowly, stiffly, she walked back and sank into the seat.

'What are you doing here?' she asked baldly.

'Signor Megras won't be coming. The villas belong to me.'

As the silence pulsed, Frankie stared back at him incredulously. 'I don't believe you.'

A slashing smile curved Santino's wide, sensual mouth. 'It is the truth. I brought you up here. I wanted to see you again.'

'Why?' Her head was spinning.

'You are my wife. It may be a long time since I have chosen to remind you of that fact, but you are *still* my wife,' Santino imparted with measured emphasis.

A jerky laugh of disbelief fell from Frankie's dry lips. 'Our marriage was annulled as soon as I went back to the UK,' she scorned, tilting her chin. 'Didn't you get the papers?'

Santino merely smiled again. 'Did you?'

Her brow furrowed, her mouth tightening. 'Mum has them. Since I was under-age, she dealt with the formalities—'

'Is that what you were told?'

'Look, I *know* that that ceremony was set aside as null and void!'

'You've been had,' Santino drawled with lazy amusement.

An angry flush washed over her cheeks. His persistence infuriated her. 'When I get home, I'll ensure that you're sent confirmation of the fact. I can assure you that we are no longer married.'

'But then we never were...in the adult sense,' Santino conceded.

Attacked without warning by a cruel Technicolor replay of her last sight of Santino, Frankie paled, her stomach giving a violent lurch. Santino with another woman, locked together in the throes of a very adult passion. A beautiful blonde, her peach-tinted nails spearing into his luxuriant black hair as he kissed her, melding every line of her curvaceous body to the lean, muscular strength of his. Frankie had been ripped apart by that glimpse of Santino as she herself had never seen him, and in that same instant she had been forced to see that they had never had a future together. In leaving, she had set them both free.

Dark golden eyes rested intently on her. 'I deeply regret the manner of our parting. You were very distressed.'

Shattered that he should have guessed what was on her mind, Frankie went rigid. In self-defence, she focused on the table. She couldn't think straight. Her emotions, usually so wonderfully well-disciplined, were in wild turmoil. She could barely accept that she was actually *with* Santino again, but even that bewildering awareness was pounded out of existence by the tremendous pain he had cruelly dredged back up out of her subconscious. With fierce determination, she blocked those memories out.

'Perhaps it was a mistake to mention that so soon but I can feel it standing between us like a wall,' Santino incised very quietly.

The assurance sent Frankie's head flying up again, a fixed smile of derision pasted to her lips. 'And I think you're imagining things. So I discovered that my saint had feet of clay.' She lifted a slim shoulder dismissively. 'All part of growing up, and irrelevant after this length of time. Now, if those villas really are yours, can we get down to business?'

'You have indeed been away a long while.' Santino signalled to the proprietor with a fluid gesture.

'That's not how we do business here. We share a drink, we talk, maybe I invite you to my home for dinner and then, possibly after dinner, we get down to business.'

Frankie's expressive eyes flashed. 'I won't be coming to your home for dinner—'

'Strive to wait until you're invited,' Santino traded gently.

Her cheeks reddened, her teeth gritting as wine arrived. 'I find this whole stupid charade juvenile!'

'As I remember it, you love the unexpected.' Santino lounged back indolently in his seat, unconcerned by her growing anger and frustration.

'I was a child then—'

'Yet at the time you kept on telling me that you were *all* woman,' Santino reminded her in a black velvet purr of wry amusement.

The worst tide of colour yet crimsoned Frankie's throat. 'So tell me,' she said sharply, absolutely desperate for a change of subject, 'are you in the tourist trade now?'

'This and that.' Hooded night-dark eyes resting on her, Santino lifted a broad shoulder in an infinitesimal shrug and a half-smile played maddeningly about his mobile mouth.

It was ridiculous that she shouldn't know what business he was in, ridiculous that she should know so very little about this male to whom she had once been married! But years ago all she had known about Santino was that the elderly village priest was his great-uncle and that during the week he worked in a bank in Cagliari, where he also had the use of an apartment.

But, whatever Santino was doing now, he appeared to be doing very well. That magnificent suit simply shrieked expensive tailoring. But then he was a Latin male, and the Latin male liked to look good and was quite capable of spending a disproportionate amount of his income on his wardrobe. Even so, Frankie wasn't used to seeing Santino in such formal attire. When he had come home to her at weekends, he had worn jeans and casual shirts. He looked so different now, like some big city business tycoon, stunningly sophisticated and smooth. The acknowledgement sharply disconcerted her.

Santino was surveying her with veiled eyes. 'I had a good reason for arranging this discreet meeting.'

'April Fool off-season?' Frankie derided brittly.

'I understand that you're on vacation and I would like to offer you the hospitality of my home,' Santino contradicted her evenly.

Frankie stared back at him wide-eyed and then a choked laugh escaped her. 'You're kidding me, right?'

Santino pressed her untouched glass of wine towards her. 'Why should I be?'

'I'm leaving for Italy immediately,' she told him, incredulous that he should advance such an invitation. 'So I'm afraid we do business now or not at all.'

'I don't give a damn about the villas,' Santino countered very drily.

'It's my job to give a damn.' Her sense of unreality was spreading by the minute. Santino here...with her. It felt so fantastically unreal. Why should Santino want to see her again after so long? Simple curiosity? Clearly he had found out where she worked in London. Was that why the villas had been offered to Finlay Travel? But how had Santino discovered where she worked?

From below her lashes she watched him as she drank, easing her parched vocal cords. He was so cool, so controlled...so *calculating*? Her spine tingled, some sixth sense spooking her. She scanned his gypsy-dark features, absorbing the stunning symmetry of each. The wide forehead, the thin, arrogant blade of a nose, the blunt high cheekbones and the chiselled curve of his sensual mouth. Her attention roved to his thick black hair, the curls ruthlessly suppressed by an expert cut, and the lustrous, very dark eyes which flared gold in emotion, and yet still a nagging sense of disorientation plagued her.

Santino both looked and *felt* like a stranger, she acknowledged dazedly, more than that even...a disturbingly intimidating stranger, who wore a cloak of natural authority and command as though he had been born to it. He was not Santino Vitale as she remembered him. Or was it that she now saw more clearly without adoration blinding her perception?

Adoration? Inwardly she shrank, but there was no denying that that single word most accurately described the emotions which Santino had once inspired in her.

'Francesca...'

'Nobody calls me that any more,' Frankie muttered waspishly, striving to rise above an ever-increasing sense of crawling mortification.

This encounter *was* a nightmare, she conceded, stricken. At sixteen, she had been so agonisingly, desperately in love with Santino. She had thrown herself at his head and done and said things that no woman in her right mind would want to recall once she reached the age of maturity! She must have seemed pathetic in his eyes, forever swearing undying love and resisting his every move to sidestep the intimacy which she had craved and which *he* had never wanted. It hadn't been Frankie who had locked her bedroom door at night...it had been Santino who'd locked *his*. That particular recollection made her feel seriously unwell.

'Look at me...' A lean brown forefinger skated a teasing path across her clenched knuckles. 'Please, Francesca...' he urged gently.

It was like being prodded by a hot wire. Her sensitive flesh scorched and she yanked her hand back out of reach, shaken by a sudden excruciating awareness of every skin-cell in her humming body. Oh, dear heaven *no*, she thought as she recognised the wanton source of that overpowering physical response. In horror, she lifted her lashes to collide with glittering gold eyes. Her breath tripped in her throat. Her heart hammered wildly against her ribs.

'What do you want?' she demanded starkly.

'Three weeks out of time,' Santino admitted softly. 'I want us to spend that time together.'

'I'm not spending *any* time with you!' Frankie jerked upright, wide green eyes alight with disbelief.

Santino rose at his leisure, grim amusement curling his eloquent mouth. In a single fluid step he reached her. Lean hands confidently tugged her out from behind the table into the circle of his arms. Frankie was so taken aback she just stood there and looked up at him in open bewilderment. She could not credit that Santino would make any form of sexual advance towards her and uneasily assumed that he was trying to be fraternally reassuring.

'Relax,' Santino urged lazily, brushing a straying strand of bright hair back from her indented brow.

At that careless touch her heartbeat lurched violently, her throat tightening. Suddenly she was struggling to get air into her lungs. He angled his dark head down and she came in conflict with dark golden eyes. Another wanton frisson of raw excitement arrowed through her. Her head swam. Her knees wobbled. And then, before she could catch her breath again, Santino brought his mouth down on hers with ruthless precision, expertly parting her soft lips to let his tongue hungrily probe the moist, tender interior within.

That single kiss was the most electrifying erotic experience Frankie had ever had. Heat flared between her thighs, making her quiver and moan in shattered response. Instinctively she pushed into the hard heat of his abrasively masculine body. He crushed her to him with satisfying strength. Then he lifted his arrogant dark head and gazed down at her, his brilliant gaze raking over her stunned face as he slowly, calmly set her back from him again. 'All this time I wondered...now I *know*,' he stressed with husky satisfaction.